Multiple Choice Questions on Paediatrics

Multiple Choice Questions on Paediatrics

ROY MEADOW
MA BM FRCP DCH DRCOG
Senior Lecturer in Paediatrics and Child Health,
University of Leeds.
Honorary Consultant Paediatrician, Leeds.

Published by
P G Publishing Pte Ltd
Singapore • Hong Kong
with special permission of
Blackwell Scientific Publications
Osney Mead, Oxford

This Asian Economy Edition is published by P G Publishing Pte Ltd,
Suite 609, Mt Elizabeth Medical Centre, Mt Elizabeth, Singapore 0922.

Reprinted with special permission of Blackwell Scientific Publications, Osney Mead, Oxford OX2 OEL.

Printed in Singapore by Koon Wah Printing Pte Ltd
First printing (Asian Economy Edition) 1983.
ISBN 9971-909-22-7

CONTENTS

PREFACE vii

ACKNOWLEDGEMENTS ix

MULTIPLE CHOICE QUESTIONS 1

CASE STUDIES 45

ANSWERS TO MULTIPLE CHOICE QUESTIONS 53

ANSWERS TO CASE STUDIES 57

PREFACE

Multiple Choice Questions play an important part in most medical examinations, (some of us may feel that they play too large a part). They are a useful method of testing factual knowledge and, in addition, can be helpful as an aid to learning and efficient reading.

I have used these questions with my tutorial groups. The students split up into pairs, discuss the questions, and arrive at an agreed answer before we discuss the answers and the topic as a group. They have found that it is best to be in pairs rather than alone or in a large group; discussion and argument seem to be optimal between two students of similar knowledge.

Whether you use this book on your own or with a partner *do* arrive at an answer of either 'True' 'False' or 'Don't know' before looking up the answers at the back of the book. Commit yourself—for that is the best way to learn. It will also help you to find out how you might improve your scoring in any multiple choice test. It is usual to give for each sub-section a mark of + 1 for a correct answer, − 1 for an incorrect answer and zero for 'Don't know'. The gambler may find he is ruining his chances by too much guessing. The cautious may find that he would do better by backing his hunches and less frequent use of the 'Don't know' option.

The first 150 multiple choice questions are grouped under system headings; the last 25 are mixed for the purpose of revision. The information required to answer these questions should be available in any good paediatric text (including I trust *Lecture Notes on Paediatrics*!). Questions are difficult to construct and I should be grateful for any criticisms, suggestions or alternative answers.

The final section contains some short clinical problems as a relief from multiple choice and to remind the reader that in practice careful attention to the clinical history is the key to correct diagnosis and effective help for the child and family.

Leeds 1979 Roy Meadow

ACKNOWLEDGEMENTS

After complaining in the past about the lengthy gestation period which most publishers require between receiving the completed manuscript and publishing a book, I gratefully acknowledge the speed and efficiency with which Mr Peter Saugman and his colleagues at Blackwell Scientific Publications have produced this book.

I am most grateful to Miss Wendy Haigh and Mrs Aileen Williams for their intelligent and careful assistance.

MULTIPLE CHOICE QUESTIONS

THE NEWBORN AND INFANT FEEDING

1. Amniocentesis can lead to the prenatal diagnosis of:
A severe rhesus haemolytic disease
B meningomyelocele
C cystic fibrosis
D anencephaly
E hyaline membrane disease

2. A newborn baby with an Apgar score of 10 should:
A be pink all over
B have a regular respiratory rate above 20 per minute
C have a heart rate about 70 per minute
D cry when a catheter is placed in the nostril
E move all limbs actively

3. A cephalhaematoma:
A is most common over the occipital region
B does not cross suture lines
C resolves within 10 days
D does not require treatment with blood transfusion
E may exacerbate jaundice in the neonatal period

4. The main problems of pre-term babies include:
A meconium aspiration
B respiratory distress syndrome
C hyperbilirubinaemia
D infections
E nerve palsy

5. Weakness of the hand muscles is a complication of:

A injury to the upper part of the Brachial plexus (Erb's palsy)
B injury to Auerbach's plexus
C injury to the lower part of the Brachial plexus (Klumpke's palsy)
D injury to the cervical spine
E intraventricular haemorrhage

6. Respiratory distress syndrome is more likely:

A in infants born to mothers who have had corticosteroids during pregnancy
B in infants of diabetic mothers
C to present within the first 12 hours of life than later
D in a 2 kg baby born at 34 weeks gestation than a 1.8 kg baby born at 37 weeks gestation
E to cause permanent lung damage than smoking 20 cigarettes a day during adult life.

7. Characteristic features of physiological jaundice include:

A onset after the first 24 hours of life
B disappearance by the 10th day of life
C a serum bilirubin level below 250 mmol/l
D itching
E associated anaemia

8. Haemorrhagic disease of the newborn:

A is most common in rhesus-positive babies
B is most common about the 2nd or 3rd day of life
C is associated with a prolonged prothrombin time
D is treated with oral Vitamin K
E is commoner in babies who are breast-fed

9. Mental handicap and eye damage are a well-recognised consequence of prenatal infection with:

A cytomegalovirus
B Epstein–Barr virus
C rubella virus
D *Treponema pallidum*
E *Toxoplasma gondii*

10. The following statements are true of neonatal convulsions:

A hypocalcaemic fits do not cause brain damage
B they are commoner in low birth weight babies
C those occurring in the first 2 days have the worst prognosis
D they are usually followed by seizures later in life
E anticonvulsant drugs are not indicated

11. Retrolental fibroplasia is:

A primarily a disease of light-for-dates infants
B a result of disordered development of the retinal blood vessels
C a result of excessively low $Pa\ O_2$
D unlikely to cause significant loss of vision
E more likely in pre-term than post-term infants

12. The perinatal mortality rate is:

A the number of stillbirths and deaths in the first 28 days of life per 1000 total births
B the number of stillbirths and deaths in the first 7 days of life per 1000 total births
C about 30% of what it was 30 years ago
D is in the range of 30–35
E is lower in the United Kingdom than in any other European country

13. An infant requires each day:

- **A** 45 mg of Vitamin C
- **B** 110 calories per kg
- **C** 150 ml of water per kg
- **D** 400 iu of Vitamin D
- **E** 6 mg of iron

14. Human milk differs from cow's milk in the following ways:

- **A** less sodium
- **B** more protein
- **C** more lactose
- **D** more fat
- **E** less phosphorus

15. Breast feeding is considered superior to bottle feeding because:

- **A** iron deficiency anaemia is less likely
- **B** most drugs ingested by the mother will be passed on to the baby in the milk
- **C** maternal antibody discourages colonisation of the gut by pathogens
- **D** bottle-fed babies are psychologically deprived
- **E** bottle-fed babies are more prone to gastroenteritis, hypernatraemia and hypocalcaemia

16. Most modern powdered or liquid milk products for babies:

- **A** have a solute load similar to breast milk
- **B** are fortified with Vitamın D, Vitamin C and iron
- **C** are derived from cow's milk
- **D** are more expensive than whole cow's milk in a bottle
- **E** are an inadequate source of food after the age of 2 months

PHYSICAL GROWTH

17. A 4-year-old child who is just below the 3rd percentile for height:

- **A** is likely to be unhealthy
- **B** is approximately 2 standard deviations below the mean normal height for that age
- **C** is likely to be just below the 3rd percentile for weight
- **D** is likely to be about the 3rd percentile for height when 2 years older
- **E** is likely to reach puberty at least a year later than a child who is on the 50th percentile for height

18. Short stature is associated with:

- **A** chronic renal disease
- **B** malabsorption
- **C** Down's syndrome
- **D** emotional deprivation
- **E** low birth weight

19. The following groups of children are particularly at risk for rickets:

- **A** those aged 5–10 years
- **B** those from Sikh families living in Britain
- **C** those from Muslim families living in Britain
- **D** mentally handicapped children with epilepsy taking long-term phenytoin
- **E** those with severe renal insufficiency

20. Important features of nutritional rickets are:

- **A** hypertonia
- **B** raised serum alkaline phosphatase
- **C** bow legs
- **D** secondary hyperparathyroidism
- **E** pica

21. A British girl aged 13 is likely to have:

A mature breast development (stage 5)
B pubic hair extending down the inner surface of the thighs
C commenced menstruation
D the ability to conceive a child
E reached at least 75% of her final adult height

22. Turner's syndrome is associated with:

A neonatal lymphoedema
B a XXX sex chromosome complement
C infertility
D severe mental handicap
E obesity

DEVELOPMENTAL SKILLS

23. A child aged 8 months is expected:

A to sit without support for 2 minutes
B to weigh between 9 and 12 kg
C to have a visible molar tooth
D to reach out and grasp an object
E to turn promptly to sounds made a foot lateral to the ear

24. A child aged 5 years is expected to:

A copy with a pencil a square shape
B have a head circumference within the range 54–56 cm
C dress and undress alone
D know his name and address
E stand on one foot for 5 seconds

25. A child aged 18 months is expected to:

- **A** build a tower of 3 cubes
- **B** pick up a toy from the floor without falling over
- **C** show unhappiness when removed from mother
- **D** use a spoon competently
- **E** be dry by day

26. A concomitant squint:

- **A** is commoner than a paralytic squint
- **B** is considered abnormal only after the age of 6 months
- **C** is commonly the result of poor visual acuity
- **D** is likely to require surgical correction
- **E** may result in permanent amblyopia

27. A child aged 3 years is expected to:

- **A** copy with a pencil a circle shape
- **B** show at least 2 carpal bones on hand X-ray
- **C** speak in sentences
- **D** walk up and down stairs
- **E** be able to hop

28. Reading backwardness is more common in:

- **A** girls
- **B** children from social classes IV and V
- **C** Down's syndrome than Turner's syndrome
- **D** the children of immigrant families
- **E** children born with spina bifida

29. A child aged 14 months is expected to:

- **A** stand without support for a second or two
- **B** wave bye-bye
- **C** have a vocabulary of at least 20 words
- **D** localise soft sounds made 3 feet above the head
- **E** understand simple commands

NERVOUS AND NEUROMUSCULAR SYSTEMS

30. A child of 7 months should have:
- **A** an open posterior fontanelle
- **B** an open anterior fontanelle
- **C** a symmetrical Moro reflex
- **D** a brisk response to sounds made $1\frac{1}{2}$ feet lateral to the ear
- **E** a down-going plantar response (negative Babinski)

31. Important causes of hypotonia in an infant aged 9 months include:
- **A** Down's syndrome
- **B** cerebral palsy
- **C** rickets
- **D** coeliac disease
- **E** severe mental retardation

32. The following conditions are generally inherited by sex-linked recessive genes:
- **A** Duchenne muscular dystrophy
- **B** temporal lobe epilepsy
- **C** meningomyelocele
- **D** haemophilia
- **E** Turner's syndrome

33. Petit mal epilepsy:
- **A** may be provoked by hyperventilation
- **B** does not start before the age of 10
- **C** is rarely associated with organic brain damage
- **D** is easily confused with vasovagal attacks
- **E** is a common sequela of breath-holding attacks

34. Febrile convulsions usually:

A occur in boys and not girls
B occur after the age of 1 year and before the age of 5
C last for less than 15 minutes
D are associated with upper respiratory tract infection
E mean that the child will have epilepsy in later life

35. Normal cerebrospinal fluid:

A appears clear
B has a glucose level similar to the blood glucose level
C contains less than 4 lymphocytes/mm^3
D contains less than 4 polymorphs/mm^3
E has a protein concentration of 0.4 –1.0 g/litre

36. The following are common symptoms and signs of meningitis in a school child:

A fever
B headache
C fits
D neck stiffness
E palpable occipital glands

37. The following are important causes of cerebral palsy:

A birth trauma
B medulloblastoma
C hyperbilirubinaemia
D intrauterine infection
E non-accidental injury of infants

38. Spasticity is characterised by, or associated with:

A clonus
B quadriplegia
C clasp-knife rigidity
D persistence of the asymmetric tonic neck reflex
E increased tendon reflexes

39. A sacral meningomyelocele is commonly associated with:

A spasticity of the lower legs
B hydrocephalus
C a neuropathic bladder
D multiple haemangiomata
E a lax anal sphincter

40. Important symptoms or signs of a space-occupying lesion are:

A headache
B visual disturbances
C neck stiffness
D earache
E a raised CSF protein

MENTAL HANDICAP

41. The following conditions cause mental handicap:

A nephrogenic diabetes insipidus
B galactosaemia
C hypothyroidism
D tuberose sclerosis
E cystinosis

42. Children attending classes for the moderately educationally subnormal (ESNM):

A are more numerous than those in classes for severely educationally subnormal (ESNS)
B are likely to have an intelligence quotient of less than 50
C are unlikely to be able to fend for themselves in later life
D commonly have other congenital abnormalities
E are most likely to come from a family of lower social class and low intelligence

43. A mongol girl:

A has 49 chromosomes

B is likely to have a first degree relative who is also a mongol

C is more likely to result from the union of a 37-year-old mother and a 30-year-old father, than from a 30-year-old mother and a 40-year-old father

D shows Barr bodies in the buccal smear

E is usually the result of chromosome non-disjunction

44. A mongol boy is likely to grow up into a man who:

A has children half of whom will be mongols

B has an intelligence quotient of less than 50

C has a life expectancy less than a man with cystic fibrosis

D is below average height

E has recurrent seizures

45. The head circumference:

A should be measured round the occipito-frontal perimeter

B is larger in boys than in girls

C is normally related to body size

D is irrelevant after the age of 5

E is normal in craniostenosis

46. The following are common features of Down's syndrome:

A hypotonia

B a small head circumference

C clinodactyly

D recurrent respiratory tract infections

E pigmented birth marks

47. Features of periodic syndrome include:
- **A** a mode age below the age of 5
- **B** an abnormal EEG
- **C** unilateral abdominal pain
- **D** low intelligence
- **E** vomiting

48. Children with nocturnal enuresis:
- **A** account for 10–15% of 5-year-olds
- **B** commonly have a first degree relative who also had nocturnal enuresis
- **C** are generally slow to acquire other skills also
- **D** should not be treated with drugs below the age of 5
- **E** usually have frequency of micturition by day

49. Tics (habit spasms):
- **A** are more common in girls than in boys
- **B** most commonly involve the hands
- **C** are best treated with antidepressant drugs
- **D** are an indication for referral to a Child Guidance Clinic
- **E** generally recur for at least 6 months

50. Faecal soiling is:
- **A** commonly associated with meningomyelocele
- **B** a frequent result of severe constipation
- **C** abnormal after the age of 5
- **D** an indication for rectal examination
- **E** the presenting feature of Hirschsprung's disease

51. Nightmares:

A are common
B are a sign of severe emotional disturbance
C occur during non-REM sleep
D cannot be remembered on waking up
E are precipitated by hypnotic drugs

52. Breath-holding attacks:

A are commoner over the age of $3\frac{1}{2}$ years
B are easily confused with a generalised seizure
C may be precipitated by a minor injury
D should be treated with sedatives
E are an important cause of brain damage

53. The following are important features of infantile autism:

A slowness in learning to talk
B failure to make warm emotional relationships
C slow development of gross motor skills
D infantile 'spasms'
E constipation

54. The following are common features of childhood migraine

A associated travel sickness
B a family history of migraine
C unilateral headache
D a headache lasting less than 2 minutes
E provocation by chocolate or cheese

55. The following are usually associated with severe psychological disturbance:

A masturbation in a pre-school child
B nightmares in an adolescent
C thumb sucking in a school child
D temper tantrums in a toddler
E head banging in an infant

CARDIOVASCULAR SYSTEM

56. The following are likely to be normal in a 5-year-old child:

A a blood pressure of 135/90
B a palpable systolic thrill
C a third heart sound
D a split second heart sound
E a pulse rate of 100 per minute

57. The blood pressure is likely to appear higher if:

A the child is standing
B the child is crying
C too large a sphygmomanometer cuff is used
D the flush method of determination is used
E the child is receiving corticosteroid therapy

58. Cardiac failure in infancy is characterised by:

A a respiratory rate of more than 40 per minute
B a heart rate of more than 150 per minute
C absent femoral pulses
D enlarged palpable liver
E feeding difficulty

59. There is an increased incidence of heart disease in:

A people who have had rheumatic fever
B children who have had rubella
C mongols
D Turner's syndrome
E children with diabetes mellitus

60. A ventricular-septal defect:

A usually causes cardiac failure in infancy
B is associated with a pan-systolic murmur
C is associated with plaeonaemic lung fields on chest X-ray
D may close spontaneously as the child becomes older
E is usually associated with a conduction defect

61. Patent ductus arteriosus:

A is a left-to-right shunt
B is associated with a high volume peripheral pulse
C generally requires surgical correction
D tends to cause clubbing of the fingers
E is associated with a characteristic murmur best heard at the back

62. Hypertension in a girl:

A may be cause by atrial septal defect
B is commoner than in a boy
C may be the result of renal disease
D is most likely to be 'essential' hypertension
E is more likely if the parents are hypertensive

63. Fallot's tetralogy is associated with:

A oligaemic lung fields on chest X-ray
B death by the age of 3 years unless corrected by surgery
C a widely split second heart sound
D a raised systolic blood pressure
E central cyanosis

64. Children aged 4:

A commonly develop otitis media
B commonly have sinusitis
C are too young to be tested by audiometry
D are too young to wear a hearing aid
E commonly have palpable cervical lymph glands

65. The following are features of acute otitis media:

A discharge from the ear
B pain in the ear
C buzzing in the ear
D a red eardrum
E neck stiffness

66. Indications for tonsillectomy are:

A recurrent colds
B recurrent wheezy bronchitis
C recurrent bouts of acute tonsillitis
D adenoidectomy
E otitis media

67. Stridor in a 2-year-old:

A may be normal
B is best heard on expiration
C may be the result of *Haemophilus influenzae* infection
D rarely lasts longer than 3 days
E may be caused by an inhaled foreign body

68. Bronchiolitis is commonly associated with:

- **A** measles
- **B** respiratory syncytial virus
- **C** onset in winter
- **D** an age of under 12 months
- **E** a respiratory rate of over 40 per minute

69. The following are commonly associated with childhood asthma:

- **A** a raised serum IgE level
- **B** a family history of enuresis
- **C** a positive skin test to house dust mite
- **D** a previous history of infantile eczema
- **E** wheezing after exercise

70. The following are useful for the treatment of status asthmaticus:

- **A** intravenous diazepam
- **B** intravenous adrenalin
- **C** disodiumcromoglycate by inhalation
- **D** intravenous aminophylline
- **E** intravenous hydrocortisone

71. Lobar pneumonia:

- **A** is commoner in children under the age of 4 than in school children
- **B** is usually caused by *Strep. pneumoniae*
- **C** is commonly caused by *Staph. pyogenes*
- **D** often gives rise to a pleural rub
- **E** generally causes the child to be ill for over 2 weeks

72. **Staphylococcal pneumonia:**
- **A** is common in childhood
- **B** is a common complication of cystic fibrosis
- **C** is characterised by lung abscesses on X-ray
- **D** is best treated with ampicillin
- **E** presents with stridor

ALIMENTARY TRACT

73. **The following are likely to be normal in an infant of 3 months:**
- **A** a liver palpable 2 cm below the right costal margin
- **B** a spleen palpable 1 cm below the left costal margin
- **C** a palpable right kidney
- **D** undescended testicles
- **E** no teeth apparent

74. **Polyhydramnios is associated with:**
- **A** renal agenesis
- **B** oesophageal atresia
- **C** rectal atresia
- **D** congenital club foot
- **E** anencephaly

75. **In infancy inguinal herniae:**
- **A** are commoner in boys
- **B** require prompt surgical correction even when they are reducible
- **C** do not strangulate in girls
- **D** are usually associated with umbilical herniae
- **E** are a feature of many syndromes involving multiple congenital abnormalities

76. Features of infantile pyloric stenosis include:

- **A** vomiting of progressive severity
- **B** anorexia
- **C** loose motions
- **D** onset within the first 21 days of life
- **E** absence of mucus in the vomit

77. Children with gastroenteritis:

- **A** usually yield a pathogenic *E. coli* in their stools
- **B** require treatment with an antibiotic which is not absorbed from the gut
- **C** may have blood in their stools
- **D** do not become severely dehydrated after the age of 4 years
- **E** often have severe abdominal pain

78. A child with gluten enteropathy:

- **A** generally presents before the age of 2 months
- **B** shows sub-total villous atrophy on jejunal biopsy
- **C** has a faecal fat content of less than 3 grams per day
- **D** has anorexia
- **E** can usually tolerate rye but not wheat

79. Important features of herpetic stomatitis include:

- **A** vesicles and ulcers on the buccal mucosa as well as the tongue and palate
- **B** inflamed gums
- **C** pain
- **D** recent contact with chicken pox
- **E** cervical lymph gland enlargement

80. Blood-stained stools in an infant are associated with:

A severe constipation
B gastroenteritis
C nose bleeds
D intussusception
E coeliac disease

81. The following are common features of cystic fibrosis:

A autosomal recessive inheritance
B presentation with intestinal obstruction in the newborn
C offensive stools as a toddler
D umbilical hernia in infancy
E staphylococcal pneumonia in the school child

82. Threadworms:

A are common in school children
B cause diarrhoea
C cause bedwetting
D cause abdominal pain
E cause eosinophilia

83. The following investigations are particularly useful in the diagnosis of cystic fibrosis:

A chest X-ray
B ECG
C full blood count
D sweat sodium concentration
E barium meal X-ray

SKELETAL SYSTEM AND CONNECTIVE TISSUE DISORDERS

84. Congenital dislocation of the hip:

- **A** usually requires correction by operative surgery before the age of 2 years
- **B** is commoner in girls
- **C** is commoner in children with spina bifida
- **D** may cause apparent shortening of one leg
- **E** is commoner in pre-term babies than those born at 40 weeks gestation

85. A schoolboy who presents with a 3-day illness caused by acute osteomyelitis is likely to have:

- **A** severe localised pain
- **B** fever
- **C** neutrophil leucocytosis
- **D** an abnormal limb X-ray
- **E** a blood culture growth of staphylococci

86. Permanent joint damage may result from:

- **A** Henoch–Schönlein syndrome
- **B** rheumatic fever
- **C** tuberculosis
- **D** Still's disease
- **E** haemophilia

87. Pathognomonic rashes of rheumatic fever include:

- **A** purpura on lateral aspects of the buttocks
- **B** erythema nodosum on the back
- **C** erythema marginatum on the trunk
- **D** erythema multiforme of the limbs
- **E** papular urticaria on the legs

88. A child with rheumatic fever is likely to:
- **A** show choreiform movements of the upper limbs
- **B** have had lobar pneumonia 2–6 weeks previously
- **C** show a sustained rise of the anti-streptolysin O titre
- **D** have a systolic cardiac murmur
- **E** be over the age of 6 years

89. Henoch–Schonlein syndrome is associated with:
- **A** thrombocytopenic purpura
- **B** mitral stenosis
- **C** glomerulonephritis
- **D** characteristic lesions in the mouth
- **E** abdominal pain

THE SKIN

90. The following birth marks usually fade and disappear by adult life:
- **A** Mongolian blue spot
- **B** strawberry naevus
- **C** port-wine stain
- **D** pigmented mole
- **E** stork mark

91. Features of childhood eczema include:
- **A** itching
- **B** involvement of extensor surfaces by school age
- **C** a family history suggesting atopy
- **D** onset before the age of 12 months
- **E** lymphadenopathy

92. Important causes of erythema nodosum include:

A tuberculosis
B sulphonamide administration
C Henoch–Schönlein syndrome
D streptococcal infection
E congenital heart disease

93. A Mongolian blue spot is common in:

A Indians
B West-Indians
C Down's syndrome
D the lumbo-sacral region
E Chinese children

94. The following conditions often have a strong genetic predisposition:

A eczema
B impetigo
C psoriasis
D erythema nodosum
E scabies

URINARY TRACT

95. The fetus in the womb:

A has a serum urea greater than 10 mmol/l
B does not pass urine until the third trimester of pregnancy
C may be associated with oligohydramnios if there is renal agenesis
D will be stillborn if there is only one kidney
E has produced the total number of nephrons by full term

96. Cloudy urine is associated with the following substances in the urine:

A chemical deposits
B bacteria
C blood
D albumin
E colouring from candy-floss

97. The following findings on microscopy of a fresh early morning midstream urine specimen from a boy of 8 are abnormal:

A a white cell count of 50 per mm^3
B a red cell count of 10 per mm^3
C a granular cast
D a hyaline cast
E motile bacteria

98. The following conditions are inherited by Mendelian patterns of inheritance:

A polycystic disease
B nephrogenic diabetes insipidus
C posterior urethral valve
D 'minimal change' nephrotic syndrome
E Henoch–Schönlein nephritis

99. The following findings in fresh urine require further investigation:

A an albumin concentration of 0.6 g/l
B a positive reaction for haemoglobin
C an ammoniacal smell
D a pH of 5
E ketonuria

100. Circumcision is usually required for the following boys:

A Jewish, after the age of 4 weeks
B Sikh
C West-Indian
D Muslim
E Hindu

101. The urine of a child with nephrotic syndrome is likely to:

A be frothy
B be of small volume
C show a highly selective differential protein clearance pattern
D contain excess white cells
E reveal microscopic haematuria

102. Post-streptococcal glomerulonephritis characteristically:

A occurs in pre-school children
B follows one or two weeks after a *Strep. pneumonia* infection
C is associated with generalised oedema
D requires confinement to bed for at least 4 weeks
E is a rare cause of end-stage renal failure

103. Nephrotic syndrome is characterised by:

A hypertension
B heavy proteinuria
C hypoalbuminaemia
D reduced serum complement
E raised blood urea

104. Urinary tract infection:

- **A** is commoner in girls
- **B** is commonly caused by *E. coli*
- **C** should be treated by a course of antibiotics lasting at least 4 weeks
- **D** is associated with vesico-ureteric reflux
- **E** is diagnosed by a colony count of more than 10^6 organisms/l

105. Routine management of a boy with urinary tract infection would include:

- **A** avoidance of bubble baths
- **B** encouragement to void frequently
- **C** a kidney X-ray
- **D** a course of chemotherapy
- **E** measurement of the blood urea

106. The following features are likely to be seen in a child of 3 with chronic renal insufficiency originating from dysplastic kidneys:

- **A** a haemoglobin of less than 8 g/dl
- **B** short stature
- **C** oliguria
- **D** bow legs
- **E** hypertension

HAEMATOLOGY AND ONCOLOGY

107. The following haematological findings would be considered normal in a 3-month-old infant:

- **A** haemoglobin concentration of 11.5 g/dl
- **B** a white cell count of 12.0×10^9/l
- **C** more lymphocytes than neutrophil polymorphs
- **D** an eosinophil count of 0.61×10^9/l
- **E** a 10% concentration of HbF

108. The following conditions are commonly controlled by sex-linked recessive genes:

A thalassaemia
B haemophilia A
C haemophilia B
D glucose-6-phosphate dehydrogenase deficiency
E hereditary spherocytosis

109. Iron deficiency anaemia is associated with:

A a low mean corpuscular volume (MCV)
B raised serum ferritin
C a mean corpuscular haemoglobin concentration of less than 32 g/dl
D acanthocytosis
E a reticulocyte count of less than 5%

110. Children from Pakistan living in Britain are more likely to develop the following conditions than children of European origin:

A Sickle cell disease
B thalassaemia
C glucose-6-phosphate dehydrogenase deficiency
D iron deficiency anaemia
E pernicious anaemia

111. The following foods are important sources of iron in childhood:

A eggs
B bread
C proprietary brands of powdered cow's milk
D potatoes
E green vegetables

112. Characteristic symptoms and signs of sickle-cell disease include:

A acute abdominal pain
B acute limb pain
C disseminated intravascular thromboses
D leucocytosis
E fever

113. Splenomegaly is a feature of:

A haemolytic anaemia
B folic acid deficiency anaemia
C septicaemia
D acute lymphoblastic leukaemia
E haemophilia

114. The following conditions are associated with thrombocytopenic purpura:

A scurvy
B Henoch–Schönlein syndrome
C leukaemia
D severe renal insufficiency
E meningococcal septicaemia

115. A nephroblastoma (Wilm's tumour) is likely to present:

A before the age of 4 years
B with abdominal pain
C with an enlarged abdomen
D with visible abnormality of the urine
E with hypertension

116. The following statements are true of malignant disease in childhood:

A it is the commonest cause of death in school children
B permanent cure does not occur
C tumours of the nervous system are the commonest form of malignancy
D it is not inherited
E new cases are twice as common as they were 20 years ago

METABOLIC DISORDERS

117. Congenital hypothyroidism (cretinism) is characterised by:

A prolonged neonatal jaundice
B single palmar creases
C feeding difficulty in infancy
D a shrill 'cerebral' cry
E hypotonia

118. Adrenogenital syndrome is associated with:

A sex-linked inheritance
B over-production of ACTH
C vomiting in the neonatal period
D undescended testicles
E convulsions in the neonatal period

119. Diabetes mellitus in childhood:

A requires treatment with insulin
B occurs most commonly in obese children
C is an important cause of childhood renal failure
D may resolve as adulthood is reached
E is commoner than it was 30 years ago

120. The following are useful for the diagnosis of cretinism:

A serum cholesterol level
B X-ray of the knees
C measurement of the head circumference
D measurement of the neck circumference
E plasma thyroxine level

121. The following conditions are causes of permanent mental handicap:

A adrenogenital syndrome
B galactosaemia
C Cushing's syndrome
D phenylketonuria
E hypoglycaemia

122. The following would be expected in a child with nephrogenic diabetes insipidus:

A urine osmolality of less than 400
B male sex
C craving for salt
D antidiuretic hormone deficiency
E failure to thrive in infancy and growth retardation

123. The Guthrie test:

A must be done on a fresh specimen of urine
B depends upon the inhibition of bacterial growth by phenylalanine
C should be done within the first 48 hours of life
D is unreliable if the baby has jaundice
E is a radio-immunoassay

THERAPEUTICS

124. Well-recognised methods of reducing a high fever include:

A taking a cold bath
B oral paracetamol
C salicylate rectal suppository
D oral barbiturates
E removal of clothes

125. A special diet is usually advised for children with:

A hypothyroidism
B a blood urea higher than 12 mmol/l
C diabetes mellitus
D hypertension
E galactosaemia

126. Games and PE at school are not advised for children with:

A epilepsy
B periodic syndrome
C recurrent respiratory tract infections
D nephrotic syndrome
E hydrocephalus

127. Swimming is not advisable for a child who has:

A epilepsy
B eczema
C chronic otitis media
D asthma
E recurrent urinary tract infection

128. Prolonged phenytoin therapy is associated with:

A coarsening of the facial features
B rickets
C gum hyperplasia
D hirsutism
E intellectual deterioration

129. Well-recognised complications of corticosteroid therapy include:

A glycosuria
B precocious puberty
C stunting of height
D raised blood pressure
E tinnitus

IMMUNISATION AND INFECTIOUS DISEASES

130. The following substances cross the placenta freely:

A immunoglobulin G
B immunoglobulin M
C pethidine
D urea
E corticosteroids

131. By the age of 3 years a child living in Britain should have been immunised against:

A tuberculosis
B poliomyelitis
C diphtheria
D mumps
E tetanus

132. The following immunisations are generally performed using a live organism:

A poliomyelitis
B measles
C rubella
D smallpox
E whooping cough

133. Pertussis vaccine should not be given:

A to a child under the age of 6 months
B to a child with cerebral palsy
C orally
D to a child who has had fits
E At the same time as another immunisation procedure

134. Rubella vaccine:

A is given by intramuscular injection
B is given to all children between the ages of 11 and 14
C should not be given to pregnant women
D should not be given to anyone thought to have had rubella
E provides immunity for a maximum of 4 years

135. BCG

A is given subcutaneously
B is given intradermally
C commonly causes enlarged painful axillary glands
D commonly causes local induration for more than 2 months
E is required by over 90% of British school children over the age of 10

136. Features of mumps in childhood include:

- **A** an incubation period of around 18 days
- **B** parotitis
- **C** orchitis
- **D** meningitis
- **E** lymphopenia

137. Features of whooping cough in infancy include:

- **A** an incubation period of around 10 days
- **B** Koplik's spots
- **C** a paroxysmal cough
- **D** pneumonia
- **E** lymphopenia

138. The following infections may be caused by farmyard animals:

- **A** glandular fever
- **B** tuberculosis
- **C** poliomyelitis
- **D** brucellosis
- **E** chicken pox

139. A child presenting with tuberculous meningitis:

- **A** is likely to have been ill for at least 2 weeks
- **B** should be notified to the Area Environmental Health Officer
- **C** may incur permanent brain damage
- **D** will have raised levels of protein and white cells in the CSF
- **E** will have a normal chest X-ray

140. Glandular fever is associated with:

- **A** histoplasmosis
- **B** Epstein–Barr virus
- **C** a polymorphonuclearleucocytosis
- **D** splenomegaly
- **E** pancreatitis

141. A child presenting with the rash of measles will generally have:

- **A** fever, cough and conjunctivitis
- **B** a rash on the face
- **C** a rash on the hands
- **D** a raised measles antibody titre
- **E** eosinophilia

142. Congenital rubella is associated with:

- **A** raised IGM level in the neonate
- **B** perceptive deafness
- **C** cataract
- **D** Down's syndrome
- **E** neonatal jaundice

143. Vaccination against smallpox is not recommended for:

- **A** anyone with eczema
- **B** most British children
- **C** clinical doctors
- **D** anyone who has had chicken pox
- **E** pregnant women

ACCIDENTS

144. The following statements apply to accidental poisoning in childhood:

A it is commoner in the pre-school child than the school child
B drugs are a commoner cause of morbidity and mortality than household and garden products
C berries and seeds rarely cause serious illness in the British Isles
D activated charcoal given orally is useful general therapy
E desferrioxamine is useful specific therapy for salicylate poisoning

145. Pharmacologically induced emesis or gastric lavage are contraindicated in the following circumstances:

A if the poison has been ingested more than 3 hours earlier
B ingestion of caustic soda
C ingestion of a piece of chalk
D ingestion of paraffin
E if the child is below the age of 2

146. Chronic lead poisoning is associated with:

A pica
B abdominal pain
C anaemia
D abnormal bone X-ray
E diarrhoea

147. Accidents are an important cause of morbidity in childhood and:

A are the commonest cause of death in school children
B deaths from poisoning are more common than from non-accidental injury (battered baby syndrome)
C deaths from burns are more common than deaths from drowning
D road accidents are the commonest cause of death
E are commoner in girls than in boys

148. The following are features of non-accidental injury (battered baby syndrome):

A a mode age of 18–24 months
B multiple fractures of the ribs
C sub-periosteal haematoma of the long bones
D sub-hyaloid haemorrhage
E sub-dural haematoma

149. Cot deaths are more common in:

A males
B social class V
C infants over the age of 6 months
D infants of low birth weight
E the winter

150. Death from road accidents would be less if:

A children were forbidden to travel in the front seat of the car
B children were forbidden to read in the car
C children were made to wear safety belts
D carry-cots for infants were strapped to the back seat of the car rather than left loose
E it was forbidden to ride a motor cycle until the age of 18

MISCELLANEOUS

151. Girls of Pakistani parents are:

- **A** likely to be Muslim (the Islam religion)
- **B** at risk for thalassaemia major
- **C** at risk for sickle-cell disease
- **D** given the title Kaur as one of their names
- **E** likely to avoid eating pork

152. Illegitimate babies:

- **A** are usually adopted
- **B** have a greater chance of being born to a mother under the age of 20 than an offspring born in wedlock
- **C** comprise about 9% of all live births
- **D** are associated with an increased perinatal mortality rate
- **E** are placed under a Supervision Order at birth

153. Vesico-ureteric reflux:

- **A** is found in about 25% of schoolgirls with 'asymptomatic' bacteriuria
- **B** requires surgical correction by the age of 8 years
- **C** may be associated with kidney damage
- **D** is identified by an intravenous pyelogram
- **E** is an important cause of nocturnal enuresis

154. A boy need not attend school if he is:

- **A** under the age of 5 years
- **B** over the age of 15 years
- **C** over the age of 15 years and has a paid job which occupies at least two hours each day
- **D** classified as suffering from severe visual impairment
- **E** subject to a 'Supervision Order'

155. Antibiotics are an important part of the treatment of:

- **A** bronchiolitis
- **B** impetigo
- **C** otitis media
- **D** acute glomerulonephritis
- **E** gastroenteritis

156. A child who is the subject of a Care Order is likely:

- **A** to be supervised by the Probation Department
- **B** to have only one living parent
- **C** to have a severe medical disorder
- **D** to have parental rights transferred to the local authority
- **E** to have regular contact with a social worker

157. A positive Tuberculin test:

- **A** is associated with previous BCG immunisation
- **B** may be absent in severe tuberculous meningitis
- **C** does not occur after the age of 1 year
- **D** should be elicited by subcutaneous injection of Tuberculin
- **E** is characterised by induration present 2 days after the test

158. Vomiting in infancy is a feature of:

- **A** Hirschsprung's disease
- **B** pyloric stenosis
- **C** hiatus hernia
- **D** adreno-genital syndrome
- **E** light-for-dates babies

159. Children with the following features cannot be adopted:

A Age over 5 years
B Hydrocephalus
C A Roman Catholic mother
D A congenital heart lesion
E Natural parents of different colour

160. The stools of breast-fed babies tend to differ from bottle-fed babies in the following ways:

A more frequent
B more loose
C more odour
D more brown
E more undigested fat

161. Important consequences of rheumatic fever in later life include:

A ankylosing spondylitis
B mitral stenosis
C coarctation of the aorta
D choreoathetoid cerebral palsy
E renal insufficiency

162. The following statements are approximately true:

A one pound weight = 450 grams
B 1000 millilitres = 1 litre
C 20 fluid ounces = 1 pint
D one litre = 1.76 pints
E one inch = 0.0254 metre

163. The following are indications for circumcision:

A hypospadias
B a long foreskin
C recurrent balanitis
D non-retractile foreskin at age of 2 years
E if the father has had cancer of the penis

164. Considering the incidence of the conditions it can be expected that a general practitioner will encounter more children presenting with:

A respiratory tract infection than urinary tract infection
B seizures than diabetes mellitus
C muscular dystrophy than cerebral palsy
D mental handicap than congenital dislocation of the hip
E spina bifida than phenylketonuria

165. Fallot's tetralogy is made up of:

A right ventricular hypertrophy
B pulmonary artery arising from left ventricle
C over-riding aorta
D pulmonary stenosis
E ventricular septal defect

166. Boys of Hindu parents:

A are frequently brought up as vegetarians
B are given the title Singh as one of their names
C are likely to avoid eating beef
D are usually circumcised
E frequently have a Mongolian blue spot on their back

167. The following disorders are commoner in the children of parents of social class V than social class I:

A accidents and poisoning
B malignant disease
C major congenital abnormalities
D measles
E asthma

168. Acute laryngotracheitis:

A occurs most commonly in the child under the age of 4 years
B generally follows a 3/4 day prodromal illness
C presents with stridor
D usually results from bacterial infection
E can cause severe respiratory distress and obstruction

169. A neonate with Trisomy 21 is more likely to have the following features than a normal neonate:

A a third fontanelle
B a cardiac murmur
C hyperbilirubinaemia
D hyaline-membrane disease
E intestinal obstruction

170. Concerning the causes of death in childhood during the last 40 years, it is true to say now that:

A death from neoplasm is twice as common
B death from accidents is twice as common
C death from infection is at least 10 times less common
D death in the first month of life is at least two times less common
E death from diabetes mellitus is more common

171. A 14-year-old boy who has recently returned from a four week holiday with grandparents in Pakistan is at risk of developing:

A smallpox
B malaria
C kwashiorkor
D rickets
E tuberculosis

172. Breathlessness on feeding is a feature of an infant with:

A pyloric stenosis
B cardiac failure
C respiratory tract infection
D tracheo-oesophageal fistula
E mental handicap

173. The following sugars are disaccharides:

A galactose
B fructose
C lactose
D maltose
E sucrose

174. Radiological evidence of chronic pyelonephritis includes:

A cortical scarring
B nephrocalcinosis
C hydronephrosis
D clubbing of the calyces
E kidneys of different size

175. The following conditions are usually associated with characteristic skin disorders:

A galactosaemia

B Sturge–Weber syndrome

C Henoch–Schönlein syndrome

D diabetes mellitus

E tuberose sclerosis

CASE STUDIES

CASE 1

A 4-week-old boy is admitted to hospital because of vomiting. He is the second child of healthy West-Indian parents. He was born at the end of a normal pregnancy and weighed 3.4 kg. He was breast fed for one week until his mother changed to bottle feeding. At that stage he began to vomit after and between feeds. For the previous two days the vomit contained slime and, on one occasion, blood. For the previous two weeks he had opened his bowels less than once a day.

On examination he is a thin, pale, drowsy baby weighing 3.6 kg. He is floppy and has an umbilical hernia of 2.5 cm diameter. The head circumference is 38 cm with an anterior fontanelle 3 cm in diameter and sunken. Blood tests reveal: haemoglobin 18 g/dl; WBC 15×10^9/l; plasma urea 15 mmol/l. The urine appears dark, is of pH 6, strongly positive for ketones, and has a trace of albumin.

a What therapeutic manoeuvre is required?
b What diagnostic manoeuvre is required?
c What is the best management of the umbilical hernia?

CASE 2

A 3-year-old girl has recurrent attacks which are described by the mother as follows: 'She suddenly gasps, stops breathing, goes red in the face then blue, then falls unconscious to the ground. Sometimes she twitches when unconscious and once she wet herself. The first one came on after she had banged her head on the table, the second when crying after I had told her she couldn't go outside. They are now happening as often as twice a day and last for at least a minute. She seems all right afterwards.'

a What are these attacks?
b What causes them?
c What is the prognosis?
d Is drug therapy indicated?

CASE 3

A baby of 5 months has recurrent episodes 'when he suddenly jumps and throws out his arms and nods his head forward'. He is otherwise healthy.

On examination he looks normal, the skull circumference is 40 cm and his developmental skills are in the range 3–5 months. The perinatal history was normal and the family history is also normal.

a What is the differential diagnosis?
b What special investigation is indicated and in what way might it be abnormal?
c What is the prognosis?

CASE 4

A boy aged 4 years is noticed by his parents to have a swollen face. His urine is frothy in the toilet. He is a bit bad tempered but does not seem ill despite the fact that he is 'just recovering from a cold'. On examination there is generalised oedema and mild ascites, the blood pressure, pulse rate and heart sounds are normal. He has had no serious previous illnesses. His father had epilepsy and there are two healthy siblings.

a What is the probable diagnosis?
b What two confirmatory investigations are required?
c What is the prognosis?
d What drug is likely to be required?

CASE 5

A 4-year-old boy became ill while staying at the family holiday cottage in Scotland. He had a 'runny nose' during the day and then at 11.00 p.m. awoke breathless and crying. He had had two similar but milder episodes, one the previous year when in the holiday cottage, and the other after a cousin's birthday party.

On examination his height is 97 cm and weight 16 kg. There is respiratory distress with flaring of the alar nasae and indrawing of the subcostal region. The respiratory rate is 44 per minute, pulse rate 100 per minute. Generalised rhonchi, most marked on expiration, can be heard.

a Which two conditions would you put at the top of your list of differential diagnoses?
b In which aspects of the family history are you most interested?
c Give at least two explanations for the way in which the circumstances and location of the attacks might be relevant?

CASE 6

A 3-year-old presents with a fever and sore mouth. For 2 days she has refused to eat and has been very miserable. On examination there are many small ulcers on the inside of her mouth. Her gums are involved also, are a dusky red, and bleeding a little. The cervical glands are enlarged and tender. Otherwise she seems healthy and in particular she has no rash on the rest of her body. Apart from a severe respiratory infection (probably bronchiolitis) at the age of 9 months she has been healthy.

a What is the diagnosis?
b What is the cause?
c What is the chance of recurrence?

CASE 7

A $1\frac{1}{2}$-year-old Cypriot child presents with poor weight gain, irritability, and feeding difficulty. He is pale. Developmental assessment suggests that he behaves more like a one-year-old than a $1\frac{1}{2}$-year-old.

The blood picture is as follows: Hb 8.0 g/dl; MCV 70 u^3; MCHC 30%; WBC 10×10^9/l; (neutrophils 30%; lymphocytes 60%); ESR 20.

a What type of anaemia is present?
b What is the likely reason for it?
c In view of the poor developmental skills what other aspects of the history is of particular importance?
d Why is the absence of splenomegaly of particular importance?

CASE 8

A 3-year-old boy is admitted to hospital because of a severe pneumonia. Physical examination reveals a rather underweight boy who is febrile and has signs of a right pleural effusion. Chest X-ray appears to show an abscess cavity in the right upper zone. It is the fourth severe respiratory tract infection that the boy has had.

He is the only child of healthy parents. The pregnancy was normal, but during the neonatal period he had prolonged jaundice and severe constipation.

a What is the most likely cause of the pneumonia?
b Suggest an underlying cause and two useful confirmatory symptoms or investigations?

CASE 9

A 22-year-old Indian mother is delivered of a 2 kg baby by breech delivery at the end of a 39 week pregnancy. The early pregnancy was spent in India, and was complicated by considerable vomiting and an 'influenza like' illness about the third month.

After delivery the baby had an Apgar score of 6 at one minute and 10 at four minutes. She appeared healthy but small. On the second day jaundice became apparent and by the fourth day her serum bilirubin was 164 μmol/l. She was slightly lethargic but taking feeds reasonably.

a What is the probable cause of the jaundice?
b Name any special treatment that is likely to be required?
c What is the probable reason for her low birth weight?

CASE 10

A mother is worried that her $2\frac{1}{2}$-year-old daughter does not talk. The girl makes noises but no distinct words. She makes her needs known by gesture. She is a healthy child. She can run and climb stairs. She copies a circle with a pencil, and can build a tower of 8 cubes. She is dry by day, but wears nappies at night. She can undress herself and eats with a spoon and fork.

She is the first child of parents who are both teachers, though the mother has not gone out to work since the daughter arrived. The pregnancy and perinatal history were normal.

a Should the mother be reassured that her daughter is essentially normal?
b What is the likely reason for the speech problem?
c What further investigation is required?

CASE 11

A 5-year-old boy develops pain in the right knee and the right hand. He is not feverish and does not feel ill. Three days later a purpuric rash becomes apparent, and is most prominent about the ankles. His blood picture shows: Hb 13 g/dl; WBC 8.2×10^9/l; platelets 180×10^9/l. There is no family history of a bleeding disorder or similar rash. Apart from occasional 'wheezy bronchitis' he has been well. He has had no immunisation because the mother 'does not believe in them'.

a What is the probable diagnosis?
b Name two additional symptoms and signs which may develop during the following weeks.
c What is the chest X-ray likely to show?

CASE 12

A 4-month-old infant presents with poor weight gain. He has always been a slow feeder, and in particular would only take small quantities of milk at a time. He has been a restless irritable baby who sweated a lot.

On examination his length is 62 cm and weight 4.8 kg. He looks pale. The pulse rate is 190/min, the respiratory rate 54/min. The blood pressure is 80/40. There is a grade 4/6 pansystolic murmur heard best to the left of the sternum. The liver is palpable 4 cm below the right costal margin. The pregnancy was complicated by severe vomiting in the first 3 months and a threatened miscarriage at 16 weeks. His birth weight was 3.1 kg.

a What is the probable diagnosis?
b Name two immediate (and simple) investigations which would help to establish a diagnosis.
c Give three important therapeutic manoeuvres.

ANSWERS TO MULTIPLE CHOICE QUESTIONS

Correct (True) responses are:

1. A B D E
2. A B D E
3. B D E
4. B C D
5. C D E
6. B C D
7. A B C
8. B C E
9. A C D E
10. A B C
11. B E
12. B C
13. B C D E
14. A C E
15. C E
16. A B C D
17. B C D
18. A B C D E
19. C D E
20. B C
21. C D E
22. A C
23. A D E
24. A C D E
25. A B C
26. A C E
27. A B C D
28. B C D E
29. A B D E
30. B D
31. A B C D E
32. A D
33. A C
34. B C D
35. A B C D
36. A B C D
37. A C D E
38. A B C D E
39. B C E
40. A B E
41. B C D
42. A E
43. C D E
44. B D
45. A B C
46. A B C D
47. E
48. A B D
49. E
50. A B C D
51. A
52. B C
53. A B
54. A B C E
55. None
56. C D E
57. B E
58. A B D E
59. A C D
60. B C D
61. A B C
62. C E
63. A E

64. A E
65. A B D
66. C
67. C D E
68. B C D E
69. A C D E
70. D E
71. B D
72. B C
73. A B C E
74. B C E
75. A B E
76. A D
77. C E
78. B D
79. A B C E
80. A B D
81. A B C E
82. A
83. A D
84. B C D
85. A B C E
86. C D E
87. C
88. C D E
89. C E
90. A B E
91. A C D E
92. A B D
93. A B D E
94. A C
95. C E
96. A B C
97. A B C E
98. A B
99. A B C
100. D
101. A B C
102. E
103. B C
104. A B D
105. B C D
106. A B D E
107. A B C E
108. B C D
109. A C E
110. B C D
111. A B C E
112. A B C D E
113. A C D
114. C
115. A C
116. None
117. A C E
118. B C
119. A E
120. A B E
121. B D E
122. A B E
123. None
124. B C E
125. C D E
126. None
127. C
128. A B C D
129. A C D
130. A C D E
131. B C E
132. A B C D
133. B C D
134. C
135. B C D E
136. A B D
137. A C D
138. B D

139. A B C D
140. B D
141. A B
142. A B C E
143. A B E
144. A B C D
145. B C D
146. A B C D
147. A D
148. B C D E
149. A B D E
150. A C D E
151. A B E
152. B C D
153. A C
154. A
155. B C
156. D E
157. A B E
158. A B C D
159. None
160. A B
161. B
162. A B C D E
163. None
164. A B D E
165. A C D E
166. A C E
167. A C D
168. A C E
169. A B E
170. C D
171. B
172. B C D
173. C D E
174. A D E
175. B C E

ANSWERS TO CASE STUDIES

CASE 1

a Rehydration with intravenous fluids. He is dehydrated and the vomiting suggests that he may not tolerate oral fluids.
b A test feed during which the abdomen is palpated for a pyloric lump (i.e. pyloric stenosis).
c Reassure the parents that umbilical herniae are common and harmless and that his will go by the age of 12 months.

CASE 2

a Breath-holding attacks.
b The child being hurt, angry or frustrated.
c Excellent, she will 'grow out of them' by the age of 5.
d No.

CASE 3

a i. Salaam attack (infantile spasms).
ii. A normal startle response in a normal baby.
b Electroencephalograph. Infantile spasms are associated with hypsarrhythmia.
c Most infants who have infantile spasms grow up to have recurrent seizures or mental handicap (or both of these).

CASE 4

a Idiopathic nephrotic syndrome.
b i. Serum albumin, which will be low.
ii. Urine protein, which will be excessive.
c Troublesome, with recurrent attacks in childhood. Eventual cure and normal adult life are likely.
d Prednisone (or other corticosteroid).

CASE 5

a i. Acute asthma.
ii. Lower respiratory tract infection, e.g. pneumonia.
b The presence in close relatives of:
i. Similar attacks.
ii. Hay fever, eczema or sensitivity rashes, i.e. 'atopy'.
c i. The 'runny nose' could be a sign of infection or allergic rhinitis (hay fever) either of which could lead to an attack of wheezing.
ii. The 'holiday house' could bring him into contact with particular allergens, e.g. pollens in the appropriate season or, more likely, house dust mite which is notorious for nestling in unfrequented holiday cottages.
iii. The 'birthday party' could cause him to have excessive excitement or exercise, either of which might bring on wheezing.
iv. Allergy to haggis and the sound of bagpipes is a good idea, but in this case cannot be allowed.

CASE 6

a Herpetic stomatitis (hepatic gingivo-stomatitis).
b Primary infection with *herpesvirus hominis* (herpes simplex virus).
c It will not recur in the severe form; subsequent reactivation will cause merely a 'cold sore' on the lip.

CASE 7

a Iron deficiency (microcytic, hypochromic).
b Insufficient iron in diet because of feeding difficulty, and slowness to chew solids because of mental handicap.
c The perinatal history, because adverse events *in utero*, at birth, and in the neonatal period are particularly likely to cause brain damage.
d Cypriots are prone to glucose-6-phosphate dehydrogenase deficiency and to thalassaemia major, either of which is associated with splenomegaly.

CASE 8

a *Staphylococcus pyogenes.* Tuberculosis is also possible.
b Cystic fibrosis
  i. Offensive loose faeces.
  ii. Sweat sodium and chloride measurement.
  iii. Analysis of faeces.
  iv. Analysis of duodenal juice.

CASE 9

a Physiological jaundice (immaturity of the liver enzyme glucuronyl transferrase).
b None is likely to be required though, if the rate of rise of bilirubin became excessive, phenobarbitone or blue light phototherapy could be helpful.
c A racial or familial characteristic.

आज के सभी ऑर्डर्स का डिक्टेशन ले चुकने के बाद मिसेज़ जी ने उठते-उठते कहा, "एक...छोटी-सी न्यूज़ है, सर!"

"[illegible]?" आकाश ने भौंहें उठाईं।

"[illegible], सर! आपने तो...लोन के लिए जो एप्लीकेशन दी थी न..."

"हाँ, वो फ्रिज ख़रीदने के लिए!"

"जी हाँ! वो लोन सैंक्शन हो गया है, सर!"

"इतनी जल्दी? लोग सुधर गए हैं!"

"आपकी संगत का असर है!"

"रियली?"

"कागज़ात ले आऊँ अभी? दस्तख़त कर देंगे?"

"ज़रूर! क्यों नहीं! नेकी और पूछ-पूछ!"

मिसेज़ जी भारी उत्साह के साथ आकाश के कमरे से निकल गईं। उसी भारी उत्साह के साथ वह वापस भी आईं, हाथ में लोन-पेपर्स लिये हुए। मेज़ पर आकाश के आगे लोन-पेपर्स फैलाकर, उँगली रख-रखकर उन्होंने बताना शुरू किया, "एक दस्तख़त यहाँ, एक यहाँ, एक यहाँ..." उसी हिसाब से आकाश दस्तख़त करता चला।

मिसेज़ जी जब लोन-पेपर्स वापस समेट रही थीं, उनके लाल लिपस्टिक में सने होंठों पर गहन-गहन मुसकान एक बार फिर उभरने लगी। आकाश ने अपने आपको तैयार कर लिया—अवश्य मिसेज़ जी अपने पिटारे में से फिर कुछ नया निकालने वाली हैं...

"सर, एक और भी न्यूज़ है!"

"आज तो आप न्यूज़ की बौछार कर रही हैं, मिसेज़ जी!"

"सर! अपनी यह जो कन्ज़्यूमर्स को-ऑपरेटिव सोसायटी है न, आई.टी.ओ. की..."

"हाँ, हाँ, जिसकी आप सुझाती हैं..."

"यस, सर! उसके बारे में न्यूज़ यह है, सर, कि बहुत जल्दी यह सोसायटी टीवी, टी.वी. और फ्रिज में भी डीलिंग शुरू करनेवाली है।"

और मिसेज़ जी की गहन मुसकान आत्म-विश्वास से और भी गहन हो गई। आकाश ने सहज पूछा, "बहुत खूब! कब तक?"

"बस, यही इसी माह!"

"यानी, अगर मैं अपना फ्रिज अभी न ख़रीदूँ, बल्कि दो इसके बाद ख़रीदूँ, तो..."

"सर, किसी भी मॉडल का फ्रिज आई.टी.ओ. की सोसायटी से ख़रीदने पर, आपको दो सौ से कम पाँच सौ रुपए तक का डिस्काउंट मिलेगा!"

अर्थचक्र

शीला झुनझुनवाला

राजकमल प्रकाशन
नयी दिल्ली पटना इलाहाबाद

मूल्य : ₹ 200

पहला संस्करण : 2011

प्रकाशक : राजकमल प्रकाशन प्रा. लि.
1-बी, नेताजी सुभाष मार्ग
नई दिल्ली-110 002

शाखाएँ : अशोक राजपथ, साइंस कॉलेज के सामने, पटना-800 006
पहली मंजिल, दरबारी बिल्डिंग, महात्मा गांधी मार्ग, इलाहाबाद-211 001

वेबसाइट : www.rajkamalprakashan.com
ई-मेल : info@rajkamalprakashan.com

आवरण : राजकमल स्टूडियो

मुद्रक : बी.के. ऑफसेट
नवीन शाहदरा, दिल्ली-110 032

ARTH-CHAKRA
Novel by Sheela Jhunjhunwala

ISBN : 978-81-267-2054-5

अर्थचक्र

आकाश के साथ तो अधिकतम आत्मीयता का नाता है शालिनी का, किन्तु सूरज शालिनी का क्या लगता है? हर सुबह सूरज ही क्यों उठाता है शालिनी को? सूरज क्षितिज से निकलता है और शालिनी अपने बिस्तर से निकलती है। गर्मियों में सूरज जल्दी निकल आता है क्षितिज से। शालिनी भी गर्मियों में बिस्तर जल्दी छोड़ देती है। सर्दियों में सूरज ज़रा देरी से, ज़रा सहमा-सहमा निकलता है क्षितिज से। शालिनी भी सर्दियों में बिस्तर देरी से ही छोड़ती है। बम्बई में सर्दी नहीं के जैसी पड़ती है, तो भी शालिनी मोटी चादर ओढ़े कसमसाती रहती है। अरे, अभी सूरज तो निकला नहीं है। अभी से बिस्तर से क्या निकलना!

यों, सूरज ने शालिनी को प्रकृति से जोड़ रखा है। आज के मशीनी युग में लोग अलार्म-घड़ी की मशीनी आवाज़ से जागते हैं। शालिनी सूरज की स्नेहभरी, नैसर्गिक थपथपाहट से जागती है। अहोभाग्य!

एक अहोभाग्य सूरज! दूसरा अहोभाग्य आकाश! आह! क्या रोमांटिक नाम है। कैसी अनन्त सम्भावनाएँ जुड़ी हैं इस नाम के साथ। तेरह बरस की तिरछी, टेढ़ी उम्र में शालिनी जब आकाश नामक पड़ोसी पर मर मिटी थी, तब मर मिटने का सबसे बड़ा आधार क्या रहा होगा--उस सलोने पड़ोसी के लम्बे पैर! स्वर का रुतबा! राजा और रंक दोनों के ही लिए एक जैसी स्नेहभरी मुसकान बिखेरते होंठ? अथवा यह सीधा-सरल नाम आकाश! पता नहीं...

आकाश में उड़ती परी एकाएक धरती पर उतर आई। अपने पंख उसने यों उतार दिए, जैसे गरम कुनकुने कमरे में दाखि़ल होने के बाद कोई अपने बदन पर से शॉल उतार दे और तहों में मोड़कर एक तरफ रख दे। अपने स्मृति-पंखों को उतारकर तहों में मोड़ती, एक तरफ़ रखती परी--शालिनी...वह केवल धरती पर नहीं उतरी थी। वह तो बाक़ायदा एक ड्राइंग-रूम में जा घुसी थी--आकाश का ड्राइंग-रूम...शालिनी का अपना ड्राइंग-रूम...

यहाँ कुछ खोज रही है शालिनी परी...

अरे, कहाँ की परी! चालीस बरस की हुई जा रही है, अब कहाँ की परी! किन्तु प्रश्न यह नहीं है कि शालिनी परी, परी है या नहीं। प्रश्न यह है कि नश्वर धरती के इस नश्वर ड्राइंग-रूम में, शालिनी नामक अ-परी, इस वक़्त आख़िर क्या खोज रही है!

बॉल-पेन! एक चौंध-सी, मन-मस्तिष्क के आर-पार निकल गई। श्वेता का बॉल-पेन! कॉलेजियन बिटिया श्वेता। सुबह की कच्ची धूप को बींधती हुई, रोज़ घर से बाहर लपक जाती है यह गिलहरी। कॉलेज पुकारता है उसे। बी.कॉम के फाइनल ईयर में पहुँच गई है। पहला पीरियड कभी उसने मिस किया हो, या पाँचेक मिनट लेट पहुँची हो, आज तक नहीं हुआ ऐसा। यह आकाश का गुण है—वक़्त की फ़ौजी पाबन्दी! श्वेता और प्रतीक दोनों ही बच्चों ने पिता के इस गुण को सीधा ग्रहण किया है।

बॉल-पेन! कहाँ है? कहाँ है? गिलहरी श्वेता एक कमरे से दूसरे कमरे में फुर्र-फुर्र जा रही है। जाने कहाँ धर दिया है! दीवार-घड़ी का लाल काँटा, क्षण-क्षण आगे बढ़ता, एक-एक सेकंड को छेद रहा है। कॉलेज की पूरी बिल्डिंग में आग लगी है। एक-एक सेकंड की देरी यानी प्रलय! श्वेता पहुँचेगी कॉलेज, तब आग बुझेगी। श्वेता, लेकिन, ऐसे कैसे पहुँच जाए कॉलेज बिना बॉल-पेन के!

यह रहा!

इधर-उधर, यहाँ-वहाँ, हर चीज़ को हटा-हटाकर देख रही शालिनी की आँखों के सामने, अचानक ही, ब्रह्म-ज्योत की तरह प्रकट होकर ढिठाई से मुसकरा रही थी वह प्लास्टिकी आकृति!

ड्राइंग-रूम के सेंटर-टेबल पर अस्त-व्यस्त पड़े अख़बारों और पत्र-पत्रिकाओं को शालिनी ने यों ही, यन्त्रवत्, हटाकर देखा ही था कि बॉल-पेन बोला, "मैं यह रहा!"

शालिनी ने भारी तसल्ली की साँस ली। साबित हो गया कि पुरानी पीढ़ी के सहयोग के बिना नई पीढ़ी का काम चल ही नहीं सकता। बॉल-पेन ढूँढ़ने जैसा सादा काम भी नई पीढ़ी अकेली कहाँ कर पाती है! गिलहरी श्वेता लपकती रहे फुर्र-फुर्र, इस कमरे से उस कमरे में। बॉल-पेन तो यहाँ धरा है, ड्राइंग-रूम के सेंटर-टेबल पर, पुरानी पीढ़ी के क़ब्ज़े में!

"अरी, श्वेता!" ज़ोर से पुकार उठी शालिनी।

घर की गहराई में से, जाने किस दिशा से, जवाब लौटा, "यस, मम्मी?" कितना आतुर, अकुलाया स्वर है श्वेता का! चार रुपल्ली के बॉल-पेन के लिए इतनी व्याकुलता! वाह!

“अरे, तेरा बॉल-पेन तो यह रहा!” शालिनी का यह वाक्य पूरा हुआ न हुआ कि श्वेता झप्प से प्रकट हो गई ड्राइंग-रूम में। श्वेता ने मानो कोई दरवाज़ा पार नहीं किया, बल्कि किसी दीवार को सीधे चीरकर सामने निकल आई वह! शालिनी सोचे बिना न रह सकी 'श्वेता की स्फूर्ति गिलहरी को भी मात देती है कई बार...'

शालिनी अपने विचार-वाक्य को, मन-ही-मन, अभी पूरा सोच भी नहीं पाई थी कि श्वेता साँय करती हुई, शालिनी की दिशा में, झपटती चली आई। बॉल-पेन एक पल शालिनी के हाथ में था और दूजे पल श्वेता के हाथ में जा चुका था। ऐसा चील-झपट्टा तो स्वयं चील भी न लगा सके! ठगी-सी देखती रह गई शालिनी अपनी बिटिया की तरफ़।

एक स्वर सुना शालिनी ने, 'थैंक्यू, मॉम!'

स्वर निस्सन्देह बिटिया का ही था, लेकिन बिटिया कहाँ थी? अभी यहाँ, सामने ही तो थी, बॉल-पेन छीनकर अपने हाथ में ले रही थी। एकाएक कहाँ चली गई? श्वेता जैसे जादुई उड़ानें भर रही थी। शालिनी ने केवल आभास पाया, श्वेता बिटिया के हाथ में पुस्तकें हैं, फाइलें हैं, पर्स भी है, सुनहरे रंग का, मैचिंग सलवार-सूट पहन रखा है उसने। श्वेता की तन-मुद्रा, मुख-मुद्रा दोनों से, एक नज़र में झलक आता है, कन्या कॉलेज जा रही है।

कॉलेज जाते-जाते श्वेता ड्राइंग-रूम के ही अन्दर, दरवाज़े के पास, अचानक यों रुक क्यों गई है? क्या बॉल-पेन जैसी ही कोई और चीज़ याद आ गई है उसे, जिसे वह भूले जा रही थी? शालिनी सहसा समझ न पाई, ऐसी कोई और चीज़ भला क्या हो सकती है...

तभी उसने श्वेता को पलटते देखा। एक पल श्वेता की पीठ दिख रही थी शालिनी को। अगले ही पल श्वेता का चेहरा आ गया शालिनी के आमने-सामने। फैंटेसी के किस सीमान्त पर आ खड़ी हुई थी शालिनी? क्यों ऐसा लग रहा था उसे कि श्वेता के चेहरे का क्षेत्रफल बढ़ रहा है? नहीं...यह श्वेता का चेहरा नहीं था, जिसकी आकृति बड़ी हो रही थी, बल्कि...यह तो स्वयं श्वेता ही थी, जो नज़दीक आ रही थी। यह फैंटेसी नहीं, भौतिकी थी कि नज़दीक आती चीज़ बड़ी दिखती जाती है...लेकिन श्वेता नज़दीक क्यों आ रही है एकाएक?

“ओह, मॉम...” बहुत हौले से बुदबुदाती है श्वेता। चटाक् से चूम लेती है श्वेता, अपनी मम्मी को। तो...फैंटेसी यह थी! चूमने के लिए पलटकर नज़दीक आ रही थी बिटिया रानी। हलाहल कलियुग आ गया हो चाहे न आया हो, हलाहल जेट-युग ज़रूर आ गया है! शालिनी मानो स्वयं को सावधान कर रही थी, 'नई पीढ़ी सारा काम कितना फटाफट निबटाती है! कॉलेज जाते-जाते, अचानक रुकना। अचानक पलटकर

मम्मी के नज़दीक आना। पल भर में चूम लेना और अगले ही पल, फिर से पलटकर, मम्मी से दूर चले जाना—ड्राइंग-रूम का दरवाज़ा पार करने के लिए!'

'माँ-बेटी का प्यार भी पल-दो पल की यांत्रिक गतिविधि रह गई है क्या?' सोचकर शालिनी छटपटा गई मन-ही-मन। याद आया...स्वयं शालिनी जब नन्ही-सी थी। माँ के साथ प्यार कैसे जताती थी वह। घंटों-घंटों माँ की गोदी में घुसी रहती थी—इतनी प्रसन्न और तृप्त कि कसमसाती भी नहीं थी। आज...माँ के साथ कितना तुरत-फुरत प्यार जता लिया जाता है। चुटकी बजाने में भी ज़्यादा वक़्त लगता होगा। माँ को चूमने में वक़्त ही क्या लगता है! इधर चूमा, उधर पलटी मारी और चल दिए कॉलेज!

'क्या मैं भी...छोटी-छोटी बातों को शिकायत का बाना पहना देती हूँ!' शालिनी ने अपने आपको डाँटा।

चौकन्नी हो गई शालिनी, क्योंकि श्वेता ड्राइंग-रूम में नहीं थी। किस क्षण निकल गई थी वह ड्राइंग-रूम से? शालिनी देख-समझ कहाँ पाई थी! इतना ज़रूर है, श्वेता अभी-अभी निकली है ड्राइंग-रूम से। मम्मी को चूमने के बाद रुकी नहीं है, क्षणांश के लिए भी। झटके के साथ परदा हटाकर निकली है ड्राइंग-रूम में से। परदा अभी भी हिल रहा है। शालिनी तुरन्त संचालित हो गई। लम्बे डग भरकर पहुँच गई ड्राइंग-रूम के दरवाज़े पर। जितनी स्फूर्ति और शक्ति से श्वेता ने परदा हटाया होगा, उतनी ही स्फूर्ति और शक्ति से शालिनी ने ड्राइंग-रूम का परदा हटाया।

आँगन में निकल आई शालिनी। अन्दाज़ा उसका सही निकला—श्वेता के पैरों ने बाहरी सड़क के कगार को अभी छुआ भर था...

शालिनी लपक गई अपनी बिटिया के पीछे, ऊँचे स्वर में बोलती हुई, "सुन! जल्दी लौटना कॉलेज से। याद है, शाम को...प्रतीक की सालगिरह की तैयारी..."

"हाँ, हाँ! याद है। जल्दी लौटूँगी!" बिटिया जवाब तो देती है, किन्तु पलटकर देखती नहीं। ओझल होती बिटिया की पीठ को निहारती रह गई है शालिनी...अभी दो जने और हैं घर में, जिन्हें विदा करना है—बेटा प्रतीक और...प्रिय बहुत प्रिय, बहुत-बहुत प्रिय आकाश! परदा हटा, ड्राइंग-रूम में वापस आने के साथ शालिनी ने स्वयं को तैयार कर लिया—जेट-युग के एक और सदस्य से आमने-सामने के लिए। प्रतीक! गत तीन महीनों में प्रतीक में भारी शारीरिक परिवर्तन आया है। उसके पैर ज़रूरत से ज़्यादा लम्बे लगने लगे हैं। पिता का प्रतिरूप बने बिना मानेगा नहीं! स्वर अचानक ही फटे बाँस जैसा हो चला है। हर हफ्ते लगता है, छोकरे की आवाज़ फिर बदल गई। आवाज़ का अन्तिम स्वरूप कैसा निखरकर सामने आएगा, पता नहीं। आकाश के स्वर में रुतबा है, तो स्नेह भी है। आकाश का स्वर अनुशासन की माँग

करता है, किन्तु साथ-साथ यह आभास भी पूरी स्पष्टता से देता है कि मैं तो अजातशत्रु का स्वर हूँ। प्रतीक के स्वर में आकाश जैसी विशेषता किसी भी तरह उभरती नहीं महसूस होती। सात-सात दिनों में बदलता प्रतीक का स्वर...बस, दिल थामकर, कौतूहल के साथ बैठे रहने की बात है, प्रतीक का व्यक्तित्व न जाने किस साँचे में ढले!

आज प्रतीक चौदह बरस का हो गया। टाँगें लम्बी तो होने लगी हैं मर्दों की तरह, लेकिन चलता है, तो कुछ ऐसे, जैसे अपनी ही लम्बी टाँगों को सँभालने का अभ्यस्त न हो। कभी-कभी तो ऐसा लबड़धोधों-सा महसूस होता है लड़का कि उस पर हँसना चाहो, तो हँस लो और यदि चिन्तित होना चाहो, तो चिन्तित हो लो!

पीठ-पीछे शालिनी ने एक परिचित ध्वनि सुनी—स्कूल-मैटाडोर के आ पहुँचने और रुकने की ध्वनि। प्रतीक चाहता तो बहुत है कि अपने कई सहपाठियों की तरह वह भी एक फैशनेबल साइकिल ख़रीदे और साइकिल पर ही स्कूल आया-जाया करे, किन्तु बम्बई की सड़कें! आकाश ने बिलकुल मना कर दिया साइकिल ले देने से। प्रतीक भारी शिकायत मन में बसाकर बैठ गया है, 'आप लोग तो मुझे दूध-पीता बच्चा समझते हैं अभी तक! अरे, क्या आँख मूँदकर साइकिल चलाऊँगा, जो कहीं भी भिड़ा दूँगा? मेरी उम्र के तमाम लड़के साँय-साँय अपनी साइकिलों पर चल रहे हैं। क्या रोज़ वे कहीं-न-कहीं एक्सीडेंट कर देते हैं?' लेकिन आकाश ने जो मना किया, वह शालिनी के भी दिल की आवाज़ थी। 'नहीं, मेरा बेटा अभी इतना बड़ा नहीं कि बम्बई की सड़कों पर साइकिल के करतब दिखाए...' लेकिन 'इतना बड़ा नहीं' है, तो आख़िर 'कितना बड़ा' है प्रतीक? आज प्रतीक की सालगिरह आई खड़ी है घर के अन्दर। आज एक बार फिर सोचना होगा, प्रतीक बड़ा है या छोटा? जो भी है, फ़िलहाल तो उसे स्कूल-मैटाडोर से ही आना-जाना है, घर और स्कूल के बीच। साइकिल ख़रीदने के लिए अगर उसने ज़्यादा ऊधम मचाया, तो ख़रीद तो देंगे, किन्तु कॉलोनी में ही, आसपास कर ले घुमक्कड़ी, अपनी साइकिल पर! बाक़ी....स्कूल तक साइकिल से आने-जाने का सवाल ही नहीं है, हाँ! ठीक है, नवीं में पहुँच गया है, इसका मतलब यह तो नहीं कि...

कितना तेज़ हॉर्न बजाती है यह स्कूल-मैटाडोर! इस देश में सही अनुपात के दर्शन कहीं नहीं होते। अरे, जिस गाड़ी से इतने सुन्दर-सलोने बच्चे आते-जाते हैं, उसका हॉर्न इतना तीखा क्यों होना चाहिए? कोमल, मधुर हॉर्न लगाने में क्या ज़्यादा पैसा ख़र्च होगा?

हॉर्न तो तीखा है ही, मैटाडोर के ड्राइवर की आवाज़ भी इतनी तेज़ है कि...

'सावधान, शालिनी!' शालिनी स्वयं से बोली, 'फिर से तू इतनी छोटी-छोटी बातों को तूल दे रही है कि....'

तीखा हॉर्न बजाता ड्राइवर तीखे स्वर में ललकार रहा था, ''प्रतीक? कम ऑन! हरी अप!''

ड्राइवर की नापसन्द आवाज़ को पसन्द करने की चेष्टा में शालिनी ने कुछ ज़्यादा ही ऊँचे स्वर में पुकारा, ''प्रतीक! तेरी गाड़ी आ गई।''

बस्ते को और अपनी लम्बी टाँगों को सँभालता प्रतीक हड़बड़ाता हुआ ड्राइंग-रूम में आया। शालिनी सन्न रह गई। कौन कहेगा प्रतीक को चौदह बरस का? शुद्ध सोलह बरस का लग रहा है। ओ, भगवान! वक़्त को इतनी तेज़ी से न बहा...

शुतुरमुर्ग रेती सूँघना चाहता हो, कुछ इसी तरह प्रतीक अपने जिस्म को बीच से मानो फोल्ड कर रहा था। शालिनी को दो पल बाद ही समझ में आया कि क्यों प्रतीक उस तरह अपनी कमर मोड़कर झुका जा रहा था—जूतों के तस्मे बाँध रहा था वह। तभी मैटाडोर का हॉर्न एक बार फिर बेताबी से बज उठा और प्रतीक ने फ़ैसला कर लिया, वह तस्मे बाँधे बिना ही लपक लेगा। वह लपका। आँखों के ऐन सामने उसकी माँ खड़ी थी, किन्तु माँ उसे नज़र नहीं आ रही थी। माँ को छूता हुआ-सा वह लपक चला। ग़नीमत थी, माँ को रौंदता हुआ नहीं निकल गया वह। 'कमबख़्त! अभी से चश्मा लगाने का इरादा है क्या तेरा?' शालिनी के होंठ आपस में कस गए। रे, दुष्ट! आज तेरी सालगिरह है, कहाँ भागा जा रहा है?

शालिनी ने तपाक से प्रतीक की बाँह पकड़ ली, ''रुक!''

घोर आश्चर्य से देखा प्रतीक ने, शालिनी की ओर, ''यस, मॉम?''

''मॉम के बच्चे! ये टॉफियाँ नहीं ले जाएगा?'' और शालिनी ने कॉर्नर-टेबल पर रखा टॉफियों का डिब्बा उठाकर प्रतीक के हाथ में थमाया, ''क्लास के एक-एक बच्चे को दो-दो टॉफियाँ देना। हरेक टीचर को तीन और...क्लास-टीचर को पाँच टॉफियाँ देना। समझे?''

''यस! यस!'' कहता प्रतीक टॉफियों के डिब्बे को बस्ते में भर रहा था। स्वयं शालिनी को अटपटा-सा लगा—इतना बड़ा लड़का टॉफियाँ बाँटेगा! लेकिन...कौन कहता है, प्रतीक बड़ा हो गया? और फिर...आजकल तो बूढ़ों में भी टॉफियाँ बाँटने-खाने का रिवाज बन गया है।

''मेरा लाल आज चौदह बरस का हो गया!'' कहती शालिनी ने, हुलसकर, प्रतीक के मस्तक पर गहरा चुम्बन लिया, किन्तु जिन क्षणों में चूम रही थी, उन्हीं क्षणों में वह, प्रतीक के व्याकुल शब्दों को सुन भी तो रही थी, ''मम्मी! प्लीज़! देर हो रही है।''

एकदम बेताब हो गया था प्रतीक, शालिनी की गिरफ़्त से अपनी बाँह छुड़ाने और मैटाडोर की दिशा में लपक जाने के लिए, किन्तु प्यार से अभिभूत हो चली शालिनी लरजते स्वर में कह रही थी, ''हैप्पी बर्थ-डे टू यू...''

"थैंक्यू, माँ! प्लीज़! शाम को!" और जेट-युग का वह सदस्य, पूरी शक्ति से तड़पकर, माँ की गिरफ़्त से आज़ाद हो गया। उसे छोड़ना नहीं चाहती थी शालिनी, किन्तु वह छूट गया—शालिनी को साफ़-साफ़ बताता हुआ कि अब मैं छोटा नहीं रहा, जब चाहूँ छूट सकता हूँ।

शालिनी ने उसे भागते देखा। व्याकुल शालिनी उसके पीछे-पीछे चिल्लाती हुई-सी भाग रही थी, "प्रतीक! प्रतीक!"

मैटाडोर की हर खिड़की से अन्दर ठूँसे बच्चों की चिल्ल-पों बाहर उफन रही थी। प्रतीक ठीक से बैठ भी नहीं पाया था कि मैटाडोर ने हौले-हौले चलना शुरू कर दिया। बैठते-बैठते प्रतीक ने पलटकर पीछे देखा, "यस, मम्मी?"

मैटाडोर का दरवाज़ा खटाक् से बन्द हुआ। प्रतीक ने खिड़की में से सिर बाहर निकाला। शामिली मैटाडोर के साथ-साथ दौड़ने-सी लगी थी, "प्रतीक! कोचिंग-क्लास छोड़ देना। स्कूटर से लौट आना। जल्दी आना।"

"मम्मी! टाटा!"

"लेट न होना। दीदी भी जल्दी आएगी। तैयारी करेंगे...सालगिरह की!"

"बाय, मम्मी!" प्रतीक ने हाथ हिलाया न हिलाया कि एक मोड़ पार कर मैटाडोर आँखों से ओझल हो गई। मैटाडोर के पीछे लपकने का अब कोई अर्थ नहीं था। रुक गई शालिनी। साँस कितनी ज़्यादा भर आई थी। खुद को हाँफते देख शालिनी को अचरज हुआ। क्या इतनी ज़्यादा दौड़ी थी शालिनी! वह लौट पड़ी। ड्राइंग-रूम में प्रवेश कर सीधे अपने बेड-रूम की ओर क़दम उठाए उसने। अटैच्ड बाथ-रूम के बन्द दरवाज़े को उसने हौले से खटखटाया, "आकाश!"

भीतर, छरछराकर चलते फव्वारे की आवाज़ रुकी नहीं। उस आवाज़ के आर-पार छनता आकाश का स्वर शालिनी के कानों तक आया, "यस, मैडम?"

"नहा चुके?"

"नहा रहा हूँ, यार!"

"आज तुम्हें जल्दी नहीं जाना है ऑफिस?"

"तो क्या नहाता-नहाता चला जाऊँ?"

"फिर न कहना, याद नहीं दिलाया!"

और शालिनी आकाश के कपड़ों में प्रेस करने की तैयारियों में जुटी। प्रेस का स्विच उसने ऑन किया ही था कि बाथ-रूम से अन्दर फव्वारे की आवाज़ बन्द हो गई। बाथ-रूम का दरवाज़ा हौले-से, ज़रा-सा खुला, जैसे कोई चोर डरते-डरते खोल रहा हो। कछुए की तरह गर्दन निकालकर आकाश ने बाहर झाँका, "ऐ, शालिनी!"

इस झाँकने और पुकारने में भी चोर तो छिपा हुआ था ही, किन्तु दोनों बच्चों को विदा करने के तनाव से अभी-अभी मुक्त हुई शालिनी इसे भाँप न सकी।

कपड़ों पर प्रेस फेरना जारी रख, उलाहने के स्वर में बोली, ''क्या शालिनी-शालिनी! नहाओ जल्दी!''

आकाश ने न तो अपना चेहरा पोंछा था, न सिर के बाल। पूरा आकाश धुला-धुला लग रहा था। ऐसे ही, आकाश का स्वर भी धुला-धुला था, ''बच्चे गए दोनों?''

''हाँ। गए।''

''और नौकरानी?''

शालिनी की नज़र आश्चर्य से उठी, ''नौकरानी?''

आकाश ज़रा झेंपा, ''मेरा मतलब है, नौकरानी...आई तो नहीं है न अभी?''

''कभी नहीं आती इतनी जल्दी।''

''ऐ, शालिनी! सुन! ज़रा पीठ पर मालिश कर दे! और साबुन रगड़ दे!''

''आकाश!''

''मैल की परतें जमी जा रही हैं!''

''ख़ाक मैल की परतें जमी जा रही हैं!''

और शालिनी प्रेस का स्विच ऑफ करती उठ पड़ी...बाथ-रूम के फ़र्श पर पलांठ लगाकर कितनी तसल्ली से बैठ गया था आकाश। उसकी गठीली पीठ पर सरसों के तेल की परत फैला चुकी शालिनी अपनी दोनों हथेलियों से, प्रियतम-पति के कन्धे मसल रही थी। शालिनी ने अपने दोनों अँगूठों से दबाव डालते हुए आकाश की गर्दन के आसपास रगों और मसल्स पर मालिश की। दो बीते ऊँची एक चौकी पर बैठी हुई थी शालिनी। आकाश अपने हाथ पीठ की तरफ मोड़-मोड़कर बताता कि कहाँ उसके मसल्स ज़्यादा अकड़े हुए हैं। वहाँ-वहाँ शालिनी ज़्यादा मालिश करती है।

मालिश करनेवाले को पता नहीं चलता क्या कि कहाँ-कहाँ मसल्स ज़्यादा अकड़े हुए हैं? अथवा...मसल्स अकड़े हुए हैं भी या नहीं? सब पता चलता है, हाँ! आकाश की पूरी पीठ में कहीं कोई अकड़न-जकड़न नहीं थी। बिलकुल भी नहीं। इसके बावजूद वह पीठ की तरफ़ हाथ मोड़-मोड़कर, छू-छूकर बता रहा था कि कहाँ ज़्यादा मालिश चाहिए। सरासर नाटक! शालिनी भी इस नाटक का बराबरी पर आनन्द ले रही थी।

अब शालिनी ने मालिश रोककर, पति की पीठ पर साबुन रगड़ना शुरू किया। नाटक का एक अंक सानन्द पूरा हो चुका था। दूसरे अंक का प्रारम्भ इन संवादों से हुआ :

''शालिनी!''

''हूँ...''

''शालिनी, आय लव यू!''

''क्या, आकाश! वही पिटीपिटाई बात!''

''नहीं, शालिनी! रियली आय लव यू!''

"बेटी बी.कॉम के फाइनल ईयर में है। खुद आयकर विभाग में इतने बड़े अधिकारी हो। किस मुँह से मजनूँ जैसी बातें करते हो?"

"मुँह तो वही है, जो पहले था—जब हमारी आँख लड़ी थी नई-नई..."

"होश में आओ। ऑफिस लेट पहुँचोगे।"

"आज तक कभी लेट पहुँचा हूँ? दस मिनट मालिश करवा ली, तो लेट पहुँचूँगा?"

"चाहे जब पहुँचो, शाम को तुम जल्दी घर लौटोगे।"

"ज़रूर जल्दी लौटूँगा! बिटवा की सालगिरह जो है!" और आकाश का चेहरा दमक उठा।

शालिनी भी जैसे स्वगत बोल पड़ी, 'चौदह बरस का हो गया प्रतीक...'

पीठ पर साबुन की रगड़ाई का प्रकरण पूरा हो चुका था। झाग-मुक्ति का एक कार्यक्रम यह हो सकता था कि आकाश चला लेता फव्वारा और खड़ा हो जाता नीचे। दूसरा कार्यक्रम यह बन सकता था कि जिसके हाथों से पीठ पर झाग पैदा हुआ था, उसी के हाथों से झाग दूर भी होता। शालिनी ने यही दूसरा कार्यक्रम पसन्द किया। बाल्टी में भरे पानी में मग्गा डाल-डालकर उसने पति की पीठ को सींचना शुरू किया। पानी के एक-एक मग्गे पर झाग सरक-सरककर बहने लगा।

आकाश ने सहसा चैतन्य और चौकन्ना होते हुए पूछा, "सालगिरह में किस-किस को बुलाया तुमने?"

शालिनी बोली, "हर साल जो करते हैं, वही इस साल किया है। कल ही सबको ख़बर भिजवा दी थी। सिर्फ़ बच्चों को बुलाया है। वो भी...सिर्फ़ आस-पड़ोस के बच्चे।"

"बच्चे कोई गिफ्ट-विफ्ट लेकर न आएँ।"

"यह भी...कह तो दिया है, हालाँकि...ख़ाली हाथ भला क्या कोई आएगा!" कहती शालिनी पति की पीठ को पूर्णतया झागमुक्त कर चुकी थी। शालिनी उठी, ताकि लटकते तौलिए को खींचकर उतार सके। तौलिया आकाश को थमाती हुई वह बाथ-रूम से निकल गई। बदन पर तौलिया रगड़ता आकाश और कपड़ों पर प्रेस करने की तैयारी दुबारा करती शालिनी अपना संवाद आगे बढ़ाते रहे।

"हाँ-हाँ, सो तो है...ख़ाली हाथ भला क्या कोई आएगा!" आकाश ने सहमति में दोहराया, "फिर भी...कह देने से इतना तो होगा कि...अनाप-शनाप महँगी चीज़ गिफ़्ट के रूप में लेकर नहीं आएगा कोई..."

शालिनी ने विषय-परिवर्तन किया, "सुनो! केक कौन लाएगा? तुम लेते आओ, तो अच्छा! या कहो तो मैं मँगवा लूँ?"

आकाश ने बनियान में सिर पिरोया, "यार! मेरा कोई भरोसा है? तुम्हीं मँगवा लो।"

भारी-भरकम ब्रीफकेस आकाश ने कार की अगली सीट पर रखा, फिर ठेलकर आगे सरकाया, ताकि स्टियरिंग के सामने स्वयं आकाश के लिए बैठने की जगह बन सके।

शालिनी को यह बात बिलकुल पसन्द नहीं कि आकाश का ब्रीफकेस हमेशा उतना भारी-भरकम बना रहे। आकाश तो अपना आधा ऑफिस मानो ब्रीफकेस के अन्दर भरकर चलता है!

किन्तु ब्रीफकेस का वज़न शालिनी को उतना चिन्तित नहीं करता, जितना चिन्तित करती है आकाश की कार की स्पीड। कार धीमी तो चला ही नहीं सकता आकाश। ज़रा भी कोई इमरजेन्सी न हो, सिर्फ़ कहीं मनपसन्द पान खाने के ही लिए जा रहा हो आकाश, तब भी अपनी कार ऐसी स्पीड से भगाएगा, मानो आसमान फट पड़ेगा, यदि आकाश की कार धीमी स्पीड से चलती नज़र आ गई। माना, बम्बई की सड़कों पर हर वाहन नियमानुसार ही चलता है, दिल्ली वाला हाल यहाँ नहीं है कि कोई भी, कहीं भी घुस गया, लेकिन स्पीड हमेशा दुर्घटनाओं से दोस्ती रखती है। आख़िर क्यों कार को व्यर्थ ही भगाया जाए? वैसे, कार चलाने की कला का मास्टर ही है आकाश! कार कोई भी हो, कैसी भी हो, आकाश ने उसे छुआ नहीं कि वह आकाश की गुलाम हुई नहीं!

आयकर विभाग में कभी भी, किसी का भी पीछा करना पड़ जाता है। आयकर अधिकारी को कार तेज़ी से चलाना आना ही चाहिए। आकाश का यह तर्क अपनी जगह ग़लत नहीं था, किन्तु शालिनी का जी धड़कता रहता।

आज भी, आकाश ने कार का द्वार बन्द किया नहीं कि शालिनी का चेहरा कार की खिड़की में से अन्दर झाँकने लगा। आकाश जानता था, शालिनी क्या कहेगी। जो आकाश जानता था, वही शालिनी ने कहा, "कार तेज़ न चलाना। बम्बई की सड़कें हैं..."

आकाश हँसा, "ओके, ओके, बिलकुल धीमी चलाऊँगा।"

शालिनी ने कहा, "बाय..."

आकाश ने भी कहा, "बाय..." और आकाश ने चला दी कार धीमे-धीमे। इतने धीमे कि कार मानो अपनी जगह से खिसकना ही न चाहती हो। पहले तो शालिनी को लगा, ज़रूर कार का इंजिन अचानक ख़राब हो गया है। दो पल बाद ही शालिनी समझी, आकाश कैसी दुष्टता कर रहा है। शालिनी अगर पैदल भी चलना शुरू करती, तो कार से आगे निकल जाती। बनावटी नाराज़गी के साथ शालिनी ने मुश्किल से चार लम्बे डग भरे होंगे कि सचमुच वह कार के साथ आ गई। एक बार फिर शालिनी ने कार की खिड़की में झाँका और गुर्राकर कहा, "आकाश!"

आकाश ने तो अपने चेहरे पर नवजात शिशु जैसा भोलापन छाप रखा था, "क्यों, मैडम!" आकाश ने पूछा, "क्या यह स्पीड भी आपको ज़्यादा लगती है?"

"आकाश! तुम पिटोगे!" शालिनी ने आँखें तरेरीं।

और आकाश, अचानक, कार को तीर की तरह भगा ले गया। शालिनी ठगी-सी रह गई। कार के पीछे लगी नम्बर-प्लेट के अंक दो-चार पल तक ही पढ़े जा सके। फिर वे इतनी तेज़ी से छोटे होकर छिटक गए कि शालिनी समझ न पाई, क्रोध करे या सन्देह करे। जा चुकी कार की दिशा में शालिनी की नज़र तीखे एतराज़ के साथ ठहरी हुई थी। फिर वह नज़र स्नेह और गर्व की नज़र में बदल गई।

भीड़-भड़क्के से आक्रान्त बम्बई की सड़कों को आकाश की कार इतनी सहजता से पार कर रही थी, जैसे मक्खन के आर-पार गरम छुरी चल रही हो। 'बेस्ट' की डबल-डेकर लाल बसें डगमग डोलकर पीछे रह जातीं, धड़धड़ाकर झटपटती फास्ट लोकल ट्रेनें भी पाँच-सात मिनट ही स्पर्धा में टिक पातीं, प्राइवेट कारों और टैक्सियों आदि की तो जैसे कोई बिसात ही नहीं थी—आकाश ने अपनी कार तीर की तरह छोड़ रखी थी।

आयकर भवन तेज़ी से प्रकट हुआ। कार आयकर भवन की ओर झपट रही थी या आयकर भवन ही कार की ओर झपट रहा था? शायद दोनों ही एक-दूसरे की ओर झपट रहे थे!...कल्पना कर आकाश बरबस मुसकरा दिया।

कार पार्क कर, लॉक कर, ब्रीफकेस को साधिकार थामे हुए आकाश ने लम्बे क़दम उठाते हुए, आयकर भवन की लिफ्ट की ओर जाना शुरू किया। ग्राउंड-फ्लोर पर खड़ी लिफ्ट, ऊपर उठने के लिए, बेताब-सी महसूस हुई और आकाश ने झटपट चलकर लिफ्ट में प्रवेश कर लिया। आयकर विभाग के कर्मचारियों के बीच आकाश ने अपने दो प्रिय सहयोगियों को लिफ्ट के अन्दर, पहले से मौजूद पाया—जनक और मिस कपूर। आकाश बेसाख़्ता बोल उठा, "गुड-मॉर्निंग, एवरीबडी..."

सभी ने समवेत स्वर में उत्तर लौटाया, "गुड-मॉर्निंग, सर!"

और लिफ्ट ने ऊपर उठना शुरू कर दिया...

आयकर भवन की चौथी मंज़िल पर है आकाश का कमरा। क्या चार का आँकड़ा भाग्यशाली होता है? पता नहीं! हाँ, सात और तेरह के बारे में ज़रूर कहा जाता है कि सात भाग्यशाली है और तेरह घोर दुर्भाग्यशाली। भला कोई तुक है? क्या किसी भी कर्मचारी का भाग्य इस आधार पर बुरे से अच्छा हो सकता है कि पहले उसका कार्यालय तेरहवीं मंज़िल पर था और अब सातवीं मंज़िल पर है?

इस झमेले से कितनी खूबसूरती से बच गया है आयकर भवन! इसमें छह से अधिक मंज़िलें ही नहीं। यदि होती सातवीं मंज़िल, तो क्या केवल उन्हीं अधिकारियों को तरक़्क़ी मिला करती, जिनके कमरे सातवीं मंज़िल पर शोभायमान होते? हिश्ट!

अनजाने में, आकाश आँखों-आँखों में गिनने लगा, 'लिफ्ट में अभी कुल कितने लोग यात्रा कर रहे हैं?'

आकाश मुसकराए बिना न रह सका—लिफ्ट में सात यात्री थे। यानी, लिफ्ट का ऑटोमेटिक इंश्योरेंश हो गया है। यह बीच में ख़राब हो ही नहीं सकती। लेकिन यही लिफ्ट यदि धड़ाम से नीचे गिर पड़े? सातों भाग्यशाली यात्री बुरी तरह घायल होंगे, कुछ की जानें भी जा सकती हैं। कोई नहीं पूछेगा कि यात्रियों की संख्या भाग्यशाली सात होने के बावजूद दुर्घटना कैसे घटी? और अगर कोई पूछ ले? तो यह अन्धविश्वासों पर सीधी चोट होगी। मुश्किल यही तो है कि अन्ध-विश्वासों को बल देतीं ख़बरें प्रायः पूरे उत्साह के साथ स्वीकार ली जाती हैं, जबकि अन्ध-विश्वासों पर चोट करती ख़बरें सहज ही नहीं स्वीकारी जातीं।

"सर!"

आकाश को लगा, उसे पुकारा जा रहा है। विचार-सागर में गोते लगा रहे आकाश को अनेक पलों तक, इतना भी होश कहाँ रहा था कि वह लिफ्ट के अन्दर है या किसी पब्लिक पार्क के अन्दर! क्या सचमुच किसी ने उसे पुकारा? आकाश को यह भी लगा, जैसे कोई उसके हाथ से ब्रीफकेस से लेना चाहता है। आकाश तुरन्त सावधान हो गया। उसके ब्रीफकेस को कोई भला कैसे ले सकता है!

"सर!"

सचमुच उसे पुकारा जा रहा था और यह स्वर जनक का था। आकाश की नज़र अपने ब्रीफकेस की ओर जा चुकी थी। स्वर तो जनक का था ही, वह प्रयास भी उसी का था। यह जनक का ही तो हाथ था, जो आकाश के हाथ से, उसके ब्रीफकेस को ले लेना चाहता था। बहुत मानता है जनक आकाश को। औपचारिक अथवा यान्त्रिक सम्मान नहीं, बल्कि हार्दिक, परम हार्दिक सम्मान झाँकता है जनक की आँखों में आकाश के लिए—हमेशा, हर कहीं...

किन्तु इसका मतलब यह कैसे हुआ कि जनक आकाश के ब्रीफकेस का वज़न ढोए। माना, जनक आयकर विभाग में अभी नया-नया आया है, जबकि आकाश है पुराना खिलाड़ी...और सीनियर्स तो अपने जूनियर्स को ऐसे मौक़े देते ही रहते हैं, जब सीनियर का भारी-भरकम ब्रीफकेस उठाकर जूनियर पीछे-पीछे लम्बे डग भर रहा हो; किन्तु नहीं...आकाश से ऐसा नहीं हो सकता...ब्रीफकेस के हैंडिल पर आकाश की उँगलियों की पकड़ मज़बूत हो गई।

"नहीं, जनक!" आकाश ने प्यार से मुसकराकर, किन्तु दृढ़ता से कहा, "यह बोझ मेरा है।"

"सर!" जनक सम्मान से झुका-झुका जा रहा था, "आप मेरे सीनियर हैं।"

किन्तु जनक को आकाश के मुँह से यही सुनने को मिला, "हर इनसान को अपना बोझ खुद उठाना चाहिए, जनक! जूनियर या सीनियर होने से क्या फ़र्क़ पड़ता है!"

मिस कपूर ने चिहुँककर कहा, "लेकिन, सर! आजकल तो हर आदमी इसी फेर में दिखता है कि अपना बोझ दूसरे के कन्धों पर रख दे।"

आकाश मुसकराया। वह जानता था, मिस कपूर ने विरोध नहीं किया है। मिस कपूर ने केवल चुटकी ली है। आकाश के साथ रंचमात्र भी वैचारिक मतभेद नहीं है मिस कपूर का। तभी तो वह आकाश के प्रिय सहयोगियों की लिस्ट में अपना नाम दर्ज करा सकी हैं! किन्तु मिस कपूर का स्वभाव है, वह चुटकियाँ लेती रहती हैं...

"जैसा आप कह रहे हैं, ज़माना वैसा नहीं है, सर!" मिस कपूर ने दोहराया।

न जाने क्यों, आकाश अपनी मुसकान को जारी न रख सका, "हाँ, मिस कपूर! मैं जानता हूँ, ज़माना वैसा नहीं है, जैसा मैं कह रहा हूँ, लेकिन...आप भी तो जानती हैं कि...जैसा ज़माना है, वैसा मैं नहीं हूँ! मैं अपना बोझ खुद ही उठाना पसन्द करता हूँ।"

लिफ्ट के सभी यात्रियों के बीच सन्नाटा खिंच गया। किसी ने नहीं सोचा था, बात का रंग यों सहसा बदरंग होने लगेगा। लिफ्ट अब चौथी मंज़िल पर रुकने की तैयारी में थी। जनक ने अपना हाथ ब्रीफकेस से विपरीत दिशा में समेट लिया था। मिस कपूर की साड़ी उनके कन्धे पर बिलकुल सही-सही व्यवस्थित थी, फिर भी उन्होंने साड़ी को नए सिरे से व्यवस्थित करना शुरू कर दिया। तभी लिफ्ट रुकी, उसका द्वार खुला और आकाश 'गुड डे!' बुदबुदाकर बाहर निकल गया। जनक और मिस कपूर को पाँचवीं मंज़िल पर पहुँचना था। वे लिफ्ट में बने रहे। लिफ्ट ने उन्हें अपने भीतर रखे-रखे ऊपर की तरफ़ पलायन किया...

आयकर भवन के लम्बे कॉरीडोर को आकाश ने आत्म-विश्वासी क़दमों से पार करना शुरू किया। कर्मचारियों और लोगों की आवन-जावन के बीच अनेक ऐसे थे, जिन्होंने आकाश को नमस्कार किया। कॉरीडोर में, दोनों तरफ़ आयकर अधिकारियों के कमरों की कतारें सजी थीं। हर कमरे के बाहर, सम्बद्ध अधिकारी की नेम-प्लेट लगी थी। अर्दलियों की फुसफुसाहटें गुज़रते आकाश को देख मन्द पड़ने लगतीं...

आकाश ने दूर से स्वयं अपने नाम की नेम-प्लेट देखी। आकाश के हर क़दम के साथ यह नेम-प्लेट नज़दीक आ रही थी...

आकाश अपनी स्टेनो मिसेज जो को डिक्टेशन दे दहा था, "...द रिटर्न इन द अबव केस वाज़ फाइल्ड डेटेड थर्ड ऑफ अक्टूबर, 1990, डिक्लेयरिंग द टोटल इन्कम ऑफ रुपीज़..."

आज के सभी ऑर्डर्स का डिक्टेशन ले चुकने के बाद मिसेज जो ने उठते-उठते कहा, "एक...छोटी-सी न्यूज़ है, सर!"

"मेरे लिए?" आकाश ने भौंहें उठाईं।

"यस, सर! आपने वो...लोन के लिए जो एप्लीकेशन दी थी न..."

"हाँ! वो फ्रिज ख़रीदने के लिए!"

"जी हाँ! वो लोन सेंक्शन हो गया है, सर!"

"इतनी जल्दी? लोग सुधर गए हैं!"

"आपकी संगत का असर है!"

"रियली?"

"कागज़ात ले आऊँ अभी? दस्तख़त कर देंगे?"

"ज़रूर! क्यों नहीं! नेकी और पूछ-पूछ!"

मिसेज जो भारी उत्साह के साथ आकाश के कमरे से निकल गईं। उसी भारी उत्साह के साथ वह वापस भी आईं, हाथ में लोन-पेपर्स लिये हुए। मेज़ पर आकाश के सामने लोन-पेपर्स फैलाकर, उँगली रख-रखकर उन्होंने बताना शुरू किया, "एक दस्तख़त यहाँ, एक यहाँ, एक यहाँ..." उसी हिसाब से आकाश दस्तख़त करता चला।

मिसेज जो जब लोन-पेपर्स वापस समेट रही थीं, उनके लाल लिपस्टिक से सजे होंठों पर गहन-गहन मुसकान एक बार फिर उभरने लगी। आकाश ने अपने आपको तैयार कर लिया—अवश्य मिसेज जो अपने पिटारे में से फिर कुछ नया निकालने वाली हैं...

"सर! एक और भी न्यूज़ है!"

"आज तो आप न्यूज़ की बौछार कर रही हैं, मिसेज जो!"

"सर! अपनी वह जो कन्ज़्यूमर्स को-ऑपरेटिव सोसायटी है न, आई.टी.ओ. की..."

"हाँ, हाँ, जिसकी आप ख़ज़ांची हैं..."

"यस, सर! उसके बारे में न्यूज़ यह है, सर, कि बहुत जल्दी यह सोसायटी रेडियो, टी.वी. और फ्रिज में भी डीलिंग शुरू करनेवाली है।"

और मिसेज जो की गहन मुसकान, आत्म-गौरव से और भी गहन हो गई। आकाश ने सहर्ष पूछा, "बहुत खूब! कब से?"

"बस, दो हफ्ते बाद!"

"यानी, अगर मैं अपना फ्रिज आज न ख़रीदूँ, बल्कि दो हफ्ते बाद ख़रीदूँ, तो..."

"सर! किसी भी मॉडल का फ्रिज आई.टी.ओ. की सोसायटी से ख़रीदने पर, बाज़ार से कम-से-कम पाँच सौ रुपए कम पर मिलेगा!"

"अरे, वाह! फिर तो मेरे फ्रिज का ऑर्डर आप ही नोट कीजिए, मिसेज जो!"

"थैंक्यू, सर!"

आकाश अपनी कुर्सी की पीठ से टिकता हुआ बोला, "आज तो, मिसेज जो, आपने पाँच सौ की बचत कराकर मेरी अमीरी बढ़ा दी। आय मस्ट थैंक्यू, मिसेज जो!"

"वेलकम, सर! वैसे...सर! इजाज़त हो, तो...एक बात कहूँ।"

"हाँ, हाँ! कहिए न! क्या कहना है?"

"सर!-बुरा न मानिएगा, लेकिन...आप सिर्फ़ पाँच सौ की बचत को इतनी इम्पोर्टेंस दे रहे हैं, जबकि...आपकी बराबरी के न जाने कितने इन्कम-टैक्स ऑफिसर्स ऐसे हैं, जिनका रोज़ का जेब-ख़र्च ही पाँच सौ से ज़्यादा है!"

आकाश के चेहरे से एक बार फिर मुसकान की रेखाएँ ग़ायब हो गईं।

"हाँ, मिसेज जो!" आकाश ने ज़रा कड़क होकर कहा, "ऐसे कई ऑफिसर्स हैं। आप अगर चाहें, तो उनमें से किसी के भी पास में आपका ट्रान्सफर करवा सकता हूँ!"

इसके जवाब में मिसेज जो "ओह, नो, सर!" कहती हुईं सामने से सरक गईं। उनकी पलायन-दक्षता पर आकाश हौले से हँस दिया।

चहक...चमक-दमक...किलकारियाँ...धौलधप्पा...सालगिरह है, भई, सालगिरह! प्रतीक कुमार की सालगिरह! दीदी हाज़िर, मम्मी हाज़िर, पप्पा हाज़िर, आसपड़ोस के दसेक बच्चे हाज़िर। बस समारोह को इससे अधिक विस्तार देना शालिनी ने चाहा भी तो नहीं था।

जन्म-दिन का केक, ख़ास प्रतीक के नाम का, बनवाया नहीं था। 'हैप्पी बर्थ-डे' अंकित बना-बनाया केक ही लाया गया था केक-शॉप से। शालिनी ने परिवार के किसी भी व्यक्ति के जन्म-दिन को, कभी ख़र्च और रुतबे के दिखावे के लिए इस्तेमाल नहीं किया। आनन्द-उल्लास का उत्सव है। क्या भारी-भरकम ख़र्च करके ही आनन्द और उल्लास को उछाला जा सकता है?

ड्राइंग-रूम बहुत अधिक नहीं सजाया गया था। शालिनी मन-ही-मन अपने पड़ोसियों का आभार मान रही थी, क्योंकि उन्होंने शालिनी के इस आग्रह को स्वीकार किया था कि प्रतीक को बधाई देने के लिए केवल बच्चे ही आएँ, बड़ा कोई न आए संग में।

किन्तु शालिनी का यह आग्रह किसी ने नहीं माना था कि प्रतीक को केवल रूखी बधाई देने ही आएँ सब, उपहार लेकर न आए कोई। स्वयं शालिनी को भी मालूम था, एक-एक बच्चा उपहार लेकर ही आएगा। आजकल गिफ्ट देना और लेना इतना सहज-सामान्य हो गया है कि गिफ्ट देकर कोई अहसान नहीं करता और गिफ्ट

स्वीकार करके भी कोई किसी पर अहसान नहीं करता! फिर...प्रतीक आख़िर बच्चा है। गिफ्ट पाने का कितना चाव होता है बच्चों में। माना प्रतीक चौदह बरस का हो गया आज, लेकिन है तो बच्चा ही...

केक पर तनकर खड़ी हैं चौदह मोमबत्तियाँ। प्रतीक फू-फू करता बुझा रहा है उन्हें। घेरकर खड़े सब बच्चे खी-खीं कर रहे हैं। तालियाँ! तालियाँ! श्वेता कितनी किलक रही है, कितने जोश के साथ बजा रही है तालियाँ। जैसे श्वेता की ही सालगिरह हो न! बुझी हुई मोमबत्तियों से धुएँ के तार जो उठ रहे थे, वे अब लुप्त हो गए हैं। प्रतीक ने केक काटना शुरू कर दिया है। ज़रा नर्वस-सा क्यों लग रहा है प्रतीक? केक काटते उसके हाथों में ज़ोर क्यों नहीं है? शालिनी ने सोचा, आगे बढ़कर वह अपने बिटवा के हाथ पकड़ ले और करने लगे सहायता, केक को जल्दी काटने में। तभी देखती क्या है कि आकाश पहुँच गया है बिटवा के पास। छुरी बिटवा के हाथ में है, बिटवा का हाथ आकाश के हाथ में है और केक कट रहा है खटाखट 'हैप्पी बर्थ-डे टू यू!' के स्वर अनेक बार उठ चुके हैं। श्वेता तो 'हैप्पी बर्थ-डे' के गीत की सभी पंक्तियाँ सस्वर गा चुकी है और सभी बच्चे इसमें श्वेता का साथ दे चुके हैं। आकाश और शालिनी ने भी तो पूरे उल्लास के साथ उन पंक्तियों को गाया था...

शालिनी हुलस से भर उठती है। लपकती है, कटे केक का एक बड़ा-सा टुकड़ा उठाती है, रख देती है प्रतीक के मुँह में। फोटोग्राफर कैमरा क्लिक-क्लिक करता है। प्रतीक भी केक का बड़ा-सा टुकड़ा शालिनी को अपने हाथ से खिलाता है। कैमरा फिर से क्लिक-क्लिक! अब आकाश का क्रम है। वह भी बिटवा को केक खिलाता है और बिटवा से केक खाता है। श्वेता क्यों पीछे रहे? केक का उतना बड़ा टुकड़ा श्वेता ने खोज कहाँ से लिया? "खोल मुँह! खोल मुँह!" श्वेता ललकार रही है। प्रतीक उतना बड़ा मुँह ही नहीं खोल पा रहा कि केक के उस टुकड़े को गड़ाप से एक निवाले में निगल सके। अचानक चमत्कार! केक के उस ज़बर्दस्त टुकड़े को श्वेता खुद खा गई। यह तो पलक झपकते हो गया। प्रतीक ने भारी प्रयास करके अपना मुँह इतना फाड़ लिया था कि महा-केक सीधा चला जाए अन्दर, लेकिन उसी पल श्वेता ने फ़ैसला किया कि केक तो वह खुद खाएगी—और वह खा गई। अचानक इतना बड़ा मुँह खोला श्वेता ने, जैसे व्हेल! केक श्वेता के मुँह में और सारे बच्चे खिलखिल-खिलखिल! प्रतीक चकित-चकित। श्वेता का मुँह केक अन्दर लेने के बाद बन्द हुआ और प्रतीक का मुँह, जो उतनी हसरत से फट-फटकर खुला था, बिना केक के ही बन्द हो गया! खी-खी-खी...हो-हो-हो...तड़-तड़-तड़ तालियाँ...जैसे श्वेता ने न जाने क्या करतब दिखा दिया हो सरकस का!

खेल खतम।

चले गए सब बच्चे—गिफ्ट केवल देकर नहीं, गिफ्ट पाकर भी। हर बच्चे को, जो भी आया था, प्रतीक ने अपने हाथ से एक-एक क़ीमती कम्पास-बॉक्स दिया। प्रतीक के लिए छोटे-बड़े पैकेट्स में, सजधज के साथ बँधी गिफ्ट्स, ड्राइंग-रूम के कोने में इकट्ठी रखी थीं। प्रतीक के हाथों में खुजली मची थी, हर पैकेट को खोलकर अन्दर छिपी गिफ्ट को चेक करने के लिए। शालिनी छेड़ रही थी प्रतीक को, "तुझे तो बड़ी गिफ्ट्स मिली है रे!"

आकाश भी शामिल था इस छेड़ में, "हमें तो कभी इतनी गिफ्ट्स एक साथ नहीं मिलीं!"

"बिकाज़ आयेम ग्रेट!" प्रतीक सीना फुलाकर कह रहा था।

श्वेता मुँह बिदका रही थी, "बड़ा आया ग्रेट!"

भाई-बहन खिसक चले गिफ्ट-पैकेट्स वाले कोने की तरफ़। सबसे पहले उन्होंने उस पैकेट को खोलना शुरू किया, जो देखने में सबसे बड़ा था। शालिनी ने डूबन-सी महसूस की। इतना बड़ा पैकेट है, न जाने क्या निकलेगा अन्दर से! शालिनी और आकाश की नज़रें मिलीं। शालिनी संकोच के साथ बोली, "एक भी बच्चा ऐसा नहीं था, जो गिफ्ट लेकर नहीं आया।"

आकाश ने मानो तसल्ली देनी चाही, "कोई बात नहीं, कोई बात नहीं..."

"मैंने तो हरेक के माँ-बाप से साफ़ कह रखा था, गिफ्ट के साथ किसी को न भेजना।"

"ठीक है, तो इसमें इतनी नर्वस क्यों हो रही हो?"

तब तक सबसे बड़ा वह पैकेट खुल चुका था। सुन्दर-सा बड़ा-सा एक भालू निकल पड़ा था उसमें से। 'सॉफ्ट टॉय! चौदह बरस के प्रतीक के लिए खिलौना-भालू? देनेवाले ने क्या कुछ भी न सोचा?' 'लेकिन नहीं...' शालिनी मन-ही-मन तर्क कर रही थी, 'ये सॉफ्ट टॉयज़ घर की सजावट में भी तो काम आते हैं। ये किसी को भी दिए जा सकते हैं...'

प्रतीक को भी उतना बड़ा खिलौना-भालू पाकर कम रोमांच नहीं हो रहा था। "मम्मी! मम्मी!" प्रतीक की किलकारी गूँजी, "हैव अ लुक!"

शालिनी बेमन से बोली, "या-या, इट्स ग्रेट..."

फिर वह आकाश से मुख़ातिब हो गई, "नर्वस कैसे न होऊँ, आकाश! क्या मैं तुम्हारे विचारों को जानती नहीं हूँ? तुम्हारे बेटे को सालगिरह की गिफ्ट देने के बहाने अगर कोई इस घर में...रिश्वत जैसी कोई चीज़ घुसा दे, तो...तुम पर क्या गुज़रेगी, क्या मुझे अन्दाज़ा नहीं?"

खिलौना-भालू को एक तरफ़ रखकर प्रतीक और श्वेता ने एक छोटे पैकेट को खोलना शुरू कर दिया था। आकाश ने प्रतीक-श्वेता पर उड़ती नज़र डाली, फिर

शालिनी की आँखों में देखा, "देखो, शालिनी! हम अपनी ओर से हमेशा सावधान रहे हैं। आज भी...बच्चों ने अगर गिफ्ट्स दी हैं, तो हर बच्चे ने यहाँ गिफ्ट पाई भी तो है!"

तब तक छोटा पैकेट पूरी तरह खुल चुका था। शालिनी और आकाश ने अपने दोनों बच्चों की आँखों को आश्चर्य से फैलते देखा। खुले पैकेट में से श्वेता एक चेन उठाकर ऊँची कर रही थी—नई, चमचमाती, सोने की चेन! शालिनी का दिल धक् से होकर रह गया। 'नहीं! यह चेन सोने की नहीं है!' शालिनी बार-बार अपने आपको इत्तला देने लगी। चमकती चेन को श्वेता ने सावधानी के साथ डिबिया में वापस रखा। डिबिया शालिनी की ओर बढ़ाती हुई वह बुदबुदाई, "मम्मी! देखो, ज़रा..."

शालिनी ने डिबिया फ़ौरन आकाश की ओर बढ़ा दी, "आकाश! अगर यह चेन सोने की है..."

आकाश ने डिबिया में से चेन क्षणांश के ही लिए उठाई, फिर वापस रख दी और चिन्तित बुदबुदाहट में कहा, "सोने की ही है! सोने को तो मैं एक नज़र में पकड़ता हूँ!" फिर आकाश ने डिबिया पर लगी स्लिप सबको पढ़कर सुनाई, "प्रिय प्रतीक को जन्म-दिन मुबारक! रेखा वर्मा की ओर से, प्यार के साथ!"

परिवार के चारों सदस्य, एक-दूसरे की ओर, ज़रा फैली आँखों से देखने लगे। पल-दो-पल का सन्नाटा, जिसे आकाश के स्वर ने तोड़ा, "प्रतीक! कौन है यह रेखा वर्मा?"

प्रतीक तपाक से सफ़ाई देने लगा, "पप्पा! पप्पा! यह मेरी दोस्त नहीं है। कभी-कभी साथ खेलते हैं। बस।"

शालिनी ने गम्भीर स्वर में बताया, "पड़ोस की लड़की है। आई थी सबके साथ। मैंने...सोचा भी नहीं था..."

आकाश ने सभी के मन की अपराध-भावना को पहचाना, जिसे दूर करने के लिए आकाश ने उसी क्षण बागडोर अपने हाथ में ले ली, "नो प्रॉब्लम! नो प्रॉब्लम! अभी तरीक़ा निकालते हैं! कौन हैं इस...रेखा वर्मा के माता-पिता?"

शालिनी बोली, "अभी, दो महीने पहले, एक नए पड़ोसी आए हैं। तुम्हारी भेंट अभी नहीं हुई है उनसे। उधर, टेन्थ रोड पर, कॉर्नर की जो बड़ी-सी कोठी है, उसे किन्हीं वर्माजी ने ख़रीदा है। हाँ, याद आया—श्रीगोपाल वर्मा। उन्हीं की इकलौती बेटी है—रेखा वर्मा।"

"यह श्रीगोपाल वर्मा करते क्या हैं?"

आकाश के इस प्रश्न के उत्तर में शालिनी इतना ही कह सकी, "यह तो नहीं पता।"

और आकाश बुदबुदा उठा, ''यह महाशय ज़रूर कुछ-न-कुछ ऐसा करते हैं, जिससे उन्हें एक आयकर अधिकारी को खुश रखने की ज़रूरत है! सोने की यह चेन पाँच हज़ार से कम की नहीं!''

चेन को सावधानी से डिबिया में वापस रख रहा आकाश क्या सोच रहा था?

निहाल हुए जा रहे थे श्रीगोपाल वर्मा। आकाश के पड़ोस में आकर बसे हुए अभी उन्हें थोड़ा-सा वक़्त ही तो गुज़रा था। आकाश के साथ विधिवत् परिचय हो सके, ऐसा अवसर भी कहाँ आया था अब तक। इतने पर भी, आकाश जैसा आयकर का बड़ा अधिकारी, बाक़ायदा सपरिवार, भेंट करने के लिए घर तक आ जाएगा—श्रीगोपाल वर्मा ने सोचा भी नहीं था। या, कम-से-कम, उन्होंने दावा तो यही किया कि उन्होंने सोचा भी नहीं था।

आकाश उनके आमने-सामने बैठा हुआ था उस वक़्त। उन्हीं के ड्राइंग-रूम के अन्दर। सोफे पर, आकाश के साथ ही बैठी थी, धीर-गम्भीर शालिनी। प्रतीक और श्वेता सोफा-चेयर्स पर चुप बैठे थे। आगे जो होने जा रहा था, वह उन्हें मालूम था, लेकिन वाह! क्या भोलापन उभार रखा था दोनों ने अपने चेहरों पर!

ठीक सामने सजे दूसरे सोफे पर श्रीगोपाल वर्मा सपत्नीक विराजमान थे। उनकी बिटिया रेखा वर्मा कॉर्नर-चेयर पर, बिना किसी रुतबे के, बैठी थी। ड्राइंग-रूम की एक-एक चीज़ से श्रीगोपाल वर्मा की अमीरी चुह रही थी, किन्तु श्रीगोपाल की इकलौती बेटी रेखा उस हद तक रुतबा-विहीन क्यों थी? सचमुच रुतबा-विहीन थी या आकाश को वैसी लग रही थी?

आकाश ने अपनी नज़र श्रीगोपाल पर केन्द्रित की। घनी, सप्रयास मुसकान आकाश के होंठों पर उभरने लगी। श्रीगोपाल पूछ रहे थे, ''क्या पीएँगे? ठंडा या गरम बोलिए!''

और आकाश बोल रहा था, ''कुछ भी नहीं, प्लीज़! घर से हम चारों सब लेकर ही आए हैं।''

फिर, आकाश एक झटके में, मुद्दे पर आ गया, ''ऐसा है, श्रीगोपाल जी! मैं एक ख़ास काम से आया हूँ आपके पास।'' और आकाश ने अपनी जेब में हाथ डाल, वही डिबिया निकाली, जो रेखा ने प्रतीक को दी थी और जिसमें से निकली थी, पड़ोसी के प्यार की प्रतीक वह सुनहरी, चमचमाती, पाँचेक हज़ार रुपयों की, सोने की चेन!

आकाश ने वह डिबिया, हाथ बढ़ाकर, श्रीगोपाल के सामने प्रस्तुत कर दी और कहा, ''यह चीज़, श्रीगोपाल जी, दरअसल...आपके घर की है, जो भूल से हमारे घर में आ गई है।''

आक्रमण सीधा और सरल था, लेकिन सांस्कृतिक था। श्रीगोपाल का रंग उड़ गया। उन्होंने अपनी पत्नी की ओर देखा। पत्नी का भी रंग उड़ा हुआ था। दोनों ने

एक-दूसरे का रंग उड़ा देखा। इससे दोनों का रंग और ज़्यादा उड़ गया। रुतबा-विहीन रेखा, भौंहों पर बल डालकर, आकाश के हाथ की डिबिया की ओर देख रही थी। प्रतीक और श्वेता, रेखा की भौंहों के बल को गम्भीरता से निहार रहे थे। क्या मज़ेदार शो-डाउन था! 'प्रतीक और श्वेता ज़रूर अभिनय की दुनिया में प्रवेश करेंगे!' शालिनी ने सोचा, 'कैसी गम्भीरता से निहार रहे हैं, कमबख़्त दोनों! मन में तो अनारदाने छूट रहे होंगे।' किन्तु स्वयं शालिनी भी तो कम गम्भीर नहीं थी। अनारदाने तो शालिनी के मन में भी छूटे जा रहे थे, एक के बाद एक!

लेकिन शालिनी जानती थी, माहौल में जल्द ही तनाव का बादल फटनेवाला है। प्रतीक और श्वेता इस बादल को तटस्थ रहकर निहार सकेंगे, किन्तु शालिनी और आकाश को तो सारा तनाव सीना तानकर झेलना होगा...

श्रीगोपाल का मरियल स्वर शालिनी के कानों तक आया, "नहीं, नहीं, हमारे घर की तो कोई भी चीज़..."

श्रीगोपाल ने अपना वाक्य अधूरा रहने दिया। आकाश ने कड़क आग्रह किया, "डिबिया हाथ में तो लीजिए! यह आप ही की है।"

डिबिया को श्रीगोपाल छूना भी नहीं चाहते थे। आकाश सोफे से उठा, दो लम्बे डग भरकर श्रीगोपाल तक पहुँचा, अछूत डिबिया को उसने श्रीगोपाल के हाथ में ज़बर्दस्ती पकड़ाया, फिर पलटकर, पुनः दो लम्बे डग भरकर वह वापस सोफे तक आया और अपनी धीर-गम्भीर शालिनी की बग़ल में, शालिनी जैसा ही धीर-गम्भीर बनकर बैठ गया।

ज़बर्दस्ती थमा दी गई डिबिया को श्रीगोपाल खोल नहीं रहे थे। खोले बिना ही उन्हें मालूम था, अन्दर क्या है। आकाश ने सूई चुभोई, "खोलकर तो देखिए!"

श्रीगोपाल हकला गए, "जी...लेकिन....मैं समझ नहीं पा रहा..."

सूई चुभोने के बाद, आकाश ने, अब भाला चुभोया, "पहले आप खोलकर देख लें। कहीं डिबिया ख़ाली न हो!"

"आप तो मुझे बिलकुल शर्मिन्दा कर रहे हैं!" श्रीगोपाल ने स्वर में हलकी आपत्ति के साथ कहा। डिबिया खोलकर देखने के लिए वह किसी सूरत में तैयार नहीं थे। आकाश दुबारा सोफे से उठा और "लाइए, मैं खोलकर दिखाता हूँ!" इन शब्दों के साथ, दुबारा दो लम्बे डग भरकर, बैठे श्रीगोपाल के आमने-सामने जाकर खड़ा हो गया। श्रीगोपाल के हाथ से डिबिया ले लेने में आकाश को कोई दिक़्क़त न हुई। डिबिया खोलकर आकाश ने सोने की उस चेन को बाक़ायदा बाहर निकाला और श्रीगोपाल को थमाते हुए कहा, "देख लीजिए, आप ही की है न?"

तब तक श्रीगोपाल अपने फॉर्म में आ चुके थे। बोले, "दरअसल...अब यह आप की हो चुकी है।"

आकाश ने भौंहें उठाईं, ''ज़बरन?''

''आपका बच्चा मेरा बच्चा है। मैंने अपने ही बच्चे को प्यार से दी है।''

''शुक्रिया! प्यार के लिए! लेकिन हम केवल उसी प्यार को रख सकते हैं, जिसे कभी वापस भी कर सकें।''

शालिनी ने भी सुर में सुर मिलाया, ''भाई जी! आप बुरा न मानिएगा।''

और आकाश ने आगे चलाया, ''इतनी क़ीमती चीज़ अगर हम रख लेंगे, तो इतनी ही क़ीमती चीज़ हमें भी, कभी-न-कभी, आपकी बिटिया के हाथ में रखनी पड़ेगी, जब कि...हमारी हैसियत इतनी बड़ी नहीं है कि...''

श्रीगोपाल ने स्वर और मुद्रा में लबालब आदेश भरकर अपनी पत्नी की ओर नज़र फेंकी, ''तिलोत्तमा?''

और तिलोत्तमा तपाक से उठ पड़ी। तपाक से ही उसने श्रीगोपाल के हाथ से चेन ले ली। इधर चेन ले रही थी और उधर, अपनी बिटिया रेखा से मुख़ातिब भी हो रही थी, ''बिटिया! तू अन्दर जा!'' जैसे कि अब यहाँ न जाने कौन-सा कर्म होगा कि जिसकी गवाह यदि बिटिया बन गई, तो शायद धरती फट जाएगी!

रेखा ने उठकर, अन्दर जाते-जाते, सिर हिलाकर, प्रतीक को साथ चलने का इशारा किया। जिस शैली में रेखा ने सिर हिलाया था, ठीक उसी शैली में सिर हिलाकर प्रतीक ने साथ, अन्दर चलने से इनकार कर दिया। रेखा अकेली ड्राइंग-रूम से बाहर निकल गई। तब तक तिलोत्तमा शालिनी तक पहुँच चुकी थी। उसने शालिनी को ज़बर्दस्ती चेन पकड़ाने का भारी प्रयास किया।

''तुम मुझसे छोटी हो, शालिनी! हो या नहीं? रख लो इसे।''

''आप बड़ी होकर छोटों को यही सिखाना चाहती हैं?''

''अरे, कुछ सिखा-विखा नहीं रही। सिर्फ़ दे रही हूँ। प्यार से। और अधिकार से।''

''मुझे सिर्फ़ एक सवाल का जवाब दीजिए, तिलोत्तमा जी! मेरे पति अगर इन्कम-टैक्स में ऑफिसर न होते...''

''बातें बाद में करेंगे। पहले इसे रख लो।''

''अगर यह सिर्फ़ एक मामूली क्लर्क होते...सिर्फ़ एक लेखक, पत्रकार या चित्रकार होते....शिक्षक होते, संगीतकार होते...तब भी क्या आप इतने ही प्यार और अधिकार से...''

''हाँ-आँ! बिलकुल!''

''नहीं, तिलोत्तमा जी! ऐसा न होता। आप भी जानती हैं, मैं भी जानती हूँ, ऐसा न होता। अब यदि इजाज़त हो, तो...''

''अरे, कहाँ तुम भी इजाज़त-विजाज़त के फेर में पड़ती हो!''

"जी, लेकिन...अब हमें चलना चाहिए। क्यों, आकाश?"

और शालिनी के संग-संग आकाश भी उठ पड़ा, "हाँ! अब हम चलें।" तब तक श्वेता और प्रतीक भी उठ चुके थे।

तिलोत्तमा का चेहरा उतर गया, किन्तु मुसकान जारी रही, "मैं तो नहीं कहूँगी कि आप लोग जाएँ..."

श्रीगोपाल ने बताया कि किस प्रकार भारतीय संस्कृति का घोर हनन हो रहा था, "देखिए, आप लोग पहली बार हमारे घर आए और...पानी भी नहीं पीया आपने! यह क्या बात हुई?"

आकाश बोला, "फिर कभी..."

शालिनी बोली, "नमस्कार!"

आकाश भी बोला, "नमस्कार!"

श्वेता और प्रतीक ने बिना कुछ बोले नमस्कार में हाथ जोड़ दिए। शालिनी लोहा मान गई दोनों बच्चों का। कैसे शान्तम्-पापम् वाली मुद्रा अपना रखी है दोनों ने। अन्दर-ही-अन्दर तो खी-खी-खी कर रहे होंगे!

श्रीगोपाल सबके नमस्कारों का सामूहिक जवाब दे रहे थे, "नमस्कार साहब, नमस्कार! अब यह जो 'सुनहरी भूल' हमसे हुई है..."

आकाश ने अफसराना ढंग से कहा, "बेहतर हो, 'सुनहरी भूल' को हम दोनों ही भूल जाएँ, ताकि दो अच्छे पड़ोसियों की तरह रह सकें।"

आकाश को सपरिवार बाहर तक छोड़ने के लिए श्रीगोपाल वर्मा संग-संग चलने लगे थे। शालिनी, श्वेता और प्रतीक, जान-बूझकर, ज़रा आगे निकल गए। इससे श्रीगोपाल और आकाश सरेआम अकेले हो गए। ऐसे मौक़े पर श्रीगोपाल वर्मा ने वही कहा, जो वह कह सकते थे, "ऐसा है, आकाश भाई साहब! आप भूल जाएँ, तो भूल जाएँ। हम नहीं भूलेंगे इस 'सुनहरी भूल' को! क्योंकि अगर हम भूल गए, तो यही भूल हम दुबारा कर बैठेंगे।"

आकाश ने भी वही जवाब दिया, जो कि दिया जाना चाहिए था, "ठीक है। भूल को याद रखना भी कोई बुरी बात नहीं!"

श्रीगोपाल वर्मा ने तपाक से कहा, "सौदा मंजूर! हम भूल को याद रखते हैं। आप हमें याद रखिए!"

आकाश बिलकुल तैयार नहीं था ऐसे बाण से बिंधने के लिए। वह इतना ही बोल सका, "जी?"

और श्रीगोपाल ने विजय-भरी नाटकीयता से हाथ जोड़ दिए, "फिर मिलेंगे! नमस्कार!"

बम्बई की सुप्रसिद्ध 'जहाँगीर आर्ट गैलेरी' के सामने आकाश ने ज्यों ही अपनी कार पार्क की, शालिनी सावधान हो गई। मॉडर्न आर्ट की पेंटिंग्स ख़रीदने का अजब चस्का है आकाश को। आकाश को बुरा लगेगा, सोचकर शालिनी कभी कहती तो नहीं थी, किन्तु वे आधुनिक कलाकृतियाँ, शालिनी को, सिवा रंगों की ऊल-जलूल लीपापोती के, और कुछ नहीं लगती थीं। कला और आधुनिकता के नाम पर, ऐसी लीपापोती के लिए, मोटी रक़में, अकसर ख़र्च करना...नहीं, आकाश की आर्थिक स्थिति इतनी सुदृढ़ नहीं थी। लॉक करने से पहले कार के शीशे चढ़ा रहे आकाश से शालिनी ने कहा, ''देखो, आकाश! मैं तुम्हारे साथ आर्ट गैलेरी के अन्दर चलूँगी ज़रूर, मगर एक शर्त पर।''

आकाश को पूर्वाभास था, वह शर्त क्या है, फिर भी उसने पूछा, ''कैसी शर्त?''

''यही कि अब तुम कोई नई पेंटिंग नहीं ख़रीदोगे। बहुत पेंटिंग्स हो गई हैं घर में।''

''लेकिन ऑफिस के लिए भी तो कुछ हों!''

''घर से ले जाओ। बहुत पड़ी हैं।''

''नहीं, शालिनी!''

बहुत बेमन से शालिनी आकाश के पीछे-पीछे चली। कलाप्रेमी दर्शकों के बिखरे-बिखरे गुच्छों के बीच से गुज़रकर दोनों ने गैलेरी में प्रवेश किया। सभी दीवारों पर छोटी-बड़ी कलाकृतियाँ सजी थीं। आकाश एक-एक पेंटिंग के सामने रुककर निहारता, तो निहारता ही रहता। शालिनी की नज़रों में जो रंगों की लीपापोती थी, वही आकाश की नज़रों में था—रंगों का उन्मुक्त उत्सव!

एक पेंटिंग के सामने आकाश कुछ ज़्यादा ही रुक गया। शालिनी समझ गई, आगे क्या होने जा रहा है। उसने आकाश की बुदबुदाहट सुनी, ''कितनी अच्छी है! है न? इसे ख़रीद लेते हैं। सिर्फ़ एक, शालिनी! प्लीज़!''

शालिनी का गणित का चोखा हिसाब था, ''एक ख़रीदो, चाहे दस। ऑफिस के लिए ख़रीद रहे हो, तो बिल का भुगतान भी ऑफिस से करवाओ।''

आकाश निरीहता से बोला, ''भुगतान ऑफिस नहीं करेगा, तुम अच्छी तरह जानती हो।''

''ओके, देन! फटाफट देखो सारी पेंटिंग्स और चलो बाहर!''

''बिना ख़रीदे?''

''हाँ! बिना ख़रीदे!''

''सुनो, शालिनी! मैंने तुमसे छिपाकर आठ सौ रुपए जोड़ रखे हैं!''

''अच्छा-आ! तो तुम भी काला धन रखने लगे? ब्लैक-मनी?''

"यस, मैडम।"

"अच्छे आयकर अधिकारी हो! ब्लैक-मनी को बाहर निकालना तुम्हारा काम है। खुद ब्लैक-मनी अन्दर किए बैठे हो!"

"कर दूँ ख़र्च? लेकर आया हूँ!"

"रोकनेवाली मैं कौन? हर इनसान अपनी ब्लैक-मनी, अपनी कमज़ोरियों पर ही, ख़र्च करता है। करो ख़र्च तुम भी!"

"यह तुमने खूब कही! कला, कलाकार और कलाकृतियाँ...ये ही तो हैं मेरी कमज़ोरियाँ..."

"कहाँ से आ गए तुम आयकर विभाग में!"

"जाने क्या दाम है इस पेंटिंग का। क्यों? मिल जाएगी आठेक सौ में?"

"मुझसे क्या पूछते हो? पूछो कलाकार से!"

"ओहो, तो इतनी नाराज़ क्यों हो रही हो?"

आत्मीय बुदबुदाहटों में हो रही थी यह नोकझोंक। न तो आकाश को आभास मिल पाया था, और न शालिनी को ही, कि उनकी बुदबुदाहटें सुनकर एक व्यक्ति चलता-चलता रुक गया है और अशालीनता होने के बावजूद, कान लगाकर सुने जा रहा है...आख़िर उस व्यक्ति से न रहा गया। शालिनी ने ज्यों ही कहा, 'पूछो कलाकार से!' त्यों ही उस व्यक्ति ने फ़ैसला कर लिया, इस जुगल-जोड़ी से बात ज़रूर करेगा।

"सर!" उस व्यक्ति ने आगे बढ़कर, शालीनता से मुसकराकर कहा, "इजाज़त हो, तो बताऊँ...आप इस प्रदर्शनी के कलाकार से बात करना चाहते हैं न? मैं ही वह कलाकार हूँ!"

और कलाकार ने अपनी परिचय-पुस्तिका आगे बढ़ा दी। परिचय-पुस्तिका लेकर आकाश ने हार्दिक उत्साह से, कलाकार से हाथ मिलाया, "नाइस टू सी यू..."

गिनती के ही मिनटों बाद, कलाकार उस पेंटिंग के आगे 'बिक चुकी' का टैग लगाता हुआ, आकाश से कह रहा था, "सर! किसी भी पूँजीपति को यह पेंटिंग मैंने आठ हज़ार से कम में न दी होती, लेकिन आपको आठ सौ में देकर भी मैं बहुत खुश हूँ। सच्चे क़द्रदान तो आप ही हैं, जिन्होंने इन्कम-टैक्स जैसे शुष्क ऑफिस में काम करते हुए भी..."

आकाश ने हँसकर टोक दिया, "नहीं, नहीं, ऐसा नहीं है। इन्कम-टैक्स का ऑफिस किसी ओर-छोर से शुष्क नहीं होता, भाई मेरे! वहाँ तो रहस्य-रोमांच और दिलेरी के ऐसे-ऐसे ताने-बाने बुने जाते हैं कि..."

शालिनी ने फुल-स्टॉप लगाया, "बस, अब आप यहाँ शुरू न हो जाइए। यह आर्ट-गैलेरी है!"

आकाश तत्काल आइन्स्टीन बन गया, ''मेरे हिसाब से तो...सारी दुनिया ही एक आर्ट-गैलेरी है!''

प्रसन्न होकर कलाकार बोला, ''सही फ़रमाया आपने!''

शालिनी फैली आँखों से देखती रह गई थी अपने आइन्स्टीन की ओर...

जॉगिंग पार्क...चिड़ियाँ अपनी चहक से सुबह का स्वागत कर रही थीं। भाँति-भाँति की पोशाकों में भाँति-भाँति के लोग जॉगिंग कर रहे थे। कुछ प्रौढ़ नर-नारी, जिनकी श्रद्धा दौड़ लगाने में नहीं थी, खड़े-खड़े तरह-तरह के व्यायाम कर रहे थे।

आकाश अकेला जॉगिंग करने निकला था। रात को अगर बहुत देर से न सोया हो, तो सूर्योदय से पहले ही आकाश जॉगिंग करने इस पार्क में आ जाया करता। बम्बई के उपनगर, खार में जब से आकाश ने फ्लैट किराए पर लिया है, तभी से इस पार्क में उसकी जॉगिंग का क्रम जारी है।

जॉगिंग में शालिनी उसका साथ नहीं देती। शालिनी को सुबह की मीठी नींद बहुत प्यारी है। इसके अलावा, प्रतीक और श्वेता को स्कूल, कॉलेज विदा भी तो करना होता है। शालिनी के इस कथन को तथ्यहीन तो नहीं माना जा सकता था, ''आकाश! तुम कसरत करो पार्क में। मैं कसरत करूँ अपने किचन में! जॉगिंग में मुझे साथ मत घसीटो, यार! डबल कसरत करवाओगे, मर जाऊँगी!''

मद्धिम-मद्धिम दौड़ लगाता आकाश, पार्क के एक कोने में मुड़ा और आगे चला। उसी कोने पर, तत्काल श्रीगोपाल वर्मा प्रकट हुए और आकाश के पीछे-पीछे जॉगिंग करते, मद्धिम-मद्धिम दौड़ने लगे, किन्तु अपने-आपमें मगन आकाश को सहसा पता न चला, महा-मानव के प्रकट होने का। श्रीगोपाल ने अपनी मद्धिम दौड़ को ज़रा तेज़ किया, ताकि आकाश के पीछे-पीछे नहीं, बल्कि संग-संग दौड़ सकें। संग दौड़ते श्रीगोपाल को देख आकाश बरबस मुसकरा दिया। श्रीगोपाल ने पहल की, ''नमस्ते, भाई साहब!''

आकाश ने भावभीनी औपचारिकता के साथ उत्तर दिया, ''ओहो, श्रीगोपाल जी! नमस्ते! कहिए, कैसे हैं?''

''बस, जॉगिंग कर रहा हूँ।''

''इस पार्क में पहली बार देखा आपको।''

''जी हाँ! पहले कहीं और जाता था। आज यहाँ आया हूँ।''

आकाश ने शुद्ध भ्राता-भाव से कहा, ''वेलकम...वेलकम...''

''अच्छा पार्क है, यहीं आना चाहिए।''

श्रीगोपाल की इस राय के साथ आकाश झटपट सहमत हो गया, ''मैं तो यहीं आता हूँ।''

“अकेले हैं क्या आज? भाभी जी नहीं हैं साथ में?” श्रीगोपाल ने पूछा।

आकाश मुसकराया, “कौन...शालिनी? और जॉगिंग? सवाल ही नहीं! अव्वल तो, प्रतीक और श्वेता के लिए, सुबह-सुबह, लंच-बॉक्स तैयार करने होते हैं, और फिर...शालिनी सुबह जल्दी जाग ही नहीं सकती। सुबह की मीठी नींद शालिनी की बहुत बड़ी कमज़ोरी है।”

श्रीगोपाल दार्शनिक अन्दाज़ में बोले, “होती है...हर इनसान की कोई-न-कोई कमज़ोरी होती है। अब देखिए न, मेरी भी कमज़ोरी है कि...”

आकाश ने मज़ाक़ किया, “न, न, श्रीगोपाल जी! अपनी कमज़ोरियाँ छिपाकर ही रखिए!”

“क्यों?”

“कमज़ोरियों को तो छिपाकर ही रखना चाहिए।”

“वो बात सही है, लेकिन भाई साहब! इनसान में कमज़ोरियाँ न हों, तो वह जीए कैसे? कमज़ोरियाँ ही तो ज़िन्दगी को जीने लायक़ बनाती हैं!”

आकाश का मज़ाकिया मूड भी, आकाश के साथ-साथ ही, जॉगिंग कर रहा था, “हाँ-आँ...लेकिन...कमज़ोरियों को छिपाकर रखने का भी अपना एक आनन्द होता है!”

“आप लेते हैं यह आनन्द?” श्रीगोपाल ने सीधा सवाल किया।

और उस सीधे सवाल के तमाम टेढ़े अर्थ, क्षण मात्र में आकाश के मन-मस्तिष्क में कौंध गए। तुरन्त याद आ गया, इस आदमी ने वचन दे रखा है, ‘सौदा मंजूर!’ वाला वचन...

आकाश ख़ामोशी से जॉगिंग करता रहा। श्रीगोपाल ने समझा कि आकाश ने उसके वाक्य को शायद ठीक से सुना नहीं, तभी तो कुछ जवाब नहीं दिया। श्रीगोपाल ने दोहराया, “कमज़ोरियों को छिपाकर रखने का आनन्द...अगर यह आनन्द आप लेते हैं, तो...”

गहरी सांकेतिकता से श्रीगोपाल ने वाक्य अधूरा छोड़ दिया। आगे के नाज़ुक संवादों के लिए आकाश मन-ही-मन स्वयं को तैयार करने लगा।

बड़ी-से-बड़ी अदालत में भी, बड़े-से-बड़े अपराधी को भी, सन्देह का लाभ मिलता है। अपराध जब तक सन्देह से पूर्णतया परे, निश्चित रूप से साबित न हो जाए, तब तक किसी व्यक्ति को दंडित नहीं किया जाता, चाहे उस पर आरोप कितना ही गम्भीर क्यों न हो। क्या श्रीगोपाल वर्मा को भी सन्देह का लाभ पाने का अधिकार नहीं है? मुमकिन है, श्रीगोपाल जो बोल रहे हैं, अपनी केवल सहजता में ही बोल रहे हैं। उनके सीधे शब्दों के पीछे टेढ़े अर्थ छिपे हुए महसूस ज़रूर हो रहे हैं, लेकिन यह आकाश की ग़लतफ़हमी भी तो हो सकती है। जब तक यह ग़लतफ़हमी दूर न हो जाए, सन्देह से पूर्णतया परे जब तक निश्चित रूप से साबित न हो जाए कि श्रीगोपाल

के मन में कुटिलता छिपी है, तब तक....श्रीगोपाल वर्मा को एक मीठा-मधुर पड़ोसी ही मानकर चलना चाहिए।

आकाश अपने इन मनोमन्थन में डूबता-उतराता, जॉगिंग को जारी रखे हुए था। श्रीगोपाल की असलियत को और भी स्पष्टता से समझने के लिए आकाश ने कमज़ोरियों वाले विषय को ही उकेरने का निर्णय ले लिया।

''कमज़ोरियों को छिपाए-छिपाए फिरने का जो...गूँगे के गुड़ जैसा आनन्द होता है, वह अपनी किस्मत में कहाँ!'' आकाश ने श्रीगोपाल वर्मा के पूरे चेहरे पर उड़ती नज़र फेरते हुए कहा, ''हमसे तो अपनी एक भी कमज़ोरी नहीं छिपती।''

''सच कहूँ?'' श्रीगोपाल ने आकाश की नज़र से नज़र लड़ाई, ''आपमें कोई कमज़ोरी है ही नहीं! छिपाएँगे क्या?''

शुद्ध मक्खन का मिसाइल छोड़ा गया था आकाश की तरफ़! आकाश ने एंटीमिसाइल छोड़ने के लिए ब्रह्म-वाक्य कहा, ''दुनिया में कोई इनसान है ऐसा, जिसमें कोई कमज़ोरी न हो?''

श्रीगोपाल बोले, ''आप जो हैं मेरे सामने!''

''छोड़िए! शर्मिन्दा करते हैं!''

''कहाँ-कहाँ नहीं पूछा, आपकी कमज़ोरियों के बारे में! कोई कुछ बताता ही नहीं!''

''देखिए, इसका एक मतलब यह निकलता है कि आपने...मेरी कमज़ोरियों को पकड़ने के लिए...बाक़ायदा मेरे पीछे जासूसी की है!'' इस बार आकाश अपनी तल्ख़ी न छिपा सका।

श्रीगोपाल वर्मा उसी पल चालू हो गए, ''हे, भगवान! यह क्या कहा आपने! मैं आपके पीछे जासूसी करूँगा? आप जैसे इन्कम-टैक्स के ऑफिसर के पीछे...मुझ जैसा अदना आदमी जासूसी करे? सोच भी कौन सकता है?''

''लेकिन अभी खुद आप ही ने तो कहा...''

''जी हाँ, कहा ज़रूर मैंने, लेकिन...मतलब वह थोड़े ही था। पूछताछ इसलिए की थी ज़रा...कि आप जैसे अच्छे इनसान के नज़दीक आने का...कोई आधार निकाल सकूँ। क्या एक अच्छे इनसान के नज़दीक आना बुरी बात है?''

''लेकिन अगर आप मेरी कमज़ोरियों की जानकारी लेकर नज़दीक आना चाहेंगे...''

और श्रीगोपाल वर्मा ने इन शब्दों के साथ हथियार डाल दिए, ''आप बुरा मान गए शायद। क्षमा करें...''

''नहीं...ऐसी कोई सीरियस बात नहीं। आइए, बैठते हैं।'' कहता हुआ आकाश जॉगिंग पार्क की एक बेंच पर बैठ गया। श्रीगोपाल वर्मा भी बेंच पर बैठे—संकोच के साथ, या संकोच के दिखावे के साथ। आकाश ने उनकी ओर रूखी मुसकान फेंकी,

फिर कहा, ''अगर मेरा अन्दाज़ा ग़लत नहीं है, तो...आज आप इस पार्क में मुझसे कोई ख़ास बात करने आए हैं।''

जॉगिंग करते लोग, कभी-कभार, उस बेंच के सामने से गुज़र रहे थे। उनका ध्यान न तो आकाश की तरफ़ था, न श्रीगोपाल की तरफ़। सूर्य ने आकाश का चेहरा सेंकने के लिए सीधी किरणें भेजना शुरू किया...वे किरणें श्रीगोपाल वर्मा की पीठ को सेंक रही थीं।

श्रीगोपाल ने गहरी साँस ली, ''ऐसा है...मैं इतना जानता हूँ, ज़िन्दगी में आपसे बहुत-कुछ सीखा जा सकता है। इसीलिए आपके नज़दीक आना चाहता हूँ। नज़दीक आने के लिए ही...मेरी हार्दिक इच्छा है कि...आपकी कुछ सेवा करूँ...लेकिन आप सेवा का मौक़ा ही नहीं देते। यहाँ तक कि...एक मामूली गिफ्ट भी आप...बाक़ायदा घर आकर वापस कर गए...''

''क्या फ़ायदा, गड़े मुरदे उखाड़ने से।'' आकाश ने औपचारिक ढंग से कहा।

श्रीगोपाल ने जारी रखा, ''जिस दिन आपने मेरे घर आकर वह चेन वापस की थी, याद है, उस दिन मैंने क्या कहा था आपसे? मैंने कहा था, 'फिर मिलेंगे!' मुझे खुशी है, आज मैं आपसे फिर मिल रहा हूँ...''

श्रीगोपाल वर्मा उठ पड़े। साथ में, आकाश भी।

''न केवल आपसे फिर मिल रहा हूँ...'' श्रीगोपाल कह रहे थे, ''बल्कि...आज मैं अकेला भी नहीं हूँ।''

आकाश समझा नहीं, ''अकेले नहीं हैं?''

श्रीगोपाल ने जॉगिंग करते हुए, पार्क की एक पगडंडी, हौले-हौले पार करनी शुरू की। आकाश उनकी बग़ल से चलता, जॉगिंग करने लगा। श्रीगोपाल ने जारी रखा, ''कोई और भी है मेरे साथ। उसकी नज़र लगातार हम दोनों पर है। ज्यों ही मैं इशारा करूँगा, वह व्यक्ति, धीमा-धीमा दौड़ता हुआ, हम दोनों के बीच से गुज़रेगा!''

''ओह! रियली!'' आकाश बुदबुदाया।

श्रीगोपाल का स्वर ज्यों-का-त्यों बना रहा, ''आप उस व्यक्ति के चेहरे पर मुसकान की एक हलकी रेखा भी नहीं देखेंगे। इस खुले पार्क में मैंने उसे मुसकराने से मना किया है।''

आकाश व्यंग्य से हँसा, ''आपकी बातें जासूसी उपन्यासों जैसी हैं।''

''जी हाँ! अब...क्यों न हम...इस उपन्यास के आख़िरी पन्ने पर पहुँच जाएँ?''

और श्रीगोपाल ने अपने दोनों हाथ इस प्रकार उठाए, मानो पार्क में टहलते-टहलते, यों ही, उनके हाथ सिर के ऊपर तक चले गए हों।

आकाश ने स्पष्ट देखा, पार्क के दूर के कोने में जॉगिंग कर रही एक युवती ने अपनी दौड़ की दिशा बदल दी है...धीमे-धीमे दौड़ रही वह युवती पार्क की

एक ऐसी पगडंडी पकड़ रही थी, जिससे वह आकाश और श्रीगोपाल के ठीक आमने-सामने दौड़ती चली आए।

आमने-सामने दौड़ी चली आ रही वह युवती निस्सन्देह गोरी थी। सूर्य की दुष्ट किरणों ने उसकी गोराई को छेड़कर सुनहरा बना दिया था। युवती के बाल पोनी-टेल की तरह बँधे थे। धीमी दौड़ के एक-एक क़दम पर वे बाल कुलाँच भर रहे थे। युवती अब इतनी नज़दीक आ चुकी थी कि आकाश उसके दोनों गालों पर ग़ौर कर सका। एक-एक क़दम पर दोनों गाल सिहर-सिहरकर अपनी चिकनी सतह का यौवन मुखर कर रहे थे। सुघड़ नासिका की अंगरक्षक-सी बनी बड़ी-बड़ी दो आँखें। लिपस्टिक-विहीन, किन्तु आमन्त्रण से सुसज्जित होंठों का जवान जोड़ा...साथ में, रनिंग-कमेंट्री जैसा, श्रीगोपाल का स्वर, ''क्या ख़याल है, भाई साहब? यह एक अनुपम कलाकृति है या नहीं? मेरे हिसाब से तो यह एक ईश्वरीय कलाकृति है, साक्षात् ईश्वर ने निर्माण किया है इसका! प्लीज़, भाई साहब! इसे आप एक कलाकृति के ही रूप में देखिए। आप तो कला और कलाकृतियों के क़द्रदान हैं न? मुझे बार-बार बताया गया है, कलाकृतियों के लिए आपके दिल में बहुत जगह है...''

जैसा कि श्रीगोपाल का वचन था, उस युवती के होंठों पर, चेहरे पर, मुसकान की हलकी-सी रेखा भी नहीं थी। तटस्थ, निर्द्वन्द्व, दौड़ती चली आ रही थी वह, जैसे संसार के किसी भी जीव से उसका कोई सरोकार न हो। ढिठाई की हद ऐसी मालूम पड़ी कि आकाश ने सोचा, 'अगर मैं अपनी जगह से दाएँ या बाएँ हटा नहीं, तो यह देवी जी बिगड़ैल बैल की तरह सीधी आकर कहीं मुझसे टकरा ही न जाएँ!'

क्यों हटे आकाश? आकाश को हटने की क्या ज़रूरत है? न हटने का पक्का फ़ैसला कर लिया उसने...और वह युवती अब बिलकुल ही नज़दीक थी। आमने-सामने दौड़ती, वह, पल-पल और नज़दीक आ रही थी।

श्रीगोपाल वर्मा ने हटकर युवती को गुज़रने की जगह दे दी। आकाश के साथ सटे-सटे दौड़ रहे श्रीगोपाल ने, सहसा दो क़दम दाएँ हटकर, दौड़ना शुरू कर दिया। इससे आकाश और श्रीगोपाल के बीच इतनी जगह निकल आई कि वह युवती उतनी जगह में से सकुशल पार हो सकती थी। आकाश और श्रीगोपाल के ऐन बीच से वह युवती, किसी से भी नज़र मिलाए बिना, साँय करती, दौड़ती निकल गई। अगले ही पल श्रीगोपाल वापस दो क़दम बाएँ हटकर दौड़ने लगे। दाएँ हटने से आकाश और श्रीगोपाल के बीच जो फ़ासला बन गया था, बाएँ हटने के साथ वह फ़ासला ख़त्म हो गया।

''भाई साहब!'' जॉगिंग करते, कुछ-कुछ हाँफते, श्रीगोपाल ने कोमल कंठ से, कुनकुनी मुद्रा में कहा, ''यह ईश्वरीय कलाकृति केवल आपके लिए है। बड़ी मशक़्क़त से इन्तज़ाम किया है इसका। आपकी 'हाँ' होने की देर है। जो कलाकृति ईश्वर की

है, वह आपकी हो जाएगी और...यक़ीन जानिए, स्वयं ईश्वर को भी इसकी ख़बर न होगी!''

क्रोध की चरम सीमा पर आकाश की ख़ामोश रह जाने की आदत थी। जॉगिंग स्थगित करके आकाश खड़ा रह गया—और वह ख़ामोश था। कितने पलों तक वह लगातार ख़ामोश रहा, स्वयं आकाश को पता न चला।

संसार की सभी पत्नियाँ एक जन्मजात दायित्व निभाती हैं—पति के आक्रोश को शान्त करने का दायित्व! पति कहीं से भी अपमानित होकर आया हो, अथवा पति किसी को भी अपमानित करके आया हो, यदि वह आक्रोश में है, तो उसे शान्त पत्नी ही करेगी। शालिनी ने कहीं लेख पढ़ा था कि कुँआरे ज़्यादा नहीं जीया करते। कारण समझ में आता है। कुँआरों का आक्रोश कौन शान्त करे? पत्नी तो होती नहीं बेचारों की! आक्रोश यदि अन्दर-ही-अन्दर घुटता रहेगा, तो उम्र को काटे बिना कैसे रहेगा!

उस वक़्त शालिनी अपने इसी जन्मजात दायित्व को निभा रही थी। आकाश का आक्रोश उबला पड़ रहा था और शालिनी उसे प्रकट और प्रच्छन्न दोनों रूपों में पुचकारे जा रही थी।

''अब मैं इस श्रीगोपाल के बच्चे को नहीं छोड़ूँगा!'' कहते आकाश की मुट्ठियाँ कस गई थीं, ''हिम्मत देखो! कितनी सफ़ाई से क्या चीज़ पेश की!''

घर से बाहर, क्रोधित आकाश जितना चुप रह जाता है, घर के अन्दर वह उतना ही बिफरता है। घर से बाहर आकाश, शान्ति से, ज़बर्दस्त फ़ैसले करता और एक्शन की बागडोर सँभालता है। घर के अन्दर, वह केवल शाब्दिक स्तर पर बिफरता है। नाज़ुक-से-नाज़ुक स्थितियों में भी, घर से बाहर, आकाश जितना शान्त रहता है, उसे देखने के बाद घर के अन्दर के, नितान्त भिन्न आकाश को क्या कोई पहचान भी पाएगा?

आकाश नाटकीयता से घर की छत की ओर देखता हुआ, न जाने किस अदृश्य अदालत में, अपील कर रहा था, ''प्यारे, आकाश! आज तेरी क़द्र हो गई!''

शालिनी बोली, ''रिलैक्स! रिलैक्स!''

किन्तु आकाश था कि बोले जा रहा था, ''पहली बार तो यों बच गया था श्रीगोपाल कि मैंने सोचा, बेचारा नया-नया पड़ोस में रहने आया है, पहचानता नहीं है मुझे, भूल कर गया है, नादान को माफ़ कर दिया जाए! लेकिन वही भूल दुबारा? ज़्यादा बेशर्मी, ज़्यादा ढिठाई के साथ? देखती जाओ तुम, शालिनी! अब कैसे मैं इस आदमी के पीछे हाथ धोकर पड़ जाता हूँ!''

''लेकिन, आकाश!'' शालिनी ने दूसरा पहलू सामने रखा, ''पड़ोस का मामला है। श्रीगोपाल को फ़ौरन शक हो जाएगा कि तुमने दुश्मनी निकाली है।''

"लो, इसमें दुश्मनी का क्या सवाल है? यह तो मेरी ड्यूटी है कि जहाँ भी काला धन हो, उसे मैं खोदूँ और बाहर निकालूँ। तुम सोचती हो, श्रीगोपाल के पास जितना धन है, सारा सफ़ेद है?"

"झगड़ा तुम दोनों का! मुसीबत मेरी!"

"क्यों? तुम्हारी क्या मुसीबत है?"

"तुम्हारा क्या! सुबह ऑफिस चल दिए। रात को लौटे, सो गए। पड़ोस का तनाव तो मैं झेलूँगी।" शालिनी ने व्यावहारिकता की बात कही, लेकिन आकाश की भौहें चढ़ गईं, "यानी, क्या एक अपराधी को सिर्फ़ इसलिए छोड़ दिया जाए कि वह पड़ोस में रहता है?"

शालिनी ने आत्म-रक्षा की, "मैंने कब कहा कि श्रीगोपाल को छोड़ दो? अगर वाक़ई उसने काला धन इकट्ठा कर रखा है, तो..."

"अगर? वाक़ई?" आकाश ने वकीलों की तरह इन दो शब्दों को पकड़ लिया, 'अगर' और 'वाक़ई' का सवाल ही कहाँ है? इस आदमी के पूरे बरताव को देखो। क्यों यह मुझे ज़बर्दस्ती घूस देना चाहता है? क्योंकि मेरे वार्ड में इसने एक नई दुकान ख़रीदी है! बात आई समझ में? मिठाई और नमकीन की दुकान! गणित का चोखा, एकदम चोखा हिसाब है। मैं इसकी दुकान पर छापा न मारूँ, चाहे इसने कुछ भी छिपा रखा हो। बदले में यह हलवाई मुझसे मांसाहार करवाएगा! जब चाहूँ, जितना चाहूँ, मांस खाता रहूँ! कमबख़्त कहता था, 'ईश्वर को भी ख़बर न होगी!'...शालिनी! क्या इतनी आसानी से ईश्वर की आँखों में धूल झोंकी जा सकती है?"

धाराप्रवाह कितना अधिक बोल गया था आकाश। वह रुका। उसे गहरी साँस लेने की ज़रूरत थी।

शालिनी ने अपनी राय दी, "तुमने श्रीगोपाल का प्रस्ताव स्वीकार तो नहीं किया है न? बस! फिर क्यों इतने उबल रहे हो?"

और आकाश फिर धाराप्रवाह शुरू हो गया, "उबल इसलिए रहा हूँ कि शर्मिन्दा हूँ...और शर्मिन्दा इसलिए हूँ कि इस मौक़े पर भी मैं अपनी सभ्यता और शालीनता की रक्षा कर रहा था! बढ़ते क्रोध के साथ मेरी ख़ामोशी बढ़ती गई थी! भला कोई बात हुई? बजाय इसके कि पूरी तरह असभ्य होकर मैं श्रीगोपाल को माँ-बहन की गालियाँ देता, मैं...मैं तो...मन्द-मन्द मुसकाने लगा था! निहायत सभ्यता के साथ, पूरी शालीनता के साथ, मन्द-मन्द मुसकाते हुए मैंने कहा था, 'नहीं, श्रीगोपालजी! ऐसी बातों में मेरी दिलचस्पी नहीं! धन्यवाद!' यानी, ऊपर से धन्यवाद भी दिया! अरे, मैं एकदम विकराल क्यों नहीं हो गया? भयानक चीत्कार करके मैं श्रीगोपाल पर टूट क्यों नहीं पड़ा? उतने भद्दे मौक़े पर भी मेरा पहले तो चुप रह जाना और फिर मुसकरा देना...क्या यह मेरी कायरता नहीं?"

शालिनी पुलकित हो गई, "आकाश! तुम्हें तो कवि होना चाहिए था!"

और शालिनी ने ऐसी मदमाती नज़र से देखा आकाश को कि अगर वह अस्सी बरस का बूढ़ा होता, तब भी चारों खाने चित्त हो जाता! जबकि आकाश अभी पैंतालीसवाँ पूरा कर रहा था। शालिनी से केवल पाँचेक बरस पहले ही तो आया था वह, इस पापी संसार में।

आकाश ने, अभी धाराप्रवाह, कम-से-कम पचास वाक्य बोले थे। जवाब में देवी जी केवल एक वाक्य बोलती हैं, 'तुम्हें तो कवि होना चाहिए था!' और सारी समस्या ख़तम हो जाती है! शालिनी को यदि देश की प्रधानमन्त्री बना दिया जाए? अपने एक-एक वाक्य से देवी जी सौ-सौ समस्याएँ हल करें!

"सुनो!" आकाश ने दीन-हीन स्वर में कहा, "मेरी एक बात मानोगी?"

"बोलो।"

और आकाश ने नहले पे दहला दे ही दिया, "कल सुबह नाश्ते में आलू की टिक्की बनाना!"

इस बार चारों खाने चित्त होने की शालिनी की बारी थी! कुछ पल पहले ही, कितना उबल रहा था आकाश! आक्रोश के गरम तवे पर बैठा आकाश किस तरह इधर-से-उधर पलट रहा था! और अभी, इस पल, एकाएक इस व्यक्ति को आलू की टिक्कियाँ याद आ गई हैं!

जिस आक्रोश ने सिर से पैर तक सान दिया हो, उसी आक्रोश को क्या इतनी आसानी से उतारकर फेंका जा सकता है? क्या आक्रोश केवल एक शॉल है? या क्रिकेट-खिलाड़ी के सिर की केवल एक कैप है? चाहो जब पहन लो, चाहो जब उतार दो! आकाश कितनी सहजता से खेल सकता है अपने आक्रोश से! आकाश जब चाहे, आक्रोश उछल पड़े। आकाश ज्यों ही इशारा करे, आक्रोश भीगी बिल्ली बन जाए! माँग-माँगकर भी इस आदमी ने क्या माँगा? सिर्फ़ आलू की टिक्की! अरे, यह तो कमाल का आदमी है! पता ही नहीं चला था शालिनी को, कब वह उठ पड़ी थी, कब उसने आकाश का चेहरा थामकर सीने से चिपटा लिया था, कब वह तपती बुदबुदाहट में बोल उठी थी, "ओह, आकाश! एकदम बच्चे हो! अभी भी!"

गैस चालू है। तवा गरम है। रिफाइंड मूँगफली के तेल का गोल घेरा, शालिनी, तवे के कगार पर बनाती है। तेल का घेरा तवे के मध्य-बिन्दु की ओर फैलता जाता है। बीच-बीच में बाधाएँ बनकर पड़ी हैं नन्ही-नन्ही पहाड़ियाँ—आलू की टिक्कियाँ! तेल का घेरा तवे के मध्य-बिन्दु तक पहुँचे, उससे पहले ही ये नन्ही पहाड़ियाँ उसे चूस-चूसकर सीत्कारने लगती हैं...हरेक नन्ही पहाड़ी के चारों ओर से सफ़ेद धुएँ के तार उठ-उठकर इठला रहे हैं...सुगन्धम्! स्वादम्!

शालिनी के हाथ में है तो जादू। आलू की टिक्कियाँ ऐसी ज़ोरदार बनाती है कि...सोचने की बात है, आकाश की अर्द्धांगिनी के रूप में शालिनी क्या अपना जीवन व्यर्थ नहीं कर रही? शालिनी को तो ताज होटल में जाकर, टिक्की-विशेषज्ञा बनकर, अपना जीवन सार्थक करना चाहिए!

आकाश और प्रतीक हड़बड़ाते हुए अन्दर आते हैं। दोनों एक-एक ख़ाली प्लेट लिये हुए हैं। आकाश लालची स्वर में बोलता है, "लाओ, लाओ, जल्दी दो!"

प्रतीक के स्वर में बेताबी है, "मॉम! प्लीज़! आई कांट वेट!"

टिक्कियों के साथ चटनी भी तो बनानी होगी। चटनी के भी तत्त्वों का जो बैलेन्स शालिनी तैयार करती है, वह बस शालिनी के ही बस की बात है। मिक्सी में चटनी के तमाम तत्त्व शालिनी डाल चुकी है। मिक्सी का ढक्कन बन्द किया है श्वेता ने। स्विच ऑन कर देती है श्वेता। घर्रर्रर्र! कमबख़्त मिक्सी! पूरा फ्लैट घरघराने लगता है इसके मारे!

आकाश और प्रतीक के हाथ से शालिनी प्लेटें छीन लेती है। मिक्सी की घर्रर्रर्र से भी ऊपर सुनाई पड़ जाए, इतना चीखकर शालिनी जैसे चुनौती दे रही है, "यहाँ खड़े-खड़े नहीं खाएगा कोई! जाओ बाहर। डाइनिंग-टेबल पर बैठो! आ जाएँगी टिक्कियाँ वहीं!"

श्वेता भी, मिक्सी की आवाज़ के आर-पार चिल्लाती है, "करेक्ट! डाइनिंग-टेबल काहे के लिए है? कबड्डी खेलने के लिए?" आकाश और प्रतीक मुँह लटकाकर किचन से निकल जाते हैं। हाय, इन्तज़ार! बेवफ़ा टिक्कियों का!

कितना चाव था आकाश को, अपनी कार अपने ही हाथों चलाने का। सपने में भी कल्पना नहीं करना चाहेगा आकाश कि उसकी कार शोफर चला रहा है और स्वामी आकाश पीछे की सीट पर पसरकर ऊँघ रहा है।

सुबह-सुबह शालिनी, आकाश के साथ, कार में जो आ बैठी, उसका कारण यह नहीं था कि कार अपने ही हाथों चलाने का आकाश का चाव, इस बीच, कहीं कम तो नहीं हो गया, इसका समाधान चाहती थी शालिनी, बल्कि वह इसलिए आ बैठी कि आयकर भवन जाता आकाश, अपनी कार वर्ली से निकालेगा ही, और वर्ली में शालिनी को अपनी एक सहेली से मिलने जाना था। इसके अलावा, आकाश से शालिनी कुछ ज़रूरी बातें भी करना चाहती थी—श्रीगोपाल को लेकर...

श्रीगोपाल को धर दबोचने के लिए आकाश ने तैयारियाँ शुरू कर दी थीं, शालिनी जानती थी। आयकर विभाग के प्रत्येक छापे के पीछे गहरी तैयारी होती है। आयकर का छापा उस कच्चे अंडे की तरह नहीं होता, जिसे आपने छिपाकर अपनी जेब में रख

लिया हो और जिसे अचानक बाहर निकालकर आप 'पार्टी' के मस्तक पर दे मारें। ऐसी चाल से 'पार्टी' को शर्मिन्दा तो किया जा सकता है, किन्तु उससे किसी प्रकार के सहयोग की आशा नहीं रखी जा सकती। ठीक विपरीत, आयकर अधिकारी हमेशा पूरी जासूसी, पूरी तैयारी करके आते हैं, 'पार्टी' या 'एसेसी' को अपनी आकस्मिक कार्रवाई से वे चौंकाते हैं, पस्त भी करते हैं, किन्तु ये अधिकारी मूलतः 'मैत्री-भाव को स्थिर रखते हैं और प्रत्येक 'एसेसी' से सहयोग की आशा रखते हैं। अधिकांश 'एसेसी' आयकर अधिकारियों की इस आशा को काफ़ी हद तक पूरा भी करते हैं।

छापा मारने से पहले की तैयारी को 'रेक्की' कहा जाता है। श्रीगोपाल की 'रेक्की' आकाश ने शुरू करवा तो दी है, लेकिन क्या छापा मारने का सही वक़्त आ गया है? शालिनी इसी मुद्दे पर आज आकाश से ज़रा बहस कर लेने के मूड में थी।

आकाश ने ज्यों ही कार स्टार्ट करके, खार टेलीफोन-एक्सचेंज के सामने से आगे बढ़ाई, शालिनी ने अपना मूड उजागर कर दिया।

"कैसी चल रही है श्रीगोपाल की रेक्की?" उसने पूछा।

"कछुआ धीमा चल रहा है, लेकिन लगातार!" आकाश हँसा।

शालिनी गम्भीर बनी रही, "श्रीगोपाल की रेक्की लम्बे समय तक चलती रहे, यह अच्छा ही है। मैं दरअसल यह समझने की कोशिश में हूँ कि...लम्बा समय यानी कितना लम्बा समय! क्या यह समय इतना लम्बा होगा कि तब तक हमें... इन्कम-टैक्स कॉलोनी में फ्लैट मिल चुका हो?"

"देखो, शालिनी! मैं पक्का तो नहीं कह सकता..."

"आकाश! कहना मैं यह चाहती हूँ...तुम मेरी पोज़ीशन भूलो नहीं। पहले हम इस प्राइवेट कॉलोनी से निकलकर सरकारी कॉलोनी में चले जाएँ। फिर करते रहना, जो करना हो, श्रीगोपाल के ख़िलाफ़! रेक्की को तब तक तो खींचो, जब तक मैं चाहती हूँ!"

"यह अच्छी कही! यानी अगर सरकारी फ्लैट दस साल तक न मिले, तो मैं दस साल तक सिर्फ़ रेक्की करता रहूँ और श्रीगोपाल को छुट्टा घूमने दूँ?" सड़क के मोड़ पर आकाश ने कार को तेज़ी के साथ मोड़ा। शालिनी साथ बैठी थी, इस कारण आकाश आज ज़्यादा स्पीड नहीं पकड़ रहा था।

शालिनी बोली, "तर्क ही करना हो, तब तो कुछ भी कहा जा सकता है, आकाश! तुम अच्छी तरह जानते हो, सरकारी फ्लैट मिलने में दस साल लगने वाले नहीं हैं। कोशिश करो, फ्लैट जल्दी मिल जाएगा। मेरा दिल कहता है।"

"यह दिल कहाँ से आ गया बीच में?" आकाश ने इस प्रकार कहा, जैसे वह शालिनी के आई.क्यू. पर सन्देह कर रहा हो।

"मैं पहले भी कह चुकी हूँ। जब तक हम श्रीगोपाल के पड़ोस में रह रहे हैं, मैं तनाव नहीं चाहती।"

"समझने की कोशिश करो, शालिनी! मैं परदे के पीछे रहकर भी तो कार्रवाई कर सकता हूँ। आई.टी.ओ. में सैकड़ों ऑफिसर्स काम करते हैं। किसी से भी कह सकता हूँ।"

"तो भी बात तुम पर आएगी और आएगी।"

"यार, दिस इज़ टू मच!"

शालिनी कुछ पल चुप रही। वह सही शब्दों का चुनाव करना चाहती थी। आख़िर उसने कहा, "आकाश! इनसान की ज़िन्दगी बड़ी पेचीदा चीज़ है। यहाँ सही काम करने के लिए भी सही वक़्त का इन्तज़ार करना पड़ता है। अगर वक़्त ही सही न हो, तो सही काम भी ग़लत हो जाता है।"

"लेकिन सही वक़्त के इन्तज़ार की भी एक हद होती है, शालिनी!"

शालिनी चिढ़ी, "तुम नहीं सुधरोगे!"

उसे जो कहना था, वह कह चुकी थी। तर्क-वितर्क-कुतर्क के जाल में वह फँसना नहीं चाहती थी। आकाश मनमौजी है। जो मन में आएगा, वही करेगा। उसके मन को प्रभावित करने के लिए शालिनी ने जितना कह दिया था, उतना पर्याप्त था।

वर्ली तक का रास्ता फिर ख़ामोशी में ही पार हुआ। जिस मोड़ पर शालिनी को उतरना था, उसके आने पर शालिनी इतना ही बोली, "बस। यहीं।"

शालिनी को सड़क के किनारे उतार, आकाश कार बढ़ा ले गया।

जहाँगीर आर्ट गैलेरी से जो पेंटिंग आकाश ने ख़रीदी थी, वह उसके कार्यालय की शोभा बढ़ा रही थी। आकाश के सामने बैठे थे जनक, मिस कपूर और मिसेज अग्रवाल। जनक द्वारा प्रस्तुत फाइल का अध्ययन आकाश कर चुका था और अब उसे, अपनी मेज़ पर, कोने में सरका रहा था। जनक अभी इंस्पेक्टर के पद पर है। मिस कपूर जनक की ही उम्र की हैं, किन्तु वह ऑफिसर के रैंक में आ चुकी हैं। जनक को भी ऑफिसर का रैंक जल्द-से-जल्द मिल जाए, इसका प्रयास आकाश समय-समय पर करता रहता था—जनक को बिना बताए। मिसेज अग्रवाल हैं सीनियर ऑफिसर। वह भारी डील-डौल की हैं। उनका रुतबा ही कुछ और है। आवाज़ कर्कश-सी होते हुए भी दयालु लगती हैं। उनकी कर्मठता, साहसिकता और ईमानदारी के अनेक क़िस्से आयकर विभाग की इमारत में गूँज चुके हैं। वह आकाश की प्रिय सहकर्मी हैं और आकाश उनका प्रिय सहकर्मी है।

मिस कपूर जनक के साथ, अतिरिक्त सावधानी से पेश आती हैं, शायद इसलिए कि दोनों की उम्र एक है, किन्तु जनक का—एक मर्द का—ओहदा छोटा है। शालीनता

से चुटकी लेकर बात करना मिस कपूर को खूब आता है, किन्तु जनक की चुटकी लेना वह प्रायः बचा जाती हैं। जब भी जनक ऑफिसर के पद पर आएगा, मिस कपूर का व्यवहार उसके प्रति निश्चित रूप से बदलेगा—आकाश का अनुमान था।

जनक अपनी नैसर्गिक सूक्ष्म दृष्टि से काम करता था। ऐसा लगता ही नहीं था, यह नौजवान आयकर विभाग में, पुराना नहीं है। इसीलिए, श्रीगोपाल वर्मा की रेक्की आकाश ने, जनक के ही द्वारा संचालित होने दी थी। वैसे भी, जनक इन्वेस्टिगेशन विभाग में नियुक्त किया गया था। नियुक्ति की दृष्टि से भी, रेक्की के संचालन के लिए वह एक सुपात्र ही था। श्रीगोपाल वर्मा की फाइल वह जिस सूक्ष्मता से तैयार करता जा रहा था, उससे आकाश को सन्तोष हुआ था। आकाश की नज़र जनक की आँखों में ठहरने लगी, ''एक बात साफ़ झलकती है इस फाइल से—श्रीगोपाल हिसाब-किताब में कुछ...ज़रूरत से ज़्यादा ही तेज़ हैं।''

''एग्ज़ैक्टली, सर!'' जनक ने कहा, ''अपने वाउचर्स, लेजर्स, कैश-बुक्स को यह शख़्स इतना क्लीन रखता है कि एक रुपए की भी हेराफेरी पकड़ में नहीं आती।''

मिस कपूर ने अनुमोदन किया, ''बुक्स के हिसाब से जितना टैक्स ड्यू होता है, श्रीगोपाल बराबर भरता रहता है, बल्कि हमेशा एडवान्स भर देता है।''

आगे के शब्द जनक के होंठों से आए, ''इसीलिए हमने पिछले तीन सालों से उस पर कोई छापा नहीं मारा है।''

मिसेज अग्रवाल के स्वर में नाराज़गी की झलक थी, ''तीन साल पहले, उसके यहाँ से सीज़ करके जो कुछ भी हम लाते थे, सब वह वापस छुड़ा ले जाता था।''

आकाश ने कहा, ''यानी, मिसेज अग्रवाल! जो कुछ भी श्रीगोपाल के पास है, सब डिक्लेयर्ड है, व्हाइट है? ब्लैक कुछ भी नहीं?''

''जी हाँ! उसकी बुक्स तो यही कहती हैं।''

''जबकि उसका बिहेवियर, उसका बरताव कुछ और कहता है। वह मुझे ज़बर्दस्ती घूस देने को बेताब है, क्योंकि वह अपने ही काले धन को पचा नहीं पा रहा...'' आकाश थोड़ा तो स्वगत बोल रहा था और थोड़ा अपने साथियों को, ब्रीफिंग दे रहा था, ''इतना काला धन वह इकट्ठा कर चुका है कि बौखला गया है और मुझे बिन-माँगी घूस एडवांस में देकर, एडवांस में पटाना चाहता है! सवाल है, यह धन उसने कहाँ छिपाया होगा...''

मिसेज अग्रवाल ने जैसे याद दिलाना चाहा, ''श्रीगोपाल की बयालीस दुकानें हैं बम्बई में।''

''यानी...मेरे वार्ड में जो नई दुकान उसने ख़रीदी है, वह तिरालीसवीं हुई!'' आकाश ने भौंहों पर बल दिया।

मिस कपूर बोलीं, "यस, सर! मिठाई और नमकीन की दुकानों की बड़ी ज़बर्दस्त मालिका है—'श्रीगोपाल स्वीट्स एंड नमकीन प्राइवेट लिमिटेड!"

जिसके अनुसन्धान में आकाश बुदबुदाया, "और हमें इस मालिका के मालिक को धर दबोचना है...देखते हैं, कब तक बच पाता है श्रीगोपाल...कब तक..."

कैसा संयोग! टेंथ रोड का नुक्कड़ पार करके, मालवाहक गाड़ी जहाँ रुकी, वहाँ से श्रीगोपाल वर्मा की कोठी आमने-सामने ही पड़ती थी। मालवाहक गाड़ी के ड्राइवर ने कोठी के गेट से निकल रही जिस महिला से पूछा, 'रंगायन अपार्टमेंट्स' कहाँ है?' वह महिला कोई और नहीं, बल्कि कोठी की स्वामिनी, श्रीगोपाल वर्मा की अर्द्धांगिनी, तिलोत्तमा वर्मा ही थी।

"चार बिल्डिंग छोड़कर पाँचवीं!" तिलोत्तमा ने मौखिक रूप से बताया और हाथ का इशारा भी किया। ड्राइवर ने चेहरा अन्दर खींचकर गाड़ी बढ़ा ले जाने की तैयारी की। तिलोत्तमा का कौतूहल जाग चुका था, "किसके यहाँ जाना है?"

"वहाँ ग्राउंड-फ्लोर पर कोई आकाश जी रहते हैं...आयकर अधिकारी..." और ड्राइवर ने गाड़ी धीमी स्पीड से आगे बढ़ा दी।

तिलोत्तमा की नज़र गाड़ी पर से हट नहीं पा रही थी। चार बिल्डिंग्स छोड़कर, पाँचवीं बिल्डिंग के सामने गाड़ी रुकने लगी थी और तिलोत्तमा के क़दम यन्त्रवत्, गाड़ी की ही दिशा में, उठने लगे थे।

पीछे की तरफ़ का, गाड़ी का शटर खड़-खड़ करता ऊपर उठा। विशाल आकृति, विशाल वज़न की अनेक चीज़ें झलक उठीं—लोहे की अलमारियाँ, रैक्स, वाशिंग-मशीनें, टी.वी, फ्रिज, पंखे, फर्नीचर, कुकिंग-रेंज...तीन मज़बूत युवक इन चीज़ों के बीच गतिशील दिखाई दिए। तिलोत्तमा ने ज़रा ऊँचे स्वर में पूछा, "क्यों, भाई, क्या लाए हो?"

जवाब तीन में से एक ने दिया, "फ्रिज है फ्रिज!"

तब तक तिलोत्तमा की दो समृद्ध सहेलियाँ उसके नज़दीक आ खड़ी हुई थीं। तिलोत्तमा ने दोनों पर बारी-बारी से नज़र डाली। मनुष्य जितनी बातें ज़बान से कर सकता है, उतनी ही बातें आँखों से भी कर सकता है। तीनों स्त्रियों ने आपस की नज़रों को आँखों-आँखों में सहलाया। तिलोत्तमा ने फिर उसी ऊँचे स्वर में पूछा, "नया फ्रिज है क्या?"

जिस युवक ने पहली बार जवाब दिया था, उसी ने कहा, "हाँ, जी, बिलकुल नया है!"

इसके साथ ही वह युवक गाड़ी में से कूदकर सड़क पर आ गया। 'रंगायन अपार्टमेंट्स' के अहाते में प्रवेश कर उसने गोरखा से पूछा, "चार नम्बर का फ्लैट किधर है? फ्रिज आया है..."

गोरखा ने आकाश-शालिनी के फ्लैट की ओर इशारा कर दिया। फ्लैट के बन्द दरवाज़े के सामने पहुँचकर वह युवक जब कॉल-बेल दबा रहा था, तब तिलोत्तमा की दोनों सहेलियाँ परस्पर बतिया रही थीं कि हम तो सब्ज़ी ख़रीदने निकली थीं, सब्ज़ी तो खुद ही ख़रीदनी चाहिए, नौकरों से ख़रीदवाओ तो कुछ ऊटपटाँग उठा लाते हैं। दोनों सहेलियाँ प्लास्टिक के झोलों में तरह-तरह की सब्ज़ियाँ थामे हुए थीं। झोले खोल-खोलकर वे तिलोत्तमा को ऐसे दिखाने लगीं, जैसे हिमालय जाकर अलौकिक जड़ी-बूटियाँ खोज लाई हों! जब कि तीनों में से एक भी महिला की दिलचस्पी सब्ज़ी-गाथा में नहीं थी। तीनों बार-बार मालवाहक गाड़ी के उठे हुए शटर के अन्दर नज़र मार रही थीं।

शालिनी की कॉल-बेल दबाने के बाद उस युवक ने दरवाज़ा खुलने का इन्तज़ार नहीं किया था। युवक एक छलाँग-सी लगाकर, उमंग-भरे मूड में, वापस अपनी मालवाहक गाड़ी की ओर लपक लिया।

शालिनी ने दरवाज़ा खोला। सामने किसी को न पाकर वह आश्चर्य करना चाह ही रही थी कि उसकी नज़र गेट पर खड़ी मालवाहक गाड़ी पर पड़ी और वह समझ गई, फ्रिज महाशय का शुभ आगमन हो गया है। शालिनी ने ख़ामोशी से अपना दरवाज़ा पार किया, ताकि सामने की सीढ़ियाँ उतर सके। तभी उसने ग़ौर किया, उसकी ओर तीन महिलाओं की पीठें घूमी हुई हैं, जिनमें से एक पीठ तिलोत्तमा की है। शेष दो पीठों को भी उसने जल्द ही पहचान लिया। वे तिलोत्तमा की प्रिय सहेलियाँ थीं, जिन्हें शालिनी ने, मन-ही-मन, 'पहली' और 'दूसरी' नाम दे रखे थे।

शालिनी के पैर थमने लगे। तीनों महानारियाँ आपस में जो खुसुर-फुसुर कर रही थीं, वह इतनी तेज़ थी कि शालिनी हर शब्द साफ़ सुन पा रही थी।

"नया-निकोर फ्रिज है, भई!"—पहली।

"मैं यही सोचती थी...कार इनके पास है, फ्रिज और वाशिंग-मशीन क्यों नहीं है!"—तिलोत्तमा।

"चलो, फ्रिज तो आ गया!"—पहली।

"वाशिंग-मशीन भी आ जाएगी।"—दूसरी।

"बड़े अफ़सरों के ये ही तो मज़े हैं! हर बड़ी चीज़ गिफ़्ट में आ जाती है!"—यह वाक्य तिलोत्तमा का था, जो पूरा हुआ-न-हुआ कि पहली बोली, "मैंने तो सुना है, कार भी इन्हें गिफ्ट में ही मिली थी!"

तिलोत्तमा ने ऐलान किया, "भई, इन्कम-टैक्स में अफसर हैं। इनके यहाँ नहीं आएगी गिफ्ट तो किसके यहाँ आएगी?"

ऐलान भले ही स्वर को दबाकर और चबाकर किया गया था, किन्तु ऐलान तो ऐलान ही होता है। शालिनी आगे नहीं सुनना चाहती थी। "तिलोत्तमा जी!" शालिनी

ने फ़ासले पर ही खड़े-खड़े, तल्ख़ आवाज़ में कहा, "कार हमें कहीं से भी गिफ्ट में नहीं मिली! उसे हमने किस्तों में ख़रीदा था। अभी तीन महीने पहले ही आख़िरी किस्त अदा की है!"

तीनों पीठें, जो शालिनी की ओर घूमी हुई थीं, पलटी खा गईं। शालिनी एक पल तीन पीठें देख रही थी और अगले ही पल तीन चेहरे देखने लगी। उनमें सबसे ज़्यादा खिसियाया हुआ चेहरा तिलोत्तमा का था।

शालिनी ने जारी रखा, "फ्रिज भी हमने लोन से लिया है। रही बात वाशिंग-मशीन की, इस बारे में अभी सोचा तक नहीं है!"

इसके जवाब में तिलोत्तमा ने मन्द-मन्द मुसकराते हुए, उत्तम आत्मीयता के साथ पूछा, "अरे, शालिनी! कैसी हो?"

"कम-से-कम आप तो न कहिए तिलोत्तमा जी, कि हम गिफ्ट लेते हैं।" शालिनी को अपना ही स्वर कर्कश महसूस हुआ, किन्तु ऐसे अवसर पर माधुर्य आए भी तो कैसे।

तिलोत्तमा ने दोनों हाथों से शालिनी के कन्धे पकड़ लिये और खिसियाई हँसी के साथ कहा, "अरे, शालिनी! यह तो आपस का मखौल था!"

शालिनी ने हौले से, किन्तु दृढ़ता से, तिलोत्तमा के हाथ हटा दिए और स्वर चबाकर पूछा, "इसे आप लोग मखौल कहती हैं?"

तिलोत्तमा शालिनी की आँखों में देखना जारी न रख सकी। फ्रिज को गाड़ी से उतार चुके उन युवकों से मुख़ातिब होती तिलोत्तमा ने कहा, "चलो, चलो, अन्दर रखो। नया फ्रिज है। किसी की नज़र न लगे।"

किन्तु शालिनी यों छोड़ने वाली नहीं थी, "तिलोत्तमा जी, मैं आपसे बात कर रही हूँ। क्या आप अपनी सहेलियों को बताएँगी कि हम गिफ्ट लेते हैं या नहीं लेते?"

कहती शालिनी की आँखों के सामने वह पूरा दृश्य घूम रहा था...इसी तिलोत्तमा के पति श्रीगोपाल ने अग्रिम रिश्वत भिजवाई थी...पाँचेक हज़ार रुपयों की, सोने की वह चमचमाती चेन...सालगिरह की सौगात देने के बहाने प्रस्तुत की गई वह अग्रिम घूस...लेकिन शालिनी और आकाश, इसी तिलोत्तमा को, इसी तिलोत्तमा के पति श्रीगोपाल को, बाक़ायदा उनके घर के अन्दर तक जाकर, सोने की वह चमचमाती चेन...वह अग्रिम घूस...वापस दे आए थे! आज वही तिलोत्तमा, खुली सड़क पर खुसुर-फुसुर कर रही है कि...यह फ्रिज तो कहीं से गिफ्ट में मिला है इन लोगों को! नहीं, शालिनी छोड़ेगी नहीं तिलोत्तमा को!

तिलोत्तमा कह रही थी, "ओहो, शालू! तुम तो हमेशा राई का पहाड़ा बना देती हो!"

शालिनी हँसी मन-ही-मन। शालिनी तिलोत्तमा के लिए शालू कब से हो गई? शालिनी की आँखें चौंधिया रही थीं, "तिलोत्तमा जी! प्लीज़! आप अपनी सहेलियों को मेरे सामने बताइए...यहीं...अभी..."

अब तो तिलोत्तमा की भी साँसें ज़रा गरम हो गईं, "हाँ, हाँ, बता रही हूँ।" और वह दोनों सहेलियों से मुख़ातिब हो गई, "सुन लो दोनों! ये लोग बिलकुल किसी से गिफ्ट नहीं लेते! बात आई समझ में? कि नहीं आई?"

सहेलियों ने मुंडी हिलाई।

"अच्छा! पुराने ज़माने के ऋषि-मुनि भी गुरु-दक्षिणा लेते थे। ये लोग गिफ्ट नहीं लेते?"—पहली।

"कितनी अच्छी बात है!"—दूसरी।

"वाक़ई!"—तिलोत्तमा।

"शालिनी जी! यह बताइए, ठंडी बोतलें कब पिला रही हैं?"—दूसरी।

"जिस दिन कहेंगी, उसी दिन आ जाएँगी हम!"—पहली।

शालिनी चुप रह गई, किन्तु भीतर की आग उसकी आँखों में सुलग रही थी। इसीलिए उसकी चुप्पी को झेलना उन महानारियों के लिए आसान नहीं था। चुप्पी आख़िर तिलोत्तमा ने तोड़ी। सहेलियों को उसने इन शब्दों में डाँटा, "अरे, तुम लोग तो ऐसे देख रही हो, जैसे फ्रिज कभी देखा न हो! चलो, चलो, सब्ज़ी नहीं काटनी? अच्छा, शालिनी! चलें? बधाई! कांग्रेच्युलेशन्स!"

पहली और दूसरी साथ-साथ बुदबुदाईं, "बधाई!"

तीनों महिलाएँ चल दीं। तब तक फ्रिज घर के अन्दर तक नहीं पहुँचा था!

कहाँ था वह पब्लिक टेलीफोन-बूथ कि जहाँ से उस व्यक्ति ने आकाश को वह ख़ास सन्देश दिया? बताना सम्भव नहीं होगा। कैसा था उस व्यक्ति का चेहरा-मोहरा? डील-डौल? यह बताना भी सम्भव नहीं होगा। जो बातें स्वयं आकाश को नहीं मालूम, वे हमें कैसे मालूम पड़ सकती हैं? वह व्यक्ति हमेशा अलग-अलग पब्लिक टेलीफोन-बूथ इस्तेमाल करता है, आकाश से बात करने के लिए, किन्तु यह राज़ आकाश को भी नहीं बताया करता कि इस बार का टेलीफोन-बूथ बम्बई के किस कोने में है। आकाश की गहरी दोस्ती है इस व्यक्ति के साथ, किन्तु उसका चेहरा कभी आकाश की आँखों के सामने नहीं आया। यहाँ तक कि उसका कोई फोटोग्राफ भी आकाश ने नहीं देखा। सहसा यक़ीन करने लायक़ बात नहीं है, किन्तु सत्य यही है। आकाश ने उस व्यक्ति का केवल स्वर सुना है...

पहले वह स्वर अकसर सुनाई देता था। फिर...पता नहीं क्या हुआ। लम्बा अरसा गुज़र गया है, आकाश को उस व्यक्ति ने टेलीफोन नहीं किया। क्या आकाश के जीवन में उस व्यक्ति की उपयोगिता यहीं तक थी? इस प्रश्न का उत्तर आकाश 'हाँ' में देना नहीं चाहता।

लम्बे अरसे की ख़ामोशी उस दिन टूटने वाली थी...बम्बई के किसी कोने के किसी टेलीफोन-बूथ में किसी व्यक्ति ने प्रवेश किया। 'किसी व्यक्ति' शब्द ही उचित है! इतना ज़रूर बताया जा सकता है कि वह टेलीफोन-बूथ ऐसा नहीं था कि जहाँ किसी की भी बातचीत कोई भी सुन सकता है। वह बूथ सही अर्थ में एक बूथ था कि जहाँ आप दाख़िल हो सकें और डायल घुमाने से पहले दरवाज़ा बन्द भी कर सकें। आप न केवल अपने स्वर को गुप्त रख सकें, बल्कि अगर चाहें तो अपना चेहरा भी छिपा लें। लड़के-लड़की की दोस्ती जब मुहब्बत में बदल रही होती है, तब इसी प्रकार के टेलीफोन-बूथ ज़्यादा इस्तेमाल होते हैं। बहरहाल...हम उसी बिन्दु पर लौट चलते हैं, जब...बम्बई के किसी टेलीफोन-बूथ में किसी व्यक्ति ने प्रवेश किया, ताकि आकाश के साथ ख़ास बातचीत हो सके। आकाश का फोन-नम्बर इस व्यक्ति ने किसी डायरी में देखने के बाद डायल नहीं किया। नम्बर उसे याद ही था। बस, केवल इतनी कामना वह कर रहा था कि इस बीच नम्बर कहीं बदल न गया हो। इन दिनों टेलीफोन विभाग इतनी तेज़ी से विकसित हो रहा है कि कब किसका फोन-नम्बर बदल जाए, भरोसा नहीं रहता।

इस व्यक्ति ने एक रुपए का सिक्का हाथ में तैयार ही रखा था, ताकि ज्यों ही दूसरे छोर पर रिसीवर उठे और 'हैलो' सुनाई दे, सिक्का बॉक्स में पिरो दिया जाए।

आकाश उस क्षण कहाँ था? अपने ऑफिस में ही तो! और कहाँ? उसकी मेज़ पर दो टेलीफोन शोभायमान थे। लाल रंग के टेलीफोन में एक्सटेन्शन के बटन लगे हुए थे। दूसरा टेलीफोन, जिसका रंग बादामी था, बिना बटनों का था। लाल टेलीफोन वह था कि जिसका नम्बर आपको डायरेक्टरी से भी मिल जाए। बादामी टेलीफोन का नम्बर किसी डायरेक्टरी में नहीं मिलेगा। लाल टेलीफोन बार-बार बजा करता, जब कि बादामी टेलीफोन केवल कभी-कभार। कहना अनावश्यक है कि बादामी टेलीफोन आकाश की 'हॉट लाइन' थी। आयकर विभाग के ख़ास अधिकारियों के पास और आकाश के कुछ ख़ास मित्रों के ही पास था इस 'हॉट लाइन' का नम्बर। शालिनी भी तो! पत्नी शालिनी के भी पास था यह ख़ास नम्बर। अकेली शालिनी ही क्यों? बेटी श्वेता और बेटे प्रतीक को भी आकाश ने यह नम्बर नोट करा रखा था। शालिनी कभी-कभार इस नम्बर को इस्तेमाल कर लिया करती। श्वेता और प्रतीक को अभी तक ऐसा मौक़ा नहीं पड़ा था।

वह व्यक्ति उस वक़्त, आकाश का कौन-सा नम्बर घुमा रहा था? लाल टेलीफोन का या बादामी? निस्सन्देह बादामी! उस व्यक्ति ने 'हॉट लाइन' का नम्बर गुप्तचरी करके हासिल नहीं किया था। स्वयं आकाश ने दिया था उसे यह नम्बर... लेकिन...एक लम्बे अरसे तक...उस व्यक्ति ने इस नम्बर पर डायल घुमाया नहीं था...आज बर्फ़ टूट रही थी!

ट्रिन-ट्रिन! ट्रिन-ट्रिन!

बादामी रंग के फोन को बजते देख, आकाश में अतिरिक्त सावधानी आ गई। जिस फाइल की जाँच वह मगन होकर कर रहा था, उसे निस्संकोच बन्द कर, आकाश ने एक तरफ़ सरका दिया। इसके साथ ही आकाश ने अपनी मेज़ के एक कोने में लगा विशेष स्विच ऑन कर दिया। इससे आकाश के कमरे के बाहर, दरवाज़े की चौखट पर एक लाल बल्ब जल उठा। यह आकाश की निजी व्यवस्था थी। निजी संकेत! सेक्रेटरी मिसेज जो के नाम! कि अगर दरवाज़े की चौखट पर लाल बल्ब जला हुआ हो, तो किसी भी शख़्स को अन्दर न जाने दिया जाए। टेलीफोन पर, या आमने-सामने बैठे किसी व्यक्ति के साथ, कोई ऐसा संवाद हो रहा है कि जिसे दूसरों के कानों तक पहुँचना नहीं चाहिए।

लाल बल्ब का स्विच ऑन कर आकाश ने बादामी टेलीफोन का रिसीवर उठा लिया और सावधान स्वर में कहा, ''हैलो!''

स्वर सुनते ही उस व्यक्ति ने रुपए का सिक्का बॉक्स में सरका दिया और साधिकार कहा, ''नमस्कार, आकाश जी!''

''नमस्कार!'' आकाश की सावधानी बढ़ी। ''तो...मेरी आवाज़ पहचान ली आपने!''

''जी हाँ! और...आपने पहचानी मेरी आवाज?''

''अपने इस अनोखे मददगार की आवाज़ को मैं ज़िन्दगी में कभी नहीं भूल सकता।'' आकाश ने उत्तर दिया।

''चलिए, वही नाता दुबारा शुरू करते हैं!''

''शुक्रिया! दोस्ती का हाथ दुबारा बढ़ाने के लिए!''

''दोस्ती का हाथ नहीं, दोस्ती की सिर्फ़ आवाज़! क्योंकि...ज़िन्दगी में कभी भी मैं आपके आमने-सामने तो आऊँगा नहीं!''

''हाँ, मुझे याद है।'' आकाश ने कहा, ''आप परदे के पीछे रहकर ही मेरी मदद करना चाहते हैं।''

''जिसकी शुरुआत मैंने तीन साल पहले की थी...'' वह व्यक्ति जैसे यादों में खो जाने लगा, ''लगातार दो सालों तक मैं आपको तरह-तरह की ख़बरें देता रहा। फिर एक साल मैं ख़ामोश रहा...''

"मैं कभी नहीं भूल सकता कि आपकी दी हुई ख़बरों के ज़ोर पर मैंने इन्कम-टैक्स के कितने छापे मारे थे और हर छापे में कैसी अनोखी सफलता पाई थी!"

"क्योंकि मैंने कभी आपको झूठी ख़बर नहीं दी...और मैंने कभी कोई पुरस्कार भी नहीं माँगा अपनी सेवाओं के लिए।"

"मुझे आप पर नाज़ है।" आकाश ने यह बात उस व्यक्ति को केवल ख़ुश करने के लिए नहीं कही। यह आकाश के दिल की सच्ची आवाज़ थी।

"आप जानते हैं..." उस व्यक्ति ने कहना जारी रखा, "यह काम तो मैं अपनी आत्मा के सुख के लिए करता हूँ। मुझे काले धन से, ब्लैक-मनी से सख़्त नफ़रत है...सख़्त नफ़रत!"

"जी हाँ, मुझे अच्छी तरह याद है..."

"यह कमबख़्त ब्लैक-मनी! इसी के ज़ोर पर उस बदमाश ने मुझसे मेरी प्रेमिका छीनी थी। वह दिन है और आज का दिन है। मैं ब्लैक-मनी के पीछे हाथ धोकर पड़ा हूँ। आपके हाथों ब्लैक-मनी पर बार-बार छापे डलवाकर मैं समाज को हिला दूँगा! देख लीजिएगा आप!"

"मुझे आप पर वाक़ई नाज़ है। इसीलिए तो मैंने बड़े ही प्यार से आपका नाम रख दिया था—आकाशवाणी! क्या मैं पूछ सकता हूँ, आकाशवाणी साल भर ख़ामोश क्यों रही?"

"क्योंकि मैं एक अजीब-सी कशमकश में फँस गया था। सोचने लगा था...अपने ही जान-पहचान वालों का काला धन चुपके-चुपके पकड़वाकर कहीं मैं...उनके साथ...गद्दारी तो नहीं कर रहा? लेकिन वह कशमकश अब दूर हो गई है। आज मैं देश के एक-एक चौराहे पर खड़ा होकर एक बार फिर चिल्लाना चाहता हूँ—प्रेमिकाओं के चोर हाय-हाय! ब्लैक-मनी हाय-हाय!"

और उस व्यक्ति का स्वर भावनाओं के अतिरेक से काँपने लगा। अपार आक्रोश का समुद्र जैसे ठाठें मार रहा था उस स्वर में...आकाश पूछे बिना न रह सका, "आर यू ओके, आकाशवाणी? हैलो, हैलो! आकाशवाणी! आप इतने जज़्बाती होकर न सोचा करें..."

"बस!" उस व्यक्ति ने घोषणा कर दी, "आज मैं इतनी ही बात करूँगा! नमस्कार!"

आकाश ने अकुलाकर संवाद के तार को जोड़े रखने की चेष्टा की, "हैलो! हैलो, आकाशवाणी!"

किन्तु दूसरे छोर पर रिसीवर रखा जा चुका था। आकाश हताशा के भँवर में डूब-सा गया, किन्तु केवल कुछ क्षणों के लिए। जल्द ही आकाश ने अपना सिर भँवर

की सतह से ऊपर, बाहर निकाल लिया था, ताकि खुलकर साँसें ले सके। हर सिक्के का दूसरा पहलू भी तो होता है। ज़िन्दादिली इसी में है कि आप दोनों पहलू ध्यान में रखें। आकाशवाणी ने बात एकाएक काट ज़रूर दी थी, लेकिन क्या यह कम महत्त्वपूर्ण था कि एक लम्बी ख़ामोशी के बाद, आकाशवाणी ने स्वयं ही सम्पर्क स्थापित किया था? अत्यधिक महत्त्व का पुराना सम्बन्ध आज फिर से जुड़ा था...भँवर में डूब जाने की भला क्या ज़रूरत! आकाशवाणी फिर से होगी, ज़रूर होगी और बार-बार होगी...हर बार आकाश को खुफिया ख़बर मिलेगी, जिनके ज़ोर पर वह काले धन पर चामत्कारिक छापे मारेगा और आयकर विभाग का नाम ऊँचा करेगा...आकाश मन-ही-मन जैसे किसी मन्त्र का जाप करने लगा, 'अरी ओ आकाशवाणी! जल्दी हो, आकाशवाणी! मेरी प्रिय आकाशवाणी...'

न केवल स्टेनो, बल्कि आकाश की सेक्रेटरी भी होने के नाते मिसेज जो अच्छी तरह जानती थीं कि यदि दरवाजे की चौखट पर लाल बल्ब जल रहा हो, तो उसका अर्थ कितना गम्भीर है। भीतर, फोन की 'हॉट-लाइन' पर या तो कोई ख़ास बातचीत हो रही है किसी के साथ, या फिर, कोई खुफ़िया बैठक चल रही है आयकर अधिकारियों की...कुछ भी नहीं, तो इतना तो निश्चित ही कि अभी आकाश किसी गहन सोच-विचार में डूबा है और किसी भी सज्जन या दुर्जन से भेंट करने के मूड में तत्काल नहीं है।

लाल बल्ब के गम्भीर अर्थ को, लेकिन, श्रीगोपाल वर्मा के सामने स्पष्ट करना टेढ़ी खीर रही थी। श्रीगोपाल वर्मा अपनी तशरीफ़ का शुभ या अशुभ टोकरा लेकर पधारे, उससे सिर्फ़ आधा मिनट पहले आकाश ने उपरोक्त लाल बल्ब का स्विच ऑन कर दिया था। जब मिसेज जो ने श्रीगोपाल से कहा कि साहब तत्काल तो मिलेंगे नहीं, और यदि तत्काल नहीं तो आख़िर कब, इसका भी कोई भरोसा नहीं, तब श्रीगोपाल अपनी आँखों में अविश्वास और एतराज़ की झलक उभरने से रोक नहीं सके थे।

"देखिए, मुझे अपनी दुकान के उद्घाटन में साहब को मौजूद ज़रूर रखना है। इसी सिलसिले में, बस, एक मिनट के लिए मिलना चाहता हूँ।"

श्रीगोपाल के इस तर्क का मिसेज जो ने यही जवाब दिया था, "एक मिनट के लिए, चाहे एक सेकंड के लिए, मुलाक़ात अभी नहीं हो सकती।"

"क्या मैं इन्तज़ार करूँ? बल्ब के बुझने का?"

"उद्घाटन का कार्ड तो आप लाए होंगे न?" मिसेज जो ने निर्ममता से कहा, "मुझे दे दीजिए। मैं साहब को दे दूँगी।"

"सॉरी! मैं आपसे सहमत नहीं।" श्रीगोपाल तनाव में आ गए, "मैं बल्ब के बुझने का इन्तज़ार करूँगा।"

"और अगर बल्ब शाम तक न बुझा?" मिसेज जो ने शुष्कता से पूछा।

श्रीगोपाल चिढ़े, "कुल कितनी शामों तक नहीं बुझेगा? अन्दर हो क्या रहा है? ब्रह्मा जी ब्रह्मांड का निर्माण करने बैठे हैं क्या?"

और श्रीगोपाल वर्मा, मिसेज जो के सामने की कुर्सी पर ऐसे विराजमान हो गए थे, जैसे आमरण अनशन करने ही बैठे हों! श्रीगोपाल के लिए ग़नीमत यह रही कि लाल बल्ब जल्द ही बुझ गया, ऐसा नहीं हुआ कि लगातार आध-पौन घंटे तक जलता रहा वह। ज्यों ही वह बुझा, श्रीगोपाल बेताबी से उठ खड़े हुए और अन्दर जाने लगे। मिसेज जो लपककर उनके सामने अड़ गईं और बोलीं, "प्लीज़! पहले आपका कार्ड मैं अन्दर ले जाना चाहूँगी।"

"उसकी ज़रूरत नहीं। वह मुझे पहचानते हैं।" श्रीगोपाल ने ज़बर्दस्ती आगे बढ़ना चाहा। मिसेज जो ने 'हाय, अब मैं क्या करूँ' वाला भाव आँखों में लबालब भरकर, अर्दली दीनू की ओर देखा। दीनू ने भारी स्फूर्ति से अपना स्टूल छोड़ दिया और मिसेज जो की बग़ल में आकर खड़ा हो गया, यानी, श्रीगोपाल का रास्ता रोककर। बोला, "ना जाइए, साब! हमारी नौकरी ख़तरे में पड़ जाएगी।"

दीनू का दीन-हीन चेहरा देखने लायक़ था। मिसेज जो ने भी झूठी मुसकान बिखेरकर दाँत दिखा दिए, "बिलकुल! हमारी नौकरी चली जाएगी!"

"ख़ामख़ा की ड्रामेबाज़ी!" श्रीगोपाल ने स्वर पीसकर कहा, "लीजिए!" और जेब से अपना कार्ड निकालकर मिसेज जो को थमा दिया। झपटकर श्रीगोपाल वापस कुर्सी में बैठ गए, दीनू भी वापस अपने स्टूल पर शोभायमान हो गया और मिसेज जो दरवाज़ा खोलकर आकाश के कमरे में समा गईं।

श्रीगोपाल का कार्ड देखकर आकाश की प्रतिक्रिया अच्छी नहीं रही। उसने मिसेज जो को घूरा, "क्या आपको याद नहीं, मिसेज जो, कि इस आदमी को अन्दर नहीं घुसने देना है?"

मिसेज जो ने अपनी विवेक-बुद्धि प्रकाशित की, "आने दीजिए, सर! आएगा, तो पाँच मिनट में चला जाएगा। रोकेंगे, तो पन्द्रह मिनट रुका रहेगा। ज़िद पर अड़ गया, तो घंटों भी रुक सकता है। बहस करेगा, सो अलग से।"

ऐसी विवेक-बुद्धि आकाश में भी थी। बस, वह उसे प्रकाशित नहीं कर रहा था। मिसेज जो की बात, इसीलिए, आकाश की समझ में झटपट आ गई।

"हुँ!" उसने एक पल सोचने का नाटक किया। अगले पल कह दिया, "ओके! भेजिए! भुगतते हैं!"

मिसेज जो जल्दी से बाहर चली गईं। दरवाज़ा उन्होंने खुला ही छोड़ दिया था, जिसे श्रीगोपाल ने तपाक से पार किया। वज़नी मुसकान के साथ श्रीगोपाल ने हाथ जोड़ दिए, "नमस्कार, भाई साहब!"

"नमस्कार, नमस्कार! आइए, श्रीगोपाल जी!" आकाश ने कुर्सी की ओर संकेत किया, "बैठिए।"

श्रीगोपाल खड़े ही रहे और बोले, "बैठूँगा नहीं! बैठ तो बाहर बहुत चुका। इस ज़िद में बैठा रहा कि मेरे हाथ से कोई भी चीज़ आप लेते नहीं हैं, लेकिन आज तो एक चीज़ अपने ही हाथ से आपके हाथ में रखकर जाऊँगा। लीजिए, साहब, इन्वीटेशन-कॉर्ड! आमन्त्रण-पत्र! नई दुकान के उद्घाटन-समारोह का! क्या आप आमन्त्रण-पत्र भी मेरे हाथ से अपने हाथ में नहीं लेंगे?"

श्रीगोपाल आत्म-विश्वास और व्यंग्य के फव्वारे छोड़ रहे थे, किन्तु आकाश ने भीगने से इनकार कर दिया। आमन्त्रण-पत्र श्रीगोपाल के हाथ से अपने हाथ में लेते हुए उसने कहा, "आप चूकते नहीं हैं!"

"खुद आया हूँ, यहाँ तक! किसी नौकर-वौकर को नहीं भेजा है। ख़ास आपको बुलाने आया हूँ।"

"अजी, आप तो पड़ोसी हैं। घर आ जाते। यहाँ तक आने की क्या ज़रूरत थी?" आकाश हँसा। दरअसल, आकाश अपने-आप पर हँस रहा था। जिस व्यक्ति को कमरे में घुसने देने पर भी उसने मनाही जारी कर रखी थी, उसी के साथ कितने मज़े-मज़े में बातें कर रहा था वह! क्या यह आकाश का आडम्बर था? अभिनय-कुशलता? या केवल मसख़री? जो भी हो, आकाश हँसा ज़रूर।

"जी हाँ, हूँ तो पड़ोसी, आपके घर ही आना चाहिए था मुझे, आमन्त्रित करने सबको...लेकिन यह बात आप दिल से नहीं कह रहे हैं—मैं जानता हूँ। और फिर...दिल से आप कहें भी तो कैसे! दो-दो बार मैंने नालायकी ही तो की है—आपके सामने!"

आकाश ने संक्षेप में निबटाने के लिए कहा, "बीती ताहि बिसार दे, आगे की सुध ले।"

श्रीगोपाल को जैसे इसी वाक्य का इन्तज़ार था, "यह आपने सही कही! मैं बीती बिसार देने को तैयार हूँ, बशर्ते आप भी तैयार हों इसके लिए! किन्तु मैं आगे की सुध ज़रूर लूँगा!"

आकाश की मुसकान ने बुझना शुरू कर दिया, "मैं आपका इशारा समझ रहा हूँ, श्रीगोपाल जी!"

श्रीगोपाल हें-हें करते बोले, "अरे, नहीं, साहब! कोई इशारा-विशारा नहीं है। आप तो, बस, यूँ ही नाराज़ होते रहते हैं। अच्छा, चलता हूँ। नमस्कार!"

किन्तु श्रीगोपाल दरवाज़े के पास खट् से रुक गए, ताकि पलटकर कह सकें, 'उद्घाटन में आपको आना ज़रूर है। भाभी जी और बच्चों समेत।'

आकाश एक बार फिर हँसा। यह हँसी श्रीगोपाल को अच्छी लगी। हँसी के जवाब में हँसी दिखाकर श्रीगोपाल दरवाज़े से बाहर निकल गए।

दुकान के उद्घाटन का आमन्त्रण! आओ, आओ, भई, आओ, आओ! फ्री में मिठाई आज तो खाओ! आओ, आओ, भई, आओ, आओ! आकाश अंकल से हाथ मिलाओ!

आमन्त्रण-पत्र को आकाश घृणा से टुकड़े-टुकड़े कर, रद्दी की टोकरी में डाल रहा था...

आज शाम को है उद्घाटन! आकाश और पूरा परिवार तैयार हो रहा था, घर से बाहर निकलने के लिए।

घर से बाहर निकलने का अर्थ यह नहीं कि उस हलवाई के बच्चे की दुकान के उद्घाटन की शोभा बनकर दाँत निपोड़ें! अरे, जहन्नुम में चले जाएँगे, मगर उद्घाटन में नहीं जाएँगे।

नहीं जाने का फ़ैसला हो चुका होने पर भी आकाश पूरी तरह निर्द्वन्द्व नहीं था। उसने बुदबुदाहट में कहा, "कमबख़्त आमन्त्रण! टुकड़े-टुकड़े कर उसे उसी पल फेंक दिया था, फिर भी...एक-एक शब्द जैसे दिमाग़ में छपकर रह गया है!"

शालिनी कन्धे के पास अपने पल्लू में पिन लगाती बोली, "नहीं जा रहे हैं न! बस! बात खत्म!"

श्वेता जीन्स में थी। ऊँची एड़ी की जूतियों में पाँव डालती बोली, "चलो, इस बहाने हम चारों साथ-साथ बाहर तो निकलें! कुछ नाटक-वाटक देखें!"

प्रतीक अपने घने बालों में कंघी फेर रहा था, "क्यों, पप्पा! हम लोग जब नहीं पहुँचेंगे, तो...श्रीगोपाल अंकल खुद आ जाएँगे हमारे यहाँ? हमें बुलाने?"

"आने दो, अगर आते हैं! आएँ और देखें यह बड़ा-सा ताला! दरवाज़े पर लटकता हुआ!" आकाश ने खिलवाड़ की तरह ताले को उछाला।

तभी प्रतीक से एक ग़लत तीर छूट गया, "क्या, पप्पा! आप भी...श्रीगोपाल अंकल से डरकर घर से भाग रहे हैं!"—और आकाश का चेहरा तनाव से एकदम कस गया।

यह जीवन है। एक पल में कुछ-का-कुछ हो जाता है। अभी पल भर पहले लग रहा था, शाम अच्छी गुज़रेगी। अगले ही पल प्रतीक नादानी करता है। आकाश को अब बमकने से नहीं रोका जा सकता। शालिनी ने व्याकुल होकर देखा आकाश की ओर। श्वेता की भी चिन्तित नज़रें आकाश पर ठहर चुकी थीं। आकाश को बिलकुल पता न चला, शालिनी-श्वेता की नज़रों का। कैसे पता चलता? आकाश तो प्रतीक को घूर रहा था। शालिनी-श्वेता ने आकाश की गुर्राहट सुनी, "क्या बोले तुम, प्रतीक? मैं श्रीगोपाल वर्मा से डरूँगा? उस हलवाई से?"

शालिनी ने तुरन्त आकाश का अनुमोदन किया, ''कुछ भी ऊटपटाँग बोल देते हो, प्रतीक! बोलना सीखो। छोटे नहीं रहे।''

लेकिन आकाश ने 'सॉरी' शब्द जैसे सुना ही नही। तैश में आकर आकाश ने बोलना जो शुरू किया, तो बोलता ही चला गया, ''तुम सोचते हो, यह मेरा आइडिया है? नो! दिस इज़ योर मम्मीज़ आइडिया! समझे? यह सिर्फ़ तुम्हारी मम्मी है, जो नहीं चाहती कि हम घर में रहें और श्रीगोपाल से आमने-सामने का ख़तरा मोल लें!''

और आकाश ने बाक़ायदा उँगली उठा-उठाकर शालिनी की ओर इशारा करना शुरू कर दिया, ''क्यों, शालिनी? क्या मैंने लगातार नहीं कहा कि हम घर से न निकलें? क्योंकि श्रीगोपाल तो हमारे घर तक आने की हिम्मत ही नहीं करेगा! ज़्यादा-से-ज़्यादा अपनी बीवी को भेजेगा...या बेटी को...और हम साफ़, मुँह पर ही, कह देंगे कि जाइए, हम नहीं आते। हम तो अपने घर में बैठेंगे! अरे, इतवार की शाम है, हमारी शाम है। पूरे हफ़्ते में मुश्किल से तो एक शाम मिलती है, जब चारों जने साथ रह सकें। यही शाम हम एक मिठाईवाले की दुकान पर गुज़ार दें? सिर्फ़ इसलिए कि वह दुकान एक...घटिया पड़ोसी की है और उसका उद्घाटन हो रहा है?''

आकाश इसलिए रुका कि उसे साँस लेनी थी। श्वेता इस मौक़े को ले उड़ी और भारी गम्भीरता से बोली, ''पप्पा! प्लीज़! इतना लम्बा भाषण?''

आकाश श्वेता को जवाब दे सकता, इससे पहले शालिनी ने टेम्पर दिखा दिया, ''सवाल है...अगर मैं चाहती हूँ कि आज की शाम पूरा परिवार बाहर निकले और नाटक देखे–वजह कोई भी हो–तो किसी को क्या तक़लीफ़ है?''

इसे कहते हैं तेजस्विता! आकाश ने कोयले से चलते इंजन की तरह भकाभक, कम-से-कम पन्द्रह वाक्य बोल डाले थे। शालिनी ने सिर्फ़ एक वाक्य उच्चारित किया, जो महा-वाक्य साबित हुआ। आकाश, जो सिंह राशि में प्रवेश कर गया था, तत्काल मिकी-माउस बन गया और परम आश्चर्य से इधर-उधर ताकने लगा, ''तक़लीफ़? किसको है तक़लीफ़? किसने कहा, तक़लीफ़ है?''

शालिनी ने मिकी-माउस की पूँछ मरोड़ी, ''और क्या...तक़लीफ़ सिर्फ़ इसलिए है कि मैं चाहती हूँ? मैं? जो कि एक औरत है? क्या अब भी यह परिवार अठारहवीं सदी में जीता है?''

आकाश ने नाटकीय अपराध-भावना से नज़रें झुका लीं। श्वेता हँसना चाह रही थी, मगर मुसकराकर रह गई और शालिनी के पीछे पहुँचकर उसे घर से बाहर निकालने के लिए धकियानी लगी। प्यार और अधिकार से श्वेता ने कहा, ''कम ऑन, मम्मी! लेट्स इन्ज्वॉय...''

शालिनी मज़े-मज़े में धक्के खाकर घर से बाहर आ गई। आकाश जब फ्लैट में ताला लगा रहा था, श्वेता ने उससे कार की चाबी छीन ली। इस परिवार की यह प्राचीन परम्परा है। जब भी पूरा परिवार एक साथ बाहर निकलता है, कार श्वेता चलाती है।

कार श्वेता चला रही थी। शालिनी आगे बैठी थी। आकाश-प्रतीक पीछे। आकाश ने कहा, "क्या दोनों मर्दों को पीछे बिठा दिया!"

श्वेता ने चोंच मारी, "प्रतीक कब से मर्द हो गया?"

प्रतीक खुश था कि पप्पा ने उसे मर्द कहा। बहन की चोंच की उसने परवाह नहीं की और जवाब लौटाया, "आय एम अ बॉर्न मर्द!"

श्वेता ने करारी होकर कहा, "जा, जा, बड़ा आया—बॉर्न मर्द!"

यह जीवन है। एक पल में कुछ-का-कुछ हो जाता है। घर से निकलते वक़्त, सहसा, कितना तनाव आ गया था, परिवार के चारों सदस्यों पर। कुछ पल बाद ही, अभी, कार-यात्रा करने में मगन, परिवार के चारों सदस्य कितने तनाव-मुक्त थे! परिवार हो तो ऐसा!

तभी, ट्रैफिक की भीड़ में से एक स्कूटर अलग छँटा और इनकी कार के आगे-आगे, सड़क के बाएँ किनारे, अपनी स्पीड जस-की-तस रखे हुए, चलता रहा। वह एक टू-व्हीलर स्कूटर था, जिसके सवार ने हेलमेट पहना हुआ था। सवार के सिर और गर्दन के ऊपरी हिस्से को हेलमेट ने छिपा रखा था, किन्तु चेहरे की तरफ़ लगा हुआ था पारदर्शी प्लास्टिक। सवार की पीठ इनकी कार की ओर होने के कारण चेहरे की शिनाख़्त लगभग असम्भव थी। इसके बावजूद श्वेता चिहुँक पड़ी, "अरे, यह तो श्रीगोपाल अंकल हैं! इधर कहाँ जा रहे हैं? अभी तो इनके यहाँ उद्घाटन की तैयारियाँ चल रही होंगी..."

आकाश ने राय दी, "तैयारियों के ही सिलसिले में लपक रहे होंगे कहीं! वैसे, कभी कार से नीचे क़दम रखते नहीं हैं। आज स्कूटर पर कैसे?"

शालिनी बोली, "होगी कोई इमरजेन्सी। कार ड्राइवर ले गया होगा कहीं। स्कूटर चलाने में ऐसी कौन-सी शर्म की बात है?"

आकाश ने आश्चर्य किया, "लेकिन, श्वेता! तुमने उन्हें पहचाना कैसे? हेलमेट के कारण पीछे से तो चेहरा दिख नहीं रहा।"

श्वेता ने कहा, "डील-डौल देखिए, कपड़े देखिए, और फिर...मैं स्कूटर भी पहचानती हूँ।"

अब तक चुप प्रतीक ने निर्णय दे दिया, "यस, ही इज़ श्रीगोपाल अंकल!"

आकाश ने बेटे की भूल सुधारी, ‘‘याद रखो, यह आदमी किसी का अंकल-वंकल नहीं है।’’

सुनते ही श्वेता एकदम खिल उठी और बोली, ‘‘ओके, देन! मैं ठोक देती हूँ।’’

‘‘क्या?’’ शालिनी ने अचरज से देखा अपनी बेटी की ओर। श्वेता ने स्पष्ट किया, ‘‘वेरी सिम्पल, मम्मी! एक हलकी-सी टक्कर! वह चारों खाने चित्त! हम चले आगे!’’

आकाश ने डाँटा, ‘‘श्वेता!’’

किन्तु श्वेता केवल शालिनी से मुख़ातिब थी, ‘‘मान लो, मम्मी, उन्होंने गाड़ी पहचान ली...तो कह देना, लड़की चला रही थी, अनाड़ी है। यह भी कह देना कि हमने तो आपको देखा ही नहीं! न तो पहले और न बाद में! वरना क्या हम रुकते नहीं? आपको गिरी हालत से क्या उठाते भी नहीं?’’

आकाश पिछली सीट पर अब आराम से बैठा न रह सका। ज़रा व्याकुलता से आगे सरका और बोला, ‘‘श्वेता! यह क्या मज़ाक है!’’

प्रतीक श्वेता के कन्धे पर थपाथप-थपाथप हाथ मारता कहने लगा, ‘‘दीदी! दीदी! सबक सिखा दे! दीदी! लिसन!’’

‘‘बोल!’’

‘‘ठोकना मत, दीदी! कट मार कट!’’

‘‘ओके! फाइन!’’ और श्वेता ने अपनी ठुड्डी ज़रा झुकाकर, आँखों को ज़रा फैलाकर, स्कूटर की पिछाड़ी को घूरना शुरू किया।

शालिनी मुसकरा पड़ी, श्वेता! बस, इतना ध्यान रखना, कोई हड्डी-वड्डी न टूटे उनकी...’’

आकाश चकराकर देखता रह गया, ‘‘शालिनी! तुम भी?’’

‘‘कुछ नहीं होगा, मॉम!’’ श्वेता का स्वर था, ‘‘उन्होंने हेलमेट पहन रखा है।’’ इसके साथ ही श्वेता ने कार के सभी यात्रियों के नाम ऑर्डर इश्यू कर दिया, ‘‘होशियार! कोई दाएँ न देखे, कोई बाएँ न देखे। सब सामने देखें—स्ट्रेट!’’

उस वक़्त जो सड़क गुज़र रही थी, उसके ऐन किनारे, मटमैले-गन्दे कीचड़ की लम्बी पट्टी चल रही थी। कीचड़ की इस पट्टी के किनारे-किनारे, श्रीगोपाल अपने स्कूटर पर लपक रहे थे। श्वेता ने स्पीड बढ़ाकर कार को स्कूटर की बग़ल में ले लिया। प्रतीक किलकारी रोक नहीं पा रहा था, ‘‘दीदी! दीदी!’’

श्वेता ने स्कूटर पर ही नज़र जमाए-जमाए प्रतीक को हड़का दिया, ‘‘चुप! गधे!’’

‘‘दीदी!’’ प्रतीक का पुलक के मारे बुरा हाल था, ‘‘रेडी...स्टडी...गो!’’

‘गो!’ होते ही श्वेता ने कार का स्टियरिंग झटके के साथ बाएँ घुमाकर, फिर वापस सीधा कर लिया। सीधी लकीर में जा रही कार ने मानो नशे की झोंक में आकर अचानक कमर मटका दी! श्रीगोपाल अकबका गए। कार के साथ टक्कर बचाने के

लिए उन्होंने अपना स्कूटर सड़क के किनारे उतार तो दिया, लेकिन स्कूटर सीधा घुस गया कीचड़ की उसी पट्टी में, जो किनारे-किनारे खिंची हुई थी। चिकने कीचड़ ने स्कूटर को लपेट-लुपूटकर, पोत-पातकर, फिसलन-पट्टी पर सर्र-सर्र इधर-से-उधर फेंक-फाँककर बराबर कर दिया। काला-कलूटा स्कूटर और काले-कलूटे श्रीगोपाल, सिर से पैर तक!

आक्थू! छी-छी-छी! अरे, कोई कार का नम्बर देखो, लेकिन कहाँ की कार और कहाँ का नम्बर! सब उड़न-छू! ही-ही!

कमिश्नर साहब के सामने आकाश जोशभरी किन्तु विनीत मुद्रा में बैठा था। कमरे में, उस वक़्त, सिवा उन दो के, तीसरा कोई नहीं था।

"सर!" आकाश ने शुरू किया, "आपसे मैं एक ख़ास इजाज़त लेने आया हूँ।"

"बोलो!" कमिश्नर साहब अपनी भव्य कुर्सी में पूरी भव्यता से विराजमान थे।

आकाश ने बताया, "सर! मैं...कल, सूरज निकलने के साथ, एक पार्टी पर ज़ोरदार छापा मारना चाहता हूँ।"

कमिश्नर साहब मुसकराए, "इसमें मेरी ख़ास इजाज़त की क्या ज़रूरत है? तुम एक ऑफिसर हो, केवल इंस्पेक्टर नहीं। यह तो तुम्हारे अधिकार में है कि तुम किसी भी पार्टी पर अचानक छापा मारकर काला धन ज़ब्त करो—बशर्ते वह पार्टी तुम्हारे वार्ड में आती हो और...पर्याप्त रेक्की भी तुमने करवा ली हो।"

आकाश मन-ही-मन व्याकुल हुआ। रेक्की...छापा मारने से पहले, आयकर विभाग के गुप्तचरों द्वारा पार्टी की चुपके-चुपके जाँच...छापा सफल तभी हो सकता है, जब रेक्की सही हुई हो। आकाश जानता था, कमिश्नर साहब के मुँह से रेक्की शब्द सुनने को ज़रूर मिलेगा उसे...अच्छी पूर्व-तैयारी करके गया था आकाश। इसके बावजूद...मन-ही-मन व्याकुल हुए बिना वह न रह सका।

"सर!" उसने संकोच के साथ कहा, "जहाँ तक वार्ड का सवाल है, पार्टी मेरे ही वार्ड में है, लेकिन...रेक्की मैंने बिलकुल नहीं करवाई है।"

यह एक ऐसा उत्तर था कि जिसकी आशा कमिश्नर साहब ने बिलकुल नहीं रखी थी। उनकी भौंहों पर बल पड़े, "रेक्की नहीं करवाई है? लेकिन, आकाश! पर्याप्त रेक्की के बिना छापे की सलाह कैसे दी जा सकती है?"

आकाश ने अजीब-सा तर्क दिया, "रेक्की के लिए वक़्त ही नहीं है, सर!"

"ऐसा कैसे हो सकता है?"

"छापा मारने का मौक़ा, कल सुबह आठ बजे के बाद, हाथ से निकल जाएगा। यह ख़बर मुझे अभी-अभी मिली है। इतने शॉर्ट नोटिस पर रेक्की कैसे ऑर्गनाइज़ की जाए?"

"अभी-अभी मिली ख़बर झूठी है या सच्ची, कुछ तो जाँच करो! तुम चाहते हो, रेक्की शब्द ही डिक्शनरी से निकाल दिया जाए?"

"नो, सर! लेकिन इस ख़बर के झूठी होने का सवाल ही नहीं उठता।" और आकाश का चेहरा दमक उठा।

"अच्छा? इतना भरोसा है अपने सोर्स पर?"

"भरोसा सही है या ग़लत, फ़ैसला आप ही करिए, सर! ख़बर कहाँ से मिली है, इस बारे में मैं तो केवल एक शब्द ही बोल सकता हूँ–आकाशवाणी!" आकाश ने ज्यों ही वाक्य पूरा किया, कमिश्नर साहब चौंक गए। उन्होंने बुदबुदाहट में दोहराया, "आकाशवाणी?"

"यस, सर!"

अब कमिश्नर साहब का चौंकना, हार्दिक प्रसन्नता में बदल गया, "अच्छा-आ! तो आकाश को आकाशवाणी फिर से सुनाई देने लगी?"

"यस, सर! साल भर की ख़ामोशी के बाद...आकाशवाणी ने एकाएक खुद ही फोन किया।"

"वेरी गुड! आय मस्ट कांग्रेच्युलेट यू!"

"थैंक्यू, सर!" आकाश ने गम्भीरता से सूचनाएँ देना शुरू किया, "अब तक आकाशवाणी के फोन चार बार आ चुके हैं। शुरू के तीन फोन तो यूँ ही...गपशप के रहे, लेकिन जो चौथा फोन आया–अभी थोड़ी देर पहले ही–उसके अनुसार...हम कई करोड़ के हीरे पकड़ सकते हैं, बशर्ते...रेक्की वग़ैरह की चिन्ता किए बग़ैर...कल...सूरज निकलने के साथ...शक्तिशाली छापा मारकर हम पार्टी को हक्का-बक्का कर दें।"

इन शब्दों के साथ आकाश अपना ब्रीफकेस खोल चुका था, जिसमें से एक लिस्ट निकालकर उसने कमिश्नर साहब के सामने प्रस्तुत कर दी, "यह उन ऑफिसरों, इन्स्पेक्टरों एवं अन्य कर्मचारियों की लिस्ट है, जिन्हें मैं इस छापे में अपने साथ ले जाना चाहता हूँ और जो साथ चलने के लिए उपलब्ध भी हैं। सबके साथ मेरी बात हो चुकी है। आप भी चेक कर लें, ताकि अन्तिम निर्णय लिया जा सके।"

"फास्ट जॉब!" बुदबुदाकर कमिश्नर साहब ने वह लिस्ट उठा ली और पढ़ना-जाँचना शुरू किया। पाँचेक मिनट में ही उन्होंने सारे नाम चेक कर लिये और उन नामों पर विचार भी कर लिया।

लिस्ट आकाश को लौटाते हुए उन्होंने मौखिक अनुमोदन कर दिया, "सुन्दर...बहुत सुन्दर..."

आकाश ने लिस्ट वापस ब्रीफकेस में रखते हुए, आशीर्वाद माँगने की तरह, एक बार फिर पूछा, "टीम ओके, सर?"

"यस!"

"तो...मैं इस टीम को...कॉन्फ्रेन्स-रूम में बुलवा लूँ, सर?"

"ज़रूर! मैं भी वहीं पहुँच रहा हूँ—सर्च-वारंट लेकर।"

"थैंक्यू वेरी मच, सर!" आकाश ने फास्ट स्पीड में बोलना शुरू किया, "हम कल सुबह साढ़े छह बजे...एक साथ पाँच स्थानों पर छापे मारेंगे। ये पाँचों स्थान रिहायशी फ्लैट्स हैं। एक फ्लैट में पार्टी खुद रहती है। बाक़ी चार में पार्टी के रिश्तेदार या पार्टनर्स हैं। पाँचों फ्लैट्स के पूरे नाम-पते—बाक़ायदा फोन-नम्बर्स समेत—खुद आकाशवाणी ने नोट करवाए हैं। यह रही इसकी लिस्ट!"

और आकाश ने ब्रीफकेस में से एक और टाइप्ड लिस्ट निकालकर कमिश्नर साहब के सामने रख दी।

कमिश्नर साहब ने लिस्ट इतनी स्फूर्ति से उठाई कि आकाश को ज़रा आश्चर्य-सा हुआ। ऑफिसरों, इन्स्पेक्टरों आदि की लिस्ट तो उन्होंने पाँचेक मिनट में ही पढ़ भी ली थी और पास भी कर दी थी। यह जो दूसरी लिस्ट सामने रखी गई है, इसमें तो पढ़ने या पास करने लायक़ कुछ है ही नहीं। इसे तो केवल शालीनता के नाते दिखाया जा रहा था उन्हें। जहाँ छापे मारने हैं, वहाँ के नाम-पते और फोन-नम्बर्स हैं। इनमें कोई रद्दोबदल तो होना नहीं है। इसके बावजूद, कमिश्नर साहब ने इस लिस्ट को उतनी स्फूर्ति से क्यों उठाया? और...इसे पढ़ने में वह इतना अधिक समय क्यों ले रहे हैं?

आकाश ने ग़ौर किया, लिस्ट को कमिश्नर साहब ने इस प्रकार पकड़ रखा था, जिससे उनका पूरा चेहरा लिस्ट की ओट में छिप-सा गया था। नहीं, नहीं, कमिश्नर साहब भला क्यों छिपाना चाहेंगे अपना चेहरा आकाश से? ज़रूर आकाश को ही ग़लतफ़हमी हो रही है...लेकिन...क्या वह लिस्ट हौले-हौले काँप नहीं रही थी? लिस्ट के काँपने का अर्थ था—स्वयं कमिश्नर साहब के हाथ काँप रहे थे! लेकिन क्यों? एकाएक कौन-सी बात हो गई ऐसी?

आकाश टोकने जा ही रहा था, "सर!"...

किन्तु तभी कमिश्नर साहब ने हौले से कहा, "गुड जॉब...वंडरफुल..."

इससे तो आकाश का सन्देह और पक्का हो गया। केवल तीन शब्द—गुड जॉब...वंडरफुल...और तीनों ही शब्द काँपते हुए...कमिश्नर साहब का स्वर जितना महीन था नहीं, उतना महीन लग क्यों रहा था? तीनों ही शब्दों में? काँपती लिस्ट, काँपते हाथ, काँपता स्वर...लिस्ट की ओट में छिपा-छिपा चेहरा...किस रहस्य-लोक में विचरण कर रहा था आकाश?

आख़िर न रहा गया। टोक देने के ही शुद्ध उद्देश्य से कहा आकाश ने, "सर!"

रूमाल निकालकर कमिश्नर साहब अपने चेहरे की ओर ले गए थे। लिस्ट की ओट होने के कारण आकाश देखे तो आख़िर कैसे देखे...कि रूमाल निकालने का

उनका उद्देश्य क्या हो सकता था? क्या वह अपने आँसू पोंछ रहे थे? हिश्ट! कैसी बचकानी कल्पना! आँसू किस वजह से? अभी कौन-सी बात हो गई है ऐसी, जो आँसू निकाल दे? लेकिन...आकाश ने साफ़ देखा...कमिश्नर साहब का चेहरा लिस्ट की ओट से बाहर आ रहा था और वह चेहरा...स्पष्ट रूप से एक ऐसा चेहरा था, जिस पर से अभी-अभी आँसू पोंछे गए थे। आकाश स्तब्ध ही रह गया यह देखकर कि कमिश्नर साहब के आँसू दुबारा बहना चाह रहे थे और इस बार उनका चेहरा लिस्ट की ओट में नहीं था। उनके चेहरे पर काँपती पीड़ा को आकाश आमने-सामने देख सकता था...आकाश की तो जैसे बोलती बन्द हो गई। उतने बड़े ऑफिसर की आँखों से आँसुओं का टप-टप गिरना...आकाश बड़ी मुश्किल से कह पाया, ''सर! आप...''

''कुछ नहीं!'' कमिश्नर साहब फीकी हँसी हँसे, ''तुम चलो कॉन्फ्रेन्स-रूम में। जब पूरी टीम आ जाए, मुझे फोन कर देना। मैं आ जाऊँगा, सर्च-वारंट लेकर।''

''लेकिन, सर! मैं आप को ऐसी हालत में छोड़कर नहीं जा सकता। पहली बार आपकी आँखों को भीगते देख रहा हूँ...'' आकाश ने ज़िद्दी स्वर में कहा।

कमिश्नर साहब के लरजते शब्द आकाश के कानों तक आए, ''आकाश! आज तुम करोड़ों के हीरे...एक इल्हामी आवाज़ के इशारे पर...ज़ब्त करने जा रहे हो! ऐसी ही एक इल्हामी आवाज़ मेरी भी ज़िन्दगी में आई थी...''

''ओह! लेकिन, सर! आपने कभी चर्चा नहीं की इसकी...'' आकाश बुदबुदाया।

कमिश्नर साहब की आँखों में भूतकाल का न जाने कौन-सा सपना तैरने लगा था, ''आकाश! जैसे तुमने अपनी मददगार आवाज़ का नाम रखा है, 'आकाशवाणी', वैसे मैंने भी अपनी उस मददगार आवाज़ का नाम रख दिया था, 'बिटिया'...'बिटिया'...''

भावुकता का जो ज्वार उमड़ रहा था कमिश्नर साहब की आवाज़ में, उसे झेलना आकाश को असम्भव-सा लग रहा था...

''हाँ, आकाश! यही नाम रखा था मैंने उस इल्हामी आवाज़ का—'बिटिया'! तब मुझे अन्दाज़ा नहीं था, कितनी नाज़ुक भूल मैं कर रहा हूँ...जिसके साथ कभी मेरी भेंट होने वाली नहीं थी, जो सिर्फ़ एक आवाज़ थी...इल्हामी आवाज़...उसके साथ प्यार का वैसा नाता मुझे जोड़ना नहीं चाहिए था।

दरअसल, मैंने नहीं, बल्कि उसने इस नाते की शुरुआत की। वही मुझे फोन पर प्यार से 'डैडी' कहकर पुकारने लगी। मुझे उसे शुरू में ही रोक देना चाहिए था, जो मैं नहीं कर पाया। उसे सचमुच एक डैडी की ज़रूरत थी। इस ज़रूरत को मैं किसी भी तरह न नकार पाया!

जबकि मुझे शुरू में ही एक लक्ष्मण-रेखा खींच लेनी चाहिए थी। यह आज से कोई दस बरस पहले की बात है। आज मैं इन्कम-टैक्स में, कमिश्नर के पद पर

बैठता हूँ। तब मैं असिस्टेंट कमिश्नर हुआ करता था। मेरा डील-डौल वैसा ही था, जैसा आज है। केवल बालों में सफ़ेदी आज के जैसी घनी नहीं थी। आज मैं भावनाओं के क्षेत्र में बहुत सध गया हूँ। दस बरस पहले ऐसा सधा हुआ नहीं था। इसीलिए, दस बरस पहले, उस अनदेखी-अनजानी लड़की ने जब मुझे डैडी कहकर पुकारा, तो मैंने भी उसे अपनी बिटिया बना लिया। यह केवल शब्दों का आडम्बरयुक्त खेल नहीं था, आकाश! मैं उस लड़की को सचमुच अपनी बिटिया की तरह चाहने लगा था।

फोन पर मैं और बिटिया किस तरह लम्बी-लम्बी बातें किया करते थे, आज भी जस-का-तस याद है...ऐसा नहीं कि उसके फोन केवल ऑफिस में आते थे। मैंने उसे घर का नम्बर दे दिया था और वह पूरे अधिकार के साथ, घर पर भी, मुझसे लम्बी बातें, फोन पर करती रहती। मेरी बीवी, मेरी सगी बिटिया, मेरे नौकर-चाकर, सब उस अनदेखी-अनजानी लड़की की आवाज़ से प्यार करने लगे थे, किन्तु उनके प्यार की सीमा थी, जबकि मेरा प्यार उसके प्रति बढ़ता ही जा रहा था। उसे आमने-सामने देखने के लिए मैं कितना व्याकुल था, याद करता हूँ, तो आज भी आश्चर्य होता है।

फोन की घंटी बजती है। जाने कैसे, पहले ही मुझे पता चल जाता है, यह फोन बिटिया का है! मैं रिसीवर उठाता हूँ, 'हैलो!'

और बिटिया का ही स्वर सुनाई पड़ता है, लाड़ से ओतप्रोत स्वर, 'हैलो, मेरे प्यारे डैडी।'

मैं भी एकदम खिल जाता हूँ, 'आह, मेरी प्यारी बिटिया!'

समझ रहे हो, आकाश, हमारा स्नेह कितना तीव्र था? वह मुझे सिर्फ़ डैडी नहीं कह पाती थी। अकसर 'प्यारे डैडी' कहा करती। मैं भी जवाब में उसे सिर्फ़ बिटिया नहीं, बल्कि 'प्यारी बिटिया' ही कहकर पुकारा करता।

'कैसी हो, प्यारी बिटिया?' मैं पूछता हूँ।

वह हँसती है, 'आप बताइए, मैं कैसी हूँ?'

मैं जवाब देता हूँ, 'कभी देखा तो है नहीं तुमको! कैसे बताऊँ, कैसी हो? बहुत चाहता हूँ, कभी आकर मिलो।'

'मिलूँगी तो कभी नहीं आपसे!' वह साफ़ इनकार कर जाती है, लेकिन इतने प्यार भरे अधिकार के साथ कि बुरा नहीं लगता।

मैं उलाहने के स्वर में कहता हूँ, 'इससे तो अच्छा है, तुम मुझे फोन ही न किया करो।'

'क्यों? क्या मैंने कभी आपको कोई...ग़लत ख़बर दी?' वह ऐसे पूछती है, जैसे मुझे अदालत में खड़ा कर रही हो!

मैं झट से स्वीकार कर लेता हूँ, 'नहीं, ऐसा नहीं...तुम्हारी दी हुई हर खबर सही निकली है। हर ख़बर के ज़ोर पर मैंने जब भी छापा मारा, लाखों का काला धन ज़ब्त किया।'

'यस!' वह उल्लसित हो जाती है, लेकिन फिर अचानक गम्भीर, 'अच्छा, प्यारे डैडी! याद है, मेरे एक सौतेले डैडी भी हैं?'

'हाँ, याद है।'

'सबसे पहला छापा मैंने अपने ही सौतेले डैडी पर डलवाया था! याद है?'

'अरे, क्यों न याद होगा! मैंने ही तो डाला था वह छापा!' मेरी इस बात से बिटिया भी अपनी किन्हीं यादों में खो जाती है। फोन पर उसका एक-एक शब्द मुझ तक स्पष्ट पहुँच रहा है, 'छापा! काले धन पर छापा! आह! काला धन! क्यों, प्यारे डैडी! यह सच है न कि काला धन सिर्फ़ काले काम ही करवाता है? यह काले धन का ही तो नशा था, जिसकी झोंक में...मेरे सौतेले डैडी ने...मुझे और मेरी मम्मी को धक्के मारकर कोठी से निकाल दिया था! तब से आज तक हम दोनों दर-दर की ठोकरें खाती फिर रही हैं...'

मैं उसे रोकता हूँ, 'क्यों पुरानी बातों को याद करती हो? भूल जाओ, बिटिया भूल जाओ।'

'नहीं भूलँगी! तभी तो मैं काले धन की दुश्मन बनी रह सकूँगी!'

'हाँ, यह बात भी सही है!' मैं सहमति में ऐसे सिर हिलाता हूँ, जैसे वह सामने ही खड़ी, मुझे सिर हिलाते देख रही है।

सहसा वह ताना मारने के मूड में आ जाती है। कहती है, 'काले धन की ख़बरों के बदले में आपसे कभी कोई इनाम तो माँगा नहीं मैंने...'

मैं उसके ताने को सर के ऊपर से निकाल देता हूँ और सहजता से कहता हूँ, 'मैंने भी क्या कभी शिकायत की...कि तुम इनाम के लालच में ख़बरें देती हो?'

वह ऐसे बात करने लगती है, जैसे अपने आपसे बोल रही हो, 'मेरे तो, बस ज़ज़्बात में आ गई है यह बात! कि जहाँ भी काला धन हो, चुपके से ज़ब्त करा दो। अब तो ज़िन्दगी भर यही काम करना है। ब्लैक-मनी ज़ब्त करवाते जाओ, खुश होते जाओ!'

मैं उसे सावधान करता हूँ, 'लेकिन, बिटिया, तुम आग से खेल रही हो।'

वह मस्त होकर कहती है, 'अरे, कुछ नहीं होगा मुझे! चिन्ता न करिए। कच्ची गोलियाँ नहीं खेलती मैं! फूँक-फूँककर क़दम रखती हूँ, हाँ! आख़िर बिटिया किसकी हूँ!'

'हाँ! हाँ! तुम मेरी बिटिया हो!'

वह बोलती जा रही है आगे, 'सौतेले डैडी को मैंने खो दिया...और फिर असली डैडी को...आपको...पा लिया! सौदा अच्छा रहा! है न?'

सुनकर मेरा गला भर आता है। मैं चुप रह जाता हूँ। नहीं चाहता, उसे पता चले कि मेरा गला भर आया। फोन पर, अचानक, वह हौले से बोलती है, 'सुनिए, डैडी! कोई आ रहा है...बाद में फोन करूँगी।'

और वह रिसीवर रख देती है। रिसीवर रखने की भी उसकी एक अदा थी। मुझे साफ़ पता चल जाता था, रिसीवर उसी ने रखा है, किसी और ने नहीं। हमेशा रिसीवर पहले वह रखती है, उसके बाद ही मैं। कई बार मैं अपने रिसीवर को देर तक थामे रह जाता हूँ, तब रख पाता हूँ...

मुझे उसने कभी नहीं बताया था कि काले धन का पता वह कैसे लगाती है। चाहे जैसे लगाती हो, उसकी दी ख़बर कभी झूठी नहीं निकली। फोन कहाँ से करती थी वह? क्या पता! जहाँ तक मैं समझ सकता हूँ, हमेशा वह अलग-अलग स्थानों का इस्तेमाल करती होगी। फोन किस वक़्त करेगी, उसका कोई ठिकाना नहीं था। एक-दो बार तो उसने मुझे रात के तीन बजे जगाकर सूचित किया था कि काला धन कहाँ है, किसके पास है, किस रूप में है...गपशप के मूड में होती, तब तो वह लम्बी बातचीत किए चली जाती, किन्तु जब विशेष सूचनाएँ दे रही होती, तब कम-से-कम शब्दों में और कम-से-कम समय में बात करने का प्रयास किया करती। एक बार...घर पर रात के लगभग डेढ़ बजे उसका फोन आया। मेरी 'हैलो' सुनते ही वह बोली, 'सुनिए, डैडी! जल्दी से काग़ज़-क़लम निकालिए और जो पता बता रही हूँ, नोट करिए...'

'हाँ, हाँ, एक मिनट...' कहकर जल्दी से मैंने काग़ज़-क़लम सँभाले।

बिटिया ने बताना और मैंने नोट करना शुरू किया, 'ऐसा है, प्यारे डैडी, खार वेस्ट में, मधु पार्क के पास...आठवें रास्ते के नुक्कड़ पर जो बिल्डिंग है न—'स्मृति-कुंज'...उसके चौथे माले के फ्लैट नम्बर 3 में सोने की ईंटें छिपी हैं। यह जो फ्लैट है न, इसमें लकड़ी की पुरानी अलमारी के पीछे कुछ चक्कर है...और...'

इसके बाद जो हुआ, आकाश! क्या उसकी कल्पना कर सकोगे? बिटिया के साथ मेरा समूचा नाता कल्पनातीत था और यह नाता टूटा भी कल्पनातीत तरीक़े से...पुरानी अलमारी के पीछे के चक्कर की बात उसके मुँह से अभी निकली ही थी कि...फोन पर...अचानक मैंने उसका तीखा चीत्कार सुना। मैं एकदम उछल पड़ा। क्या अर्थ था उसके चीत्कार का? वह बार-बार चीख़ रही थी, जैसे न जाने कौन-से दरिन्दे बढ़ने लगे थे उसकी ओर...उसकी हर चीख़ मेरे कानों में पहुँच रही थी। वे चीखें, फिर, केवल चीख़ें न रहीं। उनमें शब्द भी शामिल होने लगे '...आ-आ...नहीं...नहीं...डैडी! बचाओ, डैडी! आ...नहीं...छोड़ दो...छोड़ दो मुझे! डैडी!...आ...ये...ये मेरा गला घोंट रहे हैं...आ...मर जाऊँगी! बचाओ! डैडी!'

और मैं फोन पर ही चिल्लाने लगा, 'छोड़ दो! छोड़ दो लड़की को! मैं कहता हूँ, छोड़ दो! हैलो, बिटिया...हैलो...हैलो...'

बिटिया के हाथ से रिसीवर छूट चुका था। रिसीवर खुला रह गया था और ज़रूर बिटिया के मुँह के पास ही लटक रहा था। बिटिया का गला घोंटा जा रहा था और गला घुटने की हर आवाज़, हर रिरियाहट रिसीवर पकड़-पकड़कर मेरे कानों तक पहुँचा रहा था...मैं बार-बार चीख़ता था, 'हैलो! हैलो, बिटिया, हैलो! कौन है उधर? छोड़ दो लड़की को...छोड़ दो...'—और फिर, उधर से आती घुटी-घुटी हर आवाज़ बन्द हो गई। बिटिया मर चुकी थी! उसका गला पूरी तरह...आह...पूरी तरह घोंटा जा चुका था!''

कमरे में ऐसा सन्नाटा खिंच गया था कि वे दोनों व्यक्ति एक-दूसरे की साँसों की आवाज़ सुन सकते थे। कमिश्नर साहब ने पाइप सुलगाया। आकाश धूम्रपान नहीं करता, अन्यथा इस मौक़े पर अवश्य उसने भी अपने फेफड़ों को तम्बाकू का धुआँ दिया होता। खूब गहरे दो कश कमिश्नर साहब ने खींचे। उनके चेहरे पर ऐसी कोई कशमकश नहीं थी कि उन्होंने अपनी एक अत्यन्त निजी कथा आकाश को सुनाकर भूल तो नहीं की। आकाश पर वह स्नेह भरा अधिकार रखते थे। इसके अलावा, स्वयं आकाश एक ऐसे दौर से गुज़र रहा था, जिस दौर से कमिश्नर साहब कब के गुज़र चुके थे और उनके अनुभव का लाभ आकाश को अवश्य ही दिया जाना चाहिए था—एक इल्हामी आवाज़ से नाता जुड़ने का अनुभव...

कमरे की ख़ामोशी कमिश्नर साहब के इन शब्दों से टूटी, ''फिर मैंने 'बिटिया' की आवाज़ कभी नहीं सुनी...कभी नहीं...''

आकाश ने गहरी साँस ली, ''आय एम सॉरी, सर!''

''मैं बयान नहीं कर सकता, आकाश! उस हादसे से उबरने के लिए मुझे कितनी कोशिश करनी पड़ी। मानसिक रूप से मैं बिलकुल अपंग-सा हो गया था। मैं अपनी बीवी का, अपने पूरे परिवार का, बेहद शुक्रगुज़ार हूँ, क्योंकि उन्हीं सबके स्नेह-सहयोग से आख़िर मैं अपने खोल से बाहर निकला...सोचो तो सही, वह कैसा क्षण था... कितना भयानक क्षण! जब मेरी प्यारी बिटिया का गला घुट रहा था, बचाने के लिए वह मुझे बार-बार पुकार रही थी और मैं...और मैं सिर्फ़ इतना कर सकता था कि...टेलीफोन के रिसीवर को थामकर...सिर्फ़ अपने कमरे में बैठा रह गया था मैं! मुझे इतना भी नहीं पता था कि वह फोन कहाँ से कर रही थी। बिटिया का गला घुट जाने के बाद, रिसीवर में मुझे कुछ भी सुनाई नहीं दिया था। उसके बाद, हौले से कनेक्शन कटने की ध्वनि हुई थी। उस छोर पर लटकते रिसीवर को किन्हीं हत्यारे हाथों ने वापस क्रेडिल पर रख दिया था...फिर तो, बस, सन्नाटा-ही-सन्नाटा था मेरे जीवन में! परिवार के लोगों ने मुझे खींचकर उस सन्नाटे से बाहर निकाला...''

''मुझे बहुत ही दुःख है, सर!'' आकाश ने धीर-गम्भीर स्वर में कहा, ''मेरी वजह से वह हादसा आज आपको फिर याद आ गया।''

आशा के विपरीत, आकाश ने कमिश्नर साहब के चेहरे पर एक चमक उभरती देखी। कहने लगे, "आकाश! तुम बहुत भाग्यशाली हो!"

आकाश समझ न पाया, कमिश्नर साहब ने यह बात किस सन्दर्भ में कही। कमिश्नर साहब ने भी उसकी उलझन को भाँप लिया और स्पष्ट किया, "ऐसा है, आकाश, इन्कम-टैक्स में...और कस्टम में भी...इस तरह की इल्हामी आवाज़ों का सहारा...कभी-कभी...किसी ऑफिसर को मिल जाता है। ये ऑफिसर लाखों में एक होते हैं और बहुत भाग्यशाली माने जाते हैं।"

आकाश झेंप-सा गया, "सर!" वह बुदबुदाया।

कमिश्नर साहब ने नेक सलाह दी, "याद रखो, आकाश! ये इल्हामी आवाज़ें बहुत जज़्बाती इनसानों की होती हैं। ऐसी आवाज़ें सिर्फ़ अपने ज़ज़्बात के लिए काम करती हैं, किसी इनाम के लालच में नहीं। इसीलिए, कई बार, इन आवाज़ों के साथ गहरे प्यार का नाता जुड़ जाता है।"

"जी..."

"एक सलाह दूँ? तुम्हारी यह जो इल्हामी आवाज़ है न, यह 'आकाशवाणी'... इसके साथ कभी अपने जज़्बात को मत जुड़ने देना...यह इल्हामी आवाज़ सिर्फ़ तुम्हारी ड्यूटी का एक हिस्सा है। आवाज़ अपनी ड्यूटी निभा रही है, तुम अपनी ड्यूटी निभाओ..."

"मैं याद रखूँगा, सर..."

"कामना करता हूँ, आकाश! कल सुबह, तुम्हें और तुम्हारी पूरी टीम को, अपने अभियान में जगमगाती सफलता मिले। यह भी कामना करता हूँ कि...जज़्बात की जैसी नाज़ुक भूल मुझसे हुई, वैसी भूल तुमसे कभी न हो...कभी न हो..." कहते-कहते कमिश्नर साहब का स्वर भीगने लगा था।

आकाश उनसे इजाज़त ले, कमरे से निकल आया।

आयकर भवन का कॉन्फ्रेन्स-रूम! लगभग पच्चीस अफसर उस बैठक में हिस्सा ले रहे थे, जिनमें पाँच महिलाएँ भी शामिल थीं—मिस कपूर, मिसेज अग्रवाल, 'मिस पंड्या, मिसेज पार्कर और मिसेज जाधव। आयकर के प्रत्येक छापे में एक महिला ऑफिसर अवश्य साथ रखी जाती है। कल सुबह, चूँकि एक साथ पाँच स्थानों पर छापे मारने थे, प्रत्येक छापे के लिए एक के हिसाब से, बैठक में, पाँच महिला ऑफिसरों की मौजूदगी का आधार समझ में आता था।

आकाश का प्रिय सहायक जनक भी बैठक में मौजूद था। उसकी सम्मानपूर्ण दृष्टि बार-बार आकाश की ओर उठ जाती।

हाथ में सीलबन्द लिफ़ाफ़ा लिये कमिश्नर साहब, सभी ऑफिसरों एवं इन्स्पेक्टरों को सम्बोधित कर रहे थे, "लेडीज़ एंड जेंटलमैन! फ़ैसला किया गया है कि बम्बई के पाँच रिहायशी फ्लैटों पर, कल सुबह, एक साथ छापे मारे जाएँ, क्योंकि वहाँ काफ़ी बड़ी मात्रा में काला धन छिपा होने की सम्भावना है। इन पाँचों छापों के सर्च-वारंट्स का लिफ़ाफ़ा मैं, आप सबके सामने, आकाश को सौंपता हूँ..."

आकाश ने सम्मान के साथ उठकर, कमिश्नर साहब के हाथ से सीलबन्द लिफ़ाफ़ा ग्रहण किया। जब वह वापस अपने स्थान पर बैठ रहा था, कमिश्नर साहब ने आगे कहना जारी कर दिया, "इस लिफ़ाफ़े की सील, कल सुबह, आप सबकी मौजूदगी में टूटेगी। तभी यह जानकारी दी जाएगी कि...इन्कम-टैक्स का कौन-सा ऑफिसर कौन-से फ्लैट पर छापा मारेगा। यह ऑफिसर अपने सहायकों के रूप में किस-किस को साथ ले जाएगा, इसका फ़ैसला भी उसी वक़्त होगा...लेडीज़ एंड जेंटलमैन! कल सुबह के छापों में आप सभी को सुनहरी सफलता मिले और आप काले धन के काले नाग पर एक और गहरी चोट कर सकें, इसी मनोकामना के साथ, मैं आप सबसे विदा लेता हूँ...नमस्कार!"

और कमिश्नर साहब उठ पड़े। उनके सम्मान में सभी ने अपनी कुर्सियाँ छोड़ दीं। कमिश्नर साहब दरवाज़े से निकल गए। सब वापस अपनी कुर्सियों पर बैठने लगे। बैठक के संचालन का भार अब आकाश के कन्धों पर था। उसने सामने आकर कहना शुरू किया, "दोस्तो! जो खबर मुझे मिली है, उसके अनुसार...अभी हाल में, इस पार्टी ने, कई करोड़ का काला धन ख़र्च करके, कुछ हीरे ख़रीदे हैं। पार्टी के भागीदारों और रिश्तेदारों के जो पाँच फ्लैट्स हैं, उनमें से किसी एक फ्लैट में ये हीरे, बस दो ही दिन पहले लाकर रखे गए हैं। इन्हें ज़ब्त करने का मौक़ा हमें तभी मिल सकता है, जब हम अपनी कार्रवाई, कल सुबह आठ बजने से पहले, न केवल शुरू कर दें, बल्कि बहुत आगे तक बढ़ा दें।"

मिस कपूर ने टोका, "सर! यह तो तभी हो सकता है, जब हम सूरज की पहली किरण फूटने के साथ पाँचों फ्लैट्स पर छापे मार दें।"

"एग्ज़ैक्टली, मिस कपूर! मैं यही कहना चाहता हूँ।"

इस बार मिस पंड्या ने टोका, "लेकिन, सर! इन हीरों को ज़ब्त करने का मौक़ा हमें कल सुबह आठ बजने से पहले ही मिलेगा, बाद में नहीं—ऐसा क्यों?"

"क्योंकि, मिस पंड्या!" आकाश ने बताया, "पार्टी का कोई बहुत भरोसे का आदमी, कल सुबह, आठ बजे के आसपास, उन हीरों को लेने आनेवाला है, ताकि उन्हें छिपाकर कहीं रख दे।"

"सर!" जनक ने कुछ पूछने के लिए हाथ उठाया।

"बोलो।"

"सर! क्या हम इस आदमी का पीछा नहीं कर सकते?" जनक का सवाल बिलकुल सीधा और सरल था, किन्तु सटीक भी तो था!

आकाश मुसकराया, "नहीं, जनक! क्योंकि हम उसे पहचानते नहीं हैं। इसके अलावा, हमें यह भी तो नहीं मालूम है कि वह आदमी पाँच में से कौन-से फ्लैट पर आएगा।"

"ओह-आय-सी..." बुदबुदाकर जनक बैठ गया।

आकाश ने जारी रखा, "पाँचों फ्लैट्स पर एक साथ छापे और छापे भी उस आदमी के आने से बहुत पहले—यही एक तरीक़ा हमारे पास रह जाता है।"

मिस्टर काचलवार ने उठकर, मन्द-मन्द मुसकराकर, पूरी बैठक से कहा, "दोस्तो, जैसा कि आप सभी जानते हैं, मैं ज्योतिष विद्या में थोड़ा-बहुत दख़ल रखता हूँ। मैं दैनिक पंचांग का भी, इसी नाते, हमेशा जानकार बना रहता हूँ। मैं बता सकता हूँ कि कल सुबह का सूरज निकलेगा, ठीक छह बजकर पैंतीस मिनट पर!"

बैठक का बोझिल होता जा रहा वातावरण, मि. काचलवार के इस वक्तव्य से एकदम चुटीला हो गया। सभी के होंठों पर मुसकान की रेखाएँ देखी जा सकीं। छापे अगर सूर्योदय के साथ ही शुरू कर देने हैं, तो सूर्योदय का बिलकुल सही समय तो मालूम होना ही चाहिए न! आकाश ने भी इस उपयोगी सूचना के लिए मि. काचलवार की भूरि-भूरि प्रशंसा की। फिर कहा, "तो...मित्रो! हम सभी को, सूरज निकलने से ठीक एक घंटा पहले किसी एक स्थान पर इकट्ठे हो जाना है...और वह स्थान है—विले-पारले पश्चिम के रेलवे स्टेशन के ठीक सामने!"

यह स्थान सभी को पसन्द आया। आकाश ने सौभाग्य के संकेत में अँगूठा उठाकर चहुँओर प्रदर्शित किया। जवाब में सभी ने अपने-अपने अँगूठे उठा दिए। सभी के होंठों पर ये ही शब्द थे, "गुड-लक! गुड-लक, एवरीबडी!"

सब कॉन्फ्रेन्स-रूम से निकलने लगे। सब मुसकरा तो रहे थे, किन्तु बम्बई जैसे शहर में, जहाँ अनन्त दूरियाँ हैं, सूर्यादय से एक घंटा पहले किसी एक स्थान पर एकत्र हो जाना...ऐसा निर्णय ही सिद्ध किए दे रहा था कि सबकी मुसकानों के पीछे गम्भीर कर्तव्य-निष्ठा छिपी हुई है...

बम्बई के लिए कहावत प्रसिद्ध है कि यह शहर कभी नहीं सोता। इसका जीवन्त प्रमाण यदि देखना हो, तो सुबह चार बजे उठकर, लोकल ट्रेन के किसी भी स्टेशन तक पहुँचने का कष्ट करना होगा। भारत के किसी भी शहर में सुबह चार बजे वह चहल-पहल नहीं दिखाई देगी, जो बम्बई के लिए आम बात है। सुबह चार बजे की लोकल ट्रेनों में भी यात्रियों की संख्या कम नहीं दिखेगी।

जबकि उस वक़्त सुबह के चार नहीं, साढ़े पाँच बज चुके थे। बेशक सूर्योदय नहीं हुआ था, किन्तु चार बजने को तो डेढ़ घंटा बीत चुका था न! बम्बई के

उपनगर, विले-पारले पश्चिम का रेलवे स्टेशन चहल-पहल से ओतप्रोत हो चुका था। धड़धड़ाती लोकल ट्रेनें आ-आकर रुकतीं और रुक-रुककर जा रही थीं। प्रत्येक ट्रेन में से यात्रियों की ठेलमठेल बाहर निकल पड़ती और वैसी ही ठेलमठेल अन्दर भी घुस जाती।

जनक कौन-सी ट्रेन से उतरा था? पता नहीं! अभी-अभी तीन ट्रेनें आई और गई हैं। उनमें से किसी से भी जनक उतरा हो सकता है। महत्त्वपूर्ण यह नहीं है कि वह कौन-सी ट्रेन से उतरा। महत्त्वपूर्ण यह है कि जनक अपनी ड्यूटी पर आ गया है और अभी सूर्योदय नहीं हुआ है। सरकारी कर्मचारियों के बारे में यह धारणा कभी नहीं मिटाई जा सकेगी कि वे काम नहीं करते, किन्तु सरकार के कुछ विभाग आज भी ऐसे हैं, जहाँ जमकर काम होता है। लोग तनख़्वाह या ओवर-टाइम की चिन्ता न कर, केवल काम करते हैं। भारत की फ़ौज संसार की बेहतरीन फ़ौजों में गिनी जाती है। क्या फ़ौज के कर्मचारी सरकारी कर्मचारी नहीं? इसी तरह, और भी कई विभाग हैं सरकार के, जहाँ डंके की चोट पर काम होता है और ज़्यादातर तरक्कियाँ इसी आधार पर होती हैं कि किसने कैसा काम किया।

जनक आयकर विभाग में अभी इन्स्पेक्टर के पद पर है, लेकिन उसकी लगन, समय की उसकी पाबन्दी, उसकी सूक्ष्म दृष्टि और अन्तर्प्रेरणा...वे सभी गुण हैं जनक में, जिससे सहज ही भविष्यवाणी की जा सके कि यह व्यक्ति बहुत आगे तक जाएगा। आकाश की 'गुड बुक्स' में जनक का नाम यदि बहुत ऊपर दर्ज था, तो यों ही नहीं!

वृक्षों पर चिड़ियों ने हलके-हलके बोलना शुरू कर दिया था। जनक सोचे बिना न रह सका, 'कितने दिनों बाद, सुबह का स्वागत करती चिड़ियों की चहक सुन रहा हूँ मैं?'

लैम्प-पोस्ट के नीचे, अख़बारों का थोक विक्रेता, अपने हॉकर्स के बीच, अख़बारों का वितरण कर रहा था। जनक ने अपनी कलाई-घड़ी में देखा। पाँच बजकर पैंतीस मिनट...सूर्योदय ठीक छह-पैंतीस पर होगा, जैसा कि मि. काचलवार ने कहा है...बराबर एक घंटा पहले जनक आ पहुँचा है यहाँ। जनक ने अपने कन्धे से लटकते थरमस को सँभाला। इसमें जनक गरम चाय भरकर लाया है। वह जानता था, ऐसे ही थरमस वह आज के अधिकांश साथियों के कन्धों से लटके देखेगा।

बहुत नज़दीक, किसी कार का हॉर्न सुन जनक चौंककर, पलटकर देखने लगा। आकाश आ पहुँचा था, अपनी कार स्वयं चलाता हुआ। जनक एकदम खिल गया।

"गुड मॉर्निंग, सर!" अपने आप उसके होंठों से फूट पड़ा।

"गुड मॉर्निंग, जनक! मुझे मालूम था, तुम पहले से आए खड़े होंगे।" आकाश ने प्रशंसा के स्वर में कहा।

जनक आगे की सीट पर, आकाश के साथ कार में आ बैठा, "वक़्त की पाबन्दी का सबक आप से ही तो सीखा है, सर!"

तभी एक और कार का हॉर्न बजा। मिसेज अग्रवाल भी अपनी कार स्वयं ही ड्राइव करती हुई आ पहुँची थीं। आकाश की कार के ठीक बग़ल में मिसेज अग्रवाल की कार आकर रुक रही थी।

"गुड मॉर्निंग, आकाश जी!"

"गुड मॉर्निंग, मिसेज अगवाल! वेलकम!"

"टैक्सियों का सही इन्तज़ाम है न?"

"जी हाँ! आप चिन्ता न करें!"

एक और लोकल ट्रेन व्हिसल देती हुई आई और रुकी। स्टेशन से भीड़ का रेला बाहर निकलने लगा। लगभग 20 व्यक्ति भीड़ से अलग छँटते दिखाई दिए। वे सब आयकर विभाग के ही अफसर, इन्स्पेक्टर व अन्य सहयोगी थे। कितनी बड़ी टोली आ पहुँची थी एक साथ। उनके बीच तीन महिलाएँ अलग झलक रही थीं–मिस पंड्या, मिसेज जाधव और मिसेज पार्कर। अधिकांश के कन्धों से थरमस लटक रहे थे।

आकाश और मिसेज अग्रवाल अपनी कारों से बाहर निकल आए थे। जनक भी आकाश की कार से बाहर निकलकर खड़ा था और सभी आगन्तुकों के स्वागत में कुछ-न-कुछ बोल रहा था। आकाश सभी के लिए सुन्दर सुबह की कामनाएँ करता, सबसे हाथ मिलाता जा रहा था। मिसेज अग्रवाल भी सबके लिए शुभकामनाओं का पुलिन्दा बनी हुई थीं।

"मॉर्निंग! मॉर्निंग! वेलकम, एवरीबडी!"

"मिस कपूर नहीं दिख रहीं?"

"आती होंगी...लीजिए, आ गईं!"

अपनी कार स्वयं चला रही मिस कपूर की शोभा ही कुछ और थी। उन्होंने खिड़की से हाथ हिलाकर सबको सामूहिक रूप से विश किया। कार पार्क कर, बाहर निकल, उन्होंने दुबारा सबको विश करते हुए कहा, 'मॉर्निंग, एवरीबडी!"

"मॉर्निंग!"

"कौन-कौन आना बाक़ी है?"

"अजी, आप तो पधारिए!"

जल्द ही, जो-जो नहीं आए थे, वे सब भी आ पहुँचे। सबकी मौजूदगी में आकाश ने सर्च-वारंट्स का सील-बन्द लिफ़ाफ़ा खोला।

पक्षियों का कलरव ज़रा तेज़ हो गया था। मिस कपूर अपनी कार में बैठ चुकी थीं। साथ में चार ऑफिसर और लदे हुए थे, उसी कार में। दो टैक्सियों में अर्दली

व अन्य सहायक सवार हो चुके थे। आकाश ने मिस कपूर को फाइल सौंपते हुए कहा, "लीजिए, मिस कपूर! अपना सर्च-वारंट सँभालिए!"

"थैंक्यू, सर!"

"आप वरसोवा के छापे की नेता हैं।"

"गुड लक, सर!"

"गुड लक, मिस कपूर!"

और मिस कपूर की कार आगे बढ़ गई। सहायकों की दोनों टैक्सियाँ पीछे-पीछे लपकीं।

सूर्योदय अब ज़रा और नज़दीक था, जिससे पक्षियों का कलरव ज़रा और तेज़ हो गया था। आकाश ने मि. काचलवार को नेपियन्सी रोड के फ्लैट पर छापे का संचालन सौंपा। सर्च-वारंट की फाइल थामे मि. काचलवार एवं साथियों की टैक्सियाँ रवाना हो गईं। मिसेज पार्कर को मि. काचलवार के साथ सहायक के रूप में भेजा गया।

मिसेज अग्रवाल अपने सर्च-वारंट की फाइल ले, वी फॉर विक्ट्री का संकेत करतीं, तेज़ी से कार बढ़ा ले गईं। वार्डन रोड के फ्लैट पर छापे का संचालन उन्हीं को करना था। उनकी कार के पीछे वे दोनों टैक्सियाँ लपक चलीं, जिनमें उनके सहायक थे।

मि. सुल्तान को जोगेश्वरी के फ्लैट पर छापे का नेतृत्व करना था। वारंट की फाइल सँभालकर, साथियों समेत, जब वह टैक्सियों में बैठकर रवाना हो रहे थे, आकाश ने उन्हें सावधान किया, "जोगेश्वरी नज़दीक ही है। आप वहाँ दूसरों की बनिस्बत जल्दी पहुँच जाएँगे। ऐसा न हो कि आपका छापा भी, दूसरों की बनिस्बत जल्दी शुरू हो जाए।"

"मुझे याद है, बॉस!" मि. सुल्तान ने कहा, "पाँचों छापे एक वक़्त, एक साथ शुरू करने हैं।"

"ठीक छह-पैंतीस पर! जब सूरज निकल रहा हो..." आकाश ने दोहराया।

"यस, बॉस!"

मि. सुल्तान के साथ मिसेज जाधव को भेजा जा रहा था। "गुड लक, मिस्टर सुल्तान! गुड लक, मिसेज जाधव!" आकाश ने दोनों की ओर विजय-सूचक संकेत करने के लिए, दो उँगलियाँ उठाकर, वी फॉर विक्ट्री की मुद्रा दिखाई। जवाब में उन्होंने भी यही मुद्रा दिखाई। गाड़ियाँ रवाना हो गईं।

अब अन्त में, आकाश रवाना हो रहा था। उसके साथ था जनक और महिला-ऑफिसर के रूप में मिस पंड्या। आकाश ने पूछा, "आर यू कम्फर्टेबल, मिस पंड्या?"

"यस, सर!"

"ओके! वी शूट!"—और आकाश की कार तेज़ी से चल पड़ी। पीछे-पीछे, सहायकों की दोनों टैक्सियाँ भी उसी तेज़ी से चलीं।

सूर्योदय से पहले की, बहुत कम चहल-पहल वाली सड़कों पर आकाश ने तेज़ी से कार चलाने का अपना शौक जी भरकर पूरा किया। साथ-साथ वह जनक और मिस पंड्या से बातें भी करता जा रहा था।

"अभी-अभी एक फ्लैश आया मेरे दिमाग़ में..." आकाश ने कहा।

मिस पंड्या ने भौंहें उठाईं, "क्या, सर?"

"यही कि...पार्टी को पहले से पता नहीं चलना चाहिए कि दरवाज़े पर कौन खड़ा है। दरवाज़ा खोल देने के बाद ही पार्टी को होश आए कि सामने तो इन्कम-टैक्स वाले खड़े हैं..."

"आकाश के इस वाक्य को जनक ने पूरा किया, "सर्च-वारंट लेकर!"

आकाश ने स्पष्ट किया, "क्योंकि अगर पार्टी दरवाज़ा खोलने से पहले ही जान गई कि इन्कम-टैक्स की रेड पड़ गई है, तो यक़ीन जानो कि हीरों को अच्छी तरह छिपाने के बाद ही पार्टी दरवाज़ा खोलेगी। हीरों जैसी छोटी चीज़ को झटपट कहीं छिपा देना भला क्या मुश्किल है! फिर तो हमारा छापा ही बेकार जा सकता है!"

मिस पंड्या बुदबुदाईं, "नो, सर! ऐसा नहीं होने देंगे!"

जनक ने भी अनुमोदन किया, "कोई-न-कोई आइडिया ज़रूर निकालेंगे..."

उन्हें पहुँचना था बैंड-स्टैंड, बान्द्रा के सागर-तट पर स्थित एक बहुमंज़िला इमारत 'दरिया-दर्शन' में। उसके चौथे माले पर निवास करते हैं श्री दिव्यांग पटेल। इन्हीं दिव्यांग जी के दिव्य दर्शन करने हैं आकाश को, सूरज निकलने के साथ। 'दरिया-दर्शन' में दिव्यांग-दर्शन! कैसा कविता जैसा लग रहा है! अपनी तुकबन्दी पर आकाश मन में मुसकरा दिया।

प्रकट में आकाश ने कहा, "अपना परिचय दिए बिना दिव्यांग पटेल का दरवाज़ा खुलवाना...आप क्या सोचती हैं, मिस पंड्या, आसान रहेगा? दिव्यांग की जगह ज़रा स्वयं को रखकर सोचिए। दृश्य क्या बनता है? सुबह की पहली किरणें अभी ठीक से फूटी भी नहीं हैं। श्रीमान दिव्यांग पटेल अभी बिस्तर से निकले भी नहीं हैं। सहसा कोई दरवाज़े पर आता है। यह 'कोई' अपना नाम बताने से इनकार करता है, परिचय पूछने पर चुप रहता है! बस, बार-बार एक ही बात कहता है, 'खोलो दरवाज़ा!' क्या दिव्यांग पटेल, या कोई भी सही दिमाग़ वाला आदमी, खोलेगा अपना दरवाज़ा? नहीं खोलेगा न?"

"बात आपकी सही है, लेकिन हम भी तो इन्कम-टैक्सवाले हैं!" मिस पंड्या के स्वर में आत्म-विश्वास था, जोश भी था।

ऐसा ही स्वर था जनक का भी, "सर! अभी सूरज निकला नहीं है। निकलने तो दीजिए! उधर सूरज की किरणें फूटेंगी और इधर, हमारे मन-मस्तिष्क में भी, सूझबूझ की किरणें फूटेंगी..."

"लेट्स होप सो..."

सड़क का एक मोड़ पार करते ही वे अचानक समुद्र के आमने-सामने आ गए। कितना सुन्दर, शान्त लग रहा था सुबह का समुद्र, अपने सीने पर अँधियारे-उजियाले की आँखमिचौनी की इजाज़त देता हुआ! किन्तु वह सुबह के समुद्र का सौन्दर्य-पान करने का अवसर नहीं था। आकाश की नज़र समुद्र के उस पार दौड़ चली—क्षितिज पर! जहाँ क्षितिज के लाल-लाल गाल पर चिकोटी काटने के लिए सुबह का शैतान सूरज कभी भी प्रकट हो सकता था...

हो गया प्रकट सूरज! सिन्दूरी क्षितिज पर अंकुरित हो चुका था कुँआरे सूरज के मस्तक का कोमल कगार...

सुबह-सुबह जॉगिंग पर निकले लोग, सड़कों के किनारे जैसे स्लो-मोशन में दौड़ रहे थे। एक-दो लोगों से ही पूछना पड़ा, कहाँ है 'दरिया-दर्शन को-ऑपरेटिव हाउसिंग सोसायटी'।

तीर की तरह आकाश की कार ने 'दरिया-दर्शन सोसायटी' के अहाते में प्रवेश किया। आकाश के सहायकों की दोनों टैक्सियाँ पीछे-पीछे तीर की तरह आईं और रुकीं। सोसायटी का गार्ड, सूर्योदय होने के साथ, एक कार और दो टैक्सियों को उतनी तीव्रता से अहाते में आते देख स्तब्ध हुआ। गार्ड ने कार की दिशा में क़दम उठाए।

अपनी ओर का, कार का शीशा आकाश जल्दी-जल्दी ऊपर चढ़ा रहा था। जनक और मिस पंड्या भी अपनी-अपनी ओर के कार के शीशे ऊपर चढ़ा रहे थे—जल्दी-जल्दी। तपाक से कार ख़ाली हो गई और कार के चारों दरवाज़े खटाक्-खटाक् बन्द हो गए। जो दो टैक्सियाँ पीछे आकर रुकी थीं, वे भी तपाक से ख़ाली हो गईं। हर टैक्सी का बिल स्फूर्ति से अदा कर दिया गया। भारतवर्ष जैसे अलाल देश में अचानक स्फूर्ति का विस्फोट-सा देखकर, सोसायटी के गार्ड को यही लगा, कहीं वह सपने में तो नहीं?

कार से निकलते ही आकाश की नज़र, एक बार फिर, क्षितिज की ओर उठी। सिन्दूरी क्षितिज पर चमकीले लाल टीके की तरह मुसकरा रहा था गोल-गोल सूरज! आकाश ने भी मुसकराकर जनक और मिस पंड्या की ओर देखा, फिर अपनी कलाइ-घड़ी की ओर। जनक और मिस पंड्या ने भी अपनी-अपनी कलाइयों पर समय चेक किया। ठीक छह बजकर पैंतीस मिनट! एक मिनट भी इधर न उधर! आह, इतनी पाबन्दी के साथ काम करने का भी कैसा अवर्णनीय आनन्द है!

सोसायटी के सिक्योरिटी-गार्ड ने अंतरिक्ष से उतरे अपने इन मेहमानों से पहला सवाल पूछा, "सर! आपको किससे मिलना है?"

"मिस्टर दिव्यांग पटेल से।" आकाश ने संक्षिप्त उत्तर लौटाया।

"मिस्टर पटेल तो अभी सो रहे होंगे।" गार्ड ने ज़रा आश्चर्य से कहा।

आकाश हँसा, "आज वह जाग रहे हैं! समझो, हमारे ही इन्तज़ार में हैं! फोन कर दिया था हमने, आने से पहले!"

गार्ड को समझते देर न लगी, मामला कुछ और है। कार और टैक्सियों से उतरे एक-एक शख़्स में इतना रुतबा था कि उनकी किसी भी बात का विरोध करने की गार्ड को जैसे सूझी ही नहीं। हारे हुए स्वर में वह इतना ही बोला, "सर! ज़रा विज़िटर्स-रजिस्टर में एंट्री कर दें।"

आकाश की नज़र जनक की ओर घूमी, "जनक! यह एंट्री तुम करो और फिर...दक्षिण में दक्षिणा!"

जनक ने इशारा समझते हुए, हौले से दोहराया, "यस, सर! दक्षिण में दक्षिणा!"

आकाश अपने साथियों को समेटता हुआ लिफ्ट की ओर बढ़ गया। लिफ्ट इतनी बड़ी नहीं थी कि सब-के-सब एक साथ समा जाते। आकाश, मिस पंड्या एवं कुछ साथियों को पहली खेप के रूप में लेकर लिफ्ट ऊपर जाने लगी।

लिफ्ट चौथे माले पर आकर रुकी। आकाश व साथियों ने बाहर निकलकर लिफ्ट का दरवाज़ा बन्द किया ही था कि ख़ाली लिफ्ट ग्राउंड-फ्लोर की ओर नीचे उतरने लगी।

आकाश व साथियों ने चौथे माले के सभी फ्लैट्स के बन्द दरवाजों पर नज़र फेरी। सभी दरवाज़ों पर नेम-प्लेटें लगी थीं, जिनके बीच दिव्यांग पटेल की नेम-प्लेट फ़ौरन झलक आई।

आकाश ने मिस पंड्या की ओर प्रश्नवाचक दृष्टि उठाई। आँखों-आँखों में वह पूछ रहा था, 'सूझा कुछ? कैसे खुलवाएँ दिव्यांग पटेल का दरवाज़ा? तपाक से?'

मिस पंड्या ने बहुत धीमी आवाज़ में कहा, "सर! शायद आपको याद न हो...किन्तु एक बार आपने मुझे...गुरु-मन्त्र दिया था..."

"मिस पंड्या! यह गपशप का मौक़ा नहीं है..."

"मैं भी गपशप नहीं कर रही, सर! लेकिन आपका दिया वह गुरु-मन्त्र अभी याद आ रहा है। आपने कहा था, 'इन्कम-टैक्स ऑफिसर निहत्था चलता तो है, लेकिन निहत्था होता नहीं है, क्योंकि वह सीधी-सपाट दीवार से भी सहायता लेना जानता है!' "

"आप कहना क्या चाहती हैं?"

"जब सीधी-सपाट दीवार भी सहायता दे सकती है, तब...दूध की बोतलें क्यों नहीं?" और मिस पंड्या ने चौथे माले के फ़र्श की ओर इशारा किया। आकाश ने ग़ौर किया, जितने भी फ्लैट इस माले पर हैं, जिनमें दिव्यांग पटेल का भी फ्लैट शामिल है, सबके बन्द दरवाज़ों के सामने, फ़र्श पर, दूध की दो-दो, तीन-तीन बोतलें रखी हुई हैं। फ्लैटों के मालिक जब जागेंगे, अथवा, जब चाहेंगे, तब दरवाज़ा खोलकर इन बोतलों को उठा लेंगे।

इन बोतलों को कोई गोरखानुमा व्यक्ति, मासिक अनुबन्ध के अनुसार, यहाँ रखकर चला गया है। दिव्यांग का दरवाज़ा तपाक से खुलवाने में ये बोतलें किस प्रकार सहायक हो सकती हैं? आकाश से यह पहेली सहसा बूझी न गई। इससे पहले कि वह मिस पंड्या से कुछ पूछ पाता, मिस पंड्या ने अपना नाजुक हाथ उठाकर दिव्यांग पटेल की कॉल-बेल दबा दी थी।

फ्लैट की गहराई में, कॉल-बेल की जो टंकार हुई, उसका स्पष्ट आभास, फ्लैट के बाहर खड़े इन लोगों के कानों तक आया। टंकार बुझी-न-बुझी कि भीतर से किसी नारी ने गुजराती भाषा में पूछा, "कोण?"

मिस पंड्या ने ऊँची आवाज़ में जवाब दिया, "अरे, बहन जी! आपकी तो सारी बोतलें टूट गईं!"

आकाश लोहा मान गया मिस पंड्या की आशु-बुद्धि का। अब आगे जो होने जा रहा था, सारा सिलसिला आकाश की कल्पना में स्पष्ट हो गया।

भीतर की गुजरातन को समझ में न आया कि बाहर रखी दूध की बोतलें, वह भी सारी-की-सारी बोतलें, एकाएक कैसे टूट सकती हैं? बड़े ही आश्चर्य के साथ गुजरातन ने फ्लैट की गहराई में से पूछा, "शूँ?"

मिस पंड्या ने दोहरा दिया, "सारा दूध बह गया, बहन जी!"

और दिव्यांग पटेल के फ्लैट का दरवाज़ा खटाक् से खुल गया!

सामने एक दमदार युवती, नाइट-गाउन पहने, खड़ी थी। दरवाज़ा खोलते वक़्त उसकी नज़र फ़र्श की ओर थी। यह नज़र दूध की टूटी बोतलों की तलाश कर रही थी। सभी बोतलों को साबुत पाकर युवती को आश्चर्य हुआ। किसने की थी शैतानी उसके साथ? उसने नज़र उठाई।

तत्काल नज़र आई मिस पंड्या! फिर नज़र आया पास ही खड़ा आकाश! अगले ही क्षण, आयकर के वे तमाम कर्मचारी नज़र आ गए, जो आकाश के आसपास खड़े थे। ऐसे नज़ारे के लिए युवती क़तई तैयार नहीं थी। उसकी आँखें फैली रह गईं, साथ में मुँह भी फैल गया। भारी आश्चर्य और आशंका से उसने अपनी एक हथेली से मुँह ढक लिया।

मिस पंड्या ने मुसकराकर कहा, "सॉरी, मैडम! बोतल तो एक भी नहीं टूटी है!"

और आकाश ने चमकती आँखों के साथ पूछा, "क्या हम अन्दर आ सकते हैं, मिसेज दिव्यांग पटेल?"

वह युवती दिव्यांग पटेल की बीवी ही थी, ऐसा कोई सुबूत नहीं था आकाश के पास। उसने केवल वक्रोक्ति के ही लिए उस युवती को मिसेज दिव्यांग पटेल कहकर पुकारा था। युवती ने जब इस सम्बोधन पर कोई आपत्ति नहीं की, तब आकाश समझ गया, अन्दाज़ा सही निकला था उसका। आश्चर्य से खुले मुँह को अपनी हथेली से ढक रही उस युवती ने सामने खड़े सभी व्यक्तियों से सामूहिक प्रश्न पूछा, "कोण छो? कोण छो तमे?"

सभी की ओर से आकाश ने जवाब दिया, "हम...मिस्टर दिव्यांग पटेल के दोस्त हैं!"

तभी लिफ्ट ऊँची उठकर चौथे माले पर आई और रुकी। दरवाज़ा खुला और आकाश के शेष सभी साथी बाहर निकल, आकाश को घेरते हुए से खड़े हो गए। युवती की फैली आँखें, इन आगन्तुकों को देख और अधिक फैल गईं। आकाश ने जो जवाब दिया था, उससे युवती की आशंका और तीव्र हो चुकी थी। युवती ने थरथराते स्वर में पूछा, "दिव्यांग ना दोस्तार...छो...तमू बद्धा? ना! ना!"

आकाश ने अपनी मुसकान बुझा ली, जैसे किसी धूम्रपानी ने अपने जलते सिगरेट को अचानक मसलकर बुझा दिया हो। आकाश ने कहा, "हम इन्कम-टैक्स ऑफिसर्स हैं और सर्च-वारंट लेकर आए हैं।"

और आकाश ने सर्च-वारंट की फाइल युवती के सामने प्रस्तुत करनी चाही। युवती ने फाइल की ओर देखा तक नहीं। उसके चेहरे पर अनबूझे रंग आ रहे थे और जा रहे थे।

मिस पंड्या ने आदेशात्मक शैली में कहा, "बोतलें उठा लीजिए और हमें अन्दर आने दीजिए।"

स्थिर खड़ी युवती अचानक सक्रिय हो गई। दूध की बोतलें उठाना उसे याद भी नहीं था। उसने तपाक से, वापस अपने फ्लैट के अन्दर समा जाने की कोशिश की। निश्चित था कि भीतर जाकर वह धड़ाम से दरवाज़ा बन्द करना चाहती थी। बेहद बौखलाकर वह दोहरा रही थी, "नई...नई..."

आकाश ने एक सेकंड की भी देर न करके, दरवाज़े की चौखट पर अपना जूता अड़ा दिया। अगले ही सेकंड युवती ने ज़ोर से दरवाज़ा बन्द किया। आकाश के जूते पर दरवाज़ा खटाक् से बज उठा। आकाश और मिस पंड्या दरवाजे को खोल देने के लिए धकेलने लगे। युवती दरवाज़ा बन्द कर देने के लिए धकेलने लगी। युवती का ज़ोर ज़्यादा साबित होता, इसका सवाल ही कहाँ था! आकाश और मिस पंड्या का साथ देने के लिए और भी तो कई लोग थे! दोनों तरफ की ज़ोर-आजमाइश के

बीच, दरवाज़ा धीरे-धीरे खुलना शुरू हुआ। ज्यों-ज्यों दरवाज़ा खुल रहा था, युवती की चीख़-पुकार बढ़ती जा रही थी, ''दिव्यांग! दिव्यांग! जल्दी आव, दिव्यांग! जो तो! कोण छे!''

फ्लैट की गहराई से एक पुरुष स्वर उभरा, ''सूवा दे ने, शिल्पा!''

आकाश मन-ही-मन बोला, 'तो...इन महाशया का नाम शिल्पा है...'

इसके साथ ही आकाश एवं साथियों ने ऐसा ज़ोर लगाया कि दरवाज़ा पूरा-का-पूरा खुल गया!

शिल्पा चीख़ती हुई भीतर की तरफ़ भागी, ''दिव्यांग! डाकू! डाकू! बचाव!''

स्वयं के लिए 'डाकू' शब्द सुन आकाश को गुस्सा भी आ रहा था, हँसी भी आ रही थी। संयत रहते हुए भी आकाश चिल्ला उठा, ''प्लीज़, मैडम तमाशा न करिए। हम डाकू नहीं हैं।''

दिव्यांग भी आश्चर्यचकित होकर, फ्लैट की गहराई से बोल रहा था, ''डाकू! शूँ कहे छे! डाकू होय कईं...''

इसके साथ ही दिव्यांग ने ड्राइंग-रूम में प्रवेश भी किया। शिल्पा तो दिव्यांग से लिपट ही पड़ी। दिव्यांग को समझ में न आया, झेंपे या न झेंपे। उधर से दिव्यांग ड्राइंग-रूम में आ रहा था और इधर से, दरवाज़ा ज़बर्दस्ती खुलवा चुके आकाश एवं साथियों का प्रवेश हो रहा था। दिव्यांग का रंग उड़ गया। उसने शिल्पा के दोनों हाथों को अपने दोनों हाथों से पकड़ लिया, ताकि शिल्पा की गिरफ्त से अपने आपको छुड़ा सके।

''दिव्यांग! दिव्यांग! आ बद्धा...कोण छे? कोण छे?'' शिल्पा की आवाज़ थरथरा रही थी। आकाश ने मन-ही-मन कहा, 'कुछ...ज़रूरत से ज़्यादा ही ड्रामेबाज़ है यह औरत...'

आयकर विभाग का एक-एक कर्मचारी, अब तक, फ्लैट के अन्दर प्रवेश कर चुका था। मिस पंड्या ने आँखों-आँखों में जाँच लिया, बाहर कोई नहीं रह गया था। मिस पंड्या ने दूध की चारों बोतलों को, जो अभी तक दरवाज़े से बाहर, फ़र्श पर रखी थीं, साधिकार उठा लिया। बोतलें उठाने के लिए मिस पंड्या का आधा शरीर फ्लैट में से बाहर आया था। यह आधा शरीर वापस फ्लैट में चला गया और साथ में दूध की चारों बोतलें भी अन्दर समा गईं। भीतर से मिस पंड्या ने दरवाज़े को हौले से धक्का दिया। खट् की आवाज़ के साथ लैच भीतर से बन्द हो गया।

उधर, सिक्योरिटी-गार्ड के बूथ में, जनक ने विज़िटर्स-रजिस्टर में आकाश एवं पार्टी का नाम दर्ज़ कर दिया था। आने का उद्देश्य? यहाँ जनक ने लिखा, 'सरकारी ड्यूटी'। गार्ड बुदबुदा रहा था, ''आज की पहली एंट्री आप ही की रही, साहब!''

जनक ने रजिस्टर बन्द कर, लौटाते हुए कहा, ''हम लोग कौन हैं, मैं तुम्हें समझा चुका हूँ...अब तुम मुझे वहाँ पहुँचा दो, जहाँ से मिस्टर दिव्यांग पटेल का पिछवाड़ा दिखाई दे।''

गार्ड उलझन में पड़ा, ''साहब! क्यों नौकरी छुड़वाते हैं!''

जनक बोला, ''यानी, अपने परिचय में मैंने जो समझाया है, तुम ठीक से समझे नहीं हो।''

''समझ में तो, साहब, सब आ गया है, लेकिन...''

''देखो, मैं एक सरकारी कर्मचारी हूँ और अपनी ड्यूटी पर हूँ। अगर तुम मेरी ड्यूटी में आड़े आओगे, तो...''

जनक को वाक्य पूरा करने की ज़रूरत न रही। उससे पहले ही गार्ड ने कह दिया, ''चलिए, सरकार! क्या करें...''

और गार्ड, जनक को साथ ले, बिल्डिंग के पिछवाड़े की तरफ़ चल पड़ा। पिछवाड़े में आकर उसने ऊपर इशारा किया, ''देखिए, हुजूर! वह जो...काँच-लगी खिड़की है न चौथे माले पर...वहाँ मिस्टर पटेल का बाथ-रूम है...''

''हँ...''

गार्ड ने जारी रखा, ''उधर की दोनों बाल्कनियाँ और...आगे की...वह सलाखों वाली खिड़की भी...''

''दिव्यांग पटेल की है!'' जनक ने वाक्य पूरा किया।

''जी, साहब!''

''ओके! थैंक्स! अब तुम जा सकते हो!''

जाने से पहले गार्ड ने जनक को सलाम ठोंका। जनक ने सख़्ती से कहा, ''किसी को बताने की ज़रूरत नहीं कि इधर मैं खड़ा हूँ।''

''चुप रहेंगे, साहब!'' गार्ड ने दुबारा सलाम ठोंका, फिर चला गया।

जनक ने नज़र में पैनापन भरकर उसे ऊपर उठाया—चौथे माले की तरफ़। उसे आकाश के शब्द याद आ रहे थे, 'और फिर...दक्षिण में दक्षिणा...'

दक्षिण यानी पिछवाड़ा...दक्षिणा यानी कुछ मिलने की आशा...आकाश की सांकेतिक भाषा, जो केवल उसके साथ काम करने वाले ही समझ सकते थे...जनक के होंठों पर मुसकान उभर आई। आयकर के छापों के दौरान, पिछवाड़ों में, अकसर 'दक्षिणा' मिल जाया करती है....क्या इस बार भी...'

जैसे दो विरोधी फ़ौजें आमने-सामने खड़ी हों, वैसे ही वे आमने-सामने खड़े थे। एक तरफ़ था आकाश, अपने साथियों समेत। दूसरी तरफ़ था दिव्यांग, अपनी जीवन-संगिनी समेत!

दिव्यांग पटेल सख़्त नाराज़ था। अपने नाइट-गाउन की नॉट वह दो बार खोलकर दो बार कसकर लगा चुका था। शिल्पा, उसकी बीवी, अब डरी हुई नहीं थी। ठीक विपरीत, अब वह आवेश से तमतमा रही थी।

एक बच्ची पाँचेक वर्ष की और एक बच्चा यही कोई छह वर्ष का, शिल्पा के पैरों से, सहमे-सहमे लिपट रहे थे।

सोफे पर एक बूढ़ा व्यक्ति बिलकुल ख़ामोश और तटस्थ बैठा था—दिव्यांग का पिता। आकाश जानता था, बूढ़ा पिता ख़ामोश ज़रूर था, किन्तु तटस्थ दिखने के बावजूद तटस्थ नहीं। बूढ़े की आँखें, गोल फ्रेम के चश्मे के पीछे से, अत्यधिक सचेत होकर, इधर-उधर देखे जा रही थीं...

बीस-बीस वर्ष के दो व्यक्ति और थे, जो कोने में सिमटकर खड़े थे—जवान नौकर, जवान नौकरानी।

दिव्यांग पटेल, अचानक दीवानों की तरह चिल्लाने लगा, "मैं सबको गिरफ्तार करवा दूँगा...गिरफ्तार करवा दूँगा..."

फ्लैट की एक-एक चीज़ से दिव्यांग की अमीरी झलक रही थी। आकाश अमीरी के विरुद्ध नहीं था। वह हमेशा कहा करता, 'काश! भारत का एक-एक व्यक्ति अमीर होता—इतना अमीर कि इस देश की गणना विश्व के सबसे अमीर देशों में की जा सकती।' किन्तु आकाश काली अमीरी के सख़्त ख़िलाफ़ था। काली अमीरी...काले धन से आई हुई अमीरी...अमीर ही अगर सरकार को कर अदा नहीं करेंगे, तो सरकार चलेगी कैसे? लेकिन सबसे अधिक करों की चोरी अमीर ही तो करते हैं! करों की चोरी करने वालों को आकाश हमेशा यह समझाने की चेष्टा करता कि यदि आप सारे कर, नियमानुसार, अदा करते जाएँगे, तो भी आपके पास इतना बच रहने वाला है कि आपकी पीढ़ियाँ भी खा सकें। इससे अधिक और क्या चाहिए आपको? इसीलिए, करों की चोरी करना आपके लिए निरर्थक है, नितान्त निरर्थक...

दिव्यांग पटेल की अमीरी में कुदाल चलाने नहीं आया था आकाश। वह तो इसलिए आया था कि दिव्यांग की काली अमीरी को सफ़ेद अमीरी में बदल दे। आयकर के छापे में जो भी काला धन पकड़ा जाता है, करों की अदायगी के बाद क्या वही काला धन सफ़ेद धन में नहीं बदल जाता? कि जिसे छिपाने की ज़रूरत ही न हो? कि जिसे मनचाहे ढंग से, खुल्लमखुल्ला ख़र्च किया जा सके?

दिव्यांग पर से आकाश की नज़र हट नहीं रही थी...और दिव्यांग था कि चिल्लाए जा रहा था, "यह...यह भी कोई वक़्त है, छापा मारने का? इतनी सुबह? हद होती है...बदतमीज़ी की!"

आकाश ने कठोरता से कहा, ''यह बदतमीज़ी नहीं, मिस्टर दिव्यांग पटेल! यह ड्यूटी है। आयकर का क़ानून है कि सूरज निकलने के बाद हम कभी भी छापा मार सकते हैं—और...सूरज निकल चुका है!''

इसके साथ ही आकाश पलटकर अपने साथियों से मुख़ातिब हो गया और ललकारकर बोला, ''फैल जाओ पूरे फ्लैट में और एक-एक कोने को नज़र में ले लो!''

जिस तरह नृत्य का एक अनुशासन होता है, उसी तरह आकयर के छापों का भी गहरा अनुशासन होता है। आकाश के साथी इस अनुशासन के सधे हुए ज्ञाता थे। आकाश का आदेश मिलते ही तमाम अधिकारी एवं सहयोगी, फ्लैट में जगह-जगह ऐसी पोज़ीशन लेकर खड़े हो गए कि अब किसी भी कोने में कोई भी चीज़ छिपाने की चेष्टा उनकी नज़रों से बचकर नहीं हो सकती थी। सभी कर्मचारी ऐसी तेज़ी से हर दिशा में छितरा गए, जैसे छर्रोंवाली गोली चल गई हो और छर्रे हर दिशा में उड़े जा रहे हों। आयकर कर्मचारियों की उस स्फूर्ति को दिव्यांग ठगा-सा देखता रह गया। फ्लैट के अन्दर जितने भी दरवाज़े थे, सभी में किसी-न-किसी ने प्रवेश कर लिया।

और दिव्यांग, एक बार फिर, अपनी उस बात को चिल्ला-चिल्लाकर दोहराने लगा, ''गिरफ्तार करवा दूँगा। सबको जेल में धकेल दूँगा। आप मुझे समझते क्या हैं? किसी को नहीं छोड़ूँगा...''

''सॉरी, मिस्टर पटेल!'' आकाश ने कहा, ''ऐसा नहीं हो सकेगा। यहाँ हम एक क़दम भी ग़ैर-क़ानूनी नहीं उठाएँगे और...यहाँ हम सिर्फ़ सरकारी ड्यूटी निभा रहे हैं।''

दिव्यांग की मुट्ठियाँ कस गईं, ''ले...लेकिन...आप धोखा देकर अन्दर घुसे हैं। यह कोई आपके बाप का घर नहीं है!''

''अन्दर घुसने का हमारा तरीक़ा क्या हो, इसका फ़ैसला आप करेंगे या हम? हमें क़ानूनन अधिकार है। अन्दर घुसने के लिए हम, जैसा हमें योग्य लगे, वैसा कर सकते हैं।''

दिव्यांग इसके उत्तर में, सहसा कुछ न बोल सका। आकाश ने मिस पंड्या की ओर देखा, ''ऐसा है, मिस पंड्या...शिल्पा जी तो सामने खड़ी हैं, मगर इस फ्लैट में और भी महिलाएँ हो सकती हैं। आप...ख़ासकर...अन्दरूनी हिस्सों में देखें, फ्लैट में महिलाएँ कोई 'हरकत' न कर रही हों...''

मिस पंड्या ने तुरन्त शयन-कक्ष की तरफ़ जाना चाहा। शिल्पा भी तुरन्त रास्ता रोककर खड़ी हो गई। बोली, ''इधर कुछ नहीं है।''

मिस पंड्या एक बन्द दरवाज़े को घूर रही थीं, ''यह बन्द क्यों है?''

''अन्दर मेरा देवर है। सो रहा है। सोने दीजिए।''

''क्यों?''

"उसकी नई-नई शादी हुई है। दोनों सोते रहते हैं। देर तक..." शिल्पा का वाक्य पूरा होते ही मिस पंड्या ने फ़ैसला सुना देने की तरह कहा, "इस वक़्त दोनों जाग चुके हैं! और दोनों समझ भी चुके हैं, बाहर क्या हो रहा है। सवाल है, अन्दर क्या हो रहा है। हटिए सामने से!" और मिस पंड्या ने शिल्पा को बाक़ायदा धकियाकर सामने से हटा दिया। बन्द दरवाज़े तक पहुँचने में उन्हें तीन सेकंड भी मुश्किल से लगे होंगे।

चौथा सेकंड बीतते-बीतते मिस पंड्या ने आकाश की ओर चेहरा घुमाकर ज़ोर से कहा, "सर! काग़ज़! अन्दर काग़ज़ जल रहा है!"

मिस पंड्या ने धड़ाधड़ दरवाज़ा पीटना शुरू किया, "मत जलाइए! कुछ मत जलाइए!"

आकाश और साथी झपटकर बन्द दरवाज़े तक पहुँचे। मिस पंड्या ज़रा किनारे हट गईं, ताकि पुरुषों की शक्तिशाली हथेलियाँ दरवाज़े को ज़्यादा ज़ोर से पीट सकें। आकाश दरवाज़ा ठोक-ठोककर चिल्लाने लगा, "यह क्राइम है! जुर्म है! मत जलाइए!"

आकाश के साथियों ने ललकारा, "खोलिए दरवाज़ा! वरना तोड़ देंगे!"

और साथियों ने बन्द दरवाज़े को ऐसे ज़ोर-ज़ोर से कन्धों की टक्करें मारीं कि दरवाज़ा किसी भी क्षण चरमराना शुरू कर सकता था। दिव्यांग पुकारता हुआ सामने आया, ताकि द्वार-रक्षा कर सके, "शैलेश! शैलेश! दरवाज़ा खोलो!"

बड़े भाई की सलाह मान, शैलेश दरवाज़ा खोल देगा, इस आशा में कन्धों की टक्करें मारना रोक दिया गया, किन्तु दरवाज़ा खुलने का नाम नहीं ले रहा था। बन्द दरवाज़े के उस पार काग़ज़ के जलाए जाने की गन्ध अब आकाश सहित, सभी की नाक तक पहुँच रही थी। पल-पल क़ीमती था। आग की लपटों को महत्त्वपूर्ण काग़ज़ात भस्म करते देर ही कितनी लगती!

जबकि बन्द दरवाज़े के उस पार, शैलेश और उसकी बीवी मनीषा को कुछ और ही लग रहा था। भारी तनाव में खड़े वे दोनों आश्चर्य कर रहे थे कि काग़ज़ात को भस्म होने में भी कितना ज़्यादा वक़्त लगता है!

दिव्यांग ने फिर से ऊँचे स्वर में पुकारा, "शैलेश! जलाना नहीं कुछ! समझे? जलाना नहीं कुछ!"

दिव्यांग के एक ही शब्द 'समझे' से आकाश समझ गया कि ज़रूर सांकेतिक ढंग से शैलेश को कोई सलाह दे दी गई है। दिव्यांग 'नहीं जलाने' के लिए कह रहा है...तो क्या शैलेश के पास कोई और भी उपाय है, जिससे वह...काग़ज़ात को जलाए तो नहीं, लेकिन...काग़ज़ात को आयकर अधिकारियों की नज़रों के सामने से...नज़रों के ऐन सामने से...ग़ायब...नहीं! नहीं! आकाश ने बौखलाकर बन्द दरवाज़े पर कन्धे की टक्कर मारी, "खोलिए! खोलिए दरवाज़ा! मैं कहता हूँ..."

बन्द दरवाज़े के उस ओर, कमरे के अटैच्ड बाथ-रूम में, दयनीय हड़बड़ी के साथ घुसे हुए थे शैलेश और मनीषा। संडास के पॉट में दो मोटी फाइलें धँसी जल रही थीं। शैलेश उन्हें जल्दी-से-जल्दी भस्म करने का भगीरथ प्रयास कर रहा था। शैलेश-मनीषा के उस निजी कमरे में मिट्टी-तेल तो था नहीं, अन्यथा फाइलें कैसी फटाफट जल जातीं! काग़ज़ का इक्का-दुक्का टुकड़ा तो झटपट जल जाता है, किन्तु जब मोटी फाइल जलानी हो...कितना वक़्त लगता है! शैलेश-मनीषा को एक-एक क्षण का सौवाँ हिस्सा भी भारी पड़ रहा था। कैसा ख़राब धुआँ! तीखी बास! छी!

धुआँ बाहर निकालने के लिए मनीषा ने बाथ-रूम में लगा एग्ज़ास्ट-फैन चला दिया, मगर यहाँ भी समस्या! काग़ज़ के जल चुके टुकड़े कालिख की पँखुड़ियों की तरह पूरे बाथ-रूम में उड़ने लगे। धुआँ ज़रूर बाहर जा रहा था, मगर ये कालिख की पँखुड़ियाँ! शैलेश एग्ज़ास्ट-फैन बन्द करने लगा, किन्तु रुक गया। सख़्त बौखलाहट और कशमकश ने घेर लिया था शैलेश को। उसने बिलखती नज़रों से देखा अपनी नई-निकोर बीवी की ओर। बेचारी मनीषा! विवाह के बाद की समस्याओं के लिए उसे भाँति-भाँति के लोगों ने भाँति-भाँति की सलाहें दी थीं, किन्तु किसी ने भी नहीं सुझाया था कि मस्त मोटी फाइलों को अगर अचानक, फटाफट जलाना पड़ जाए, तो क्या करना चाहिए और क्या नहीं! पति की बिलखती नज़रों के जवाब में मनीषा की भी नज़रें बिलखने लगीं।

बाहर से दरवाज़ा जो पीटा जा रहा था; 'खोलो! खोलो!' की ललकार के चाबुक जो चल रहे थे, उसका तनाव अलग से!

शैलेश ने पॉट के पास उकड़ूँ बैठकर जलती फाइलों को इधर-उधर किया, ताकि जो न जल रहा हो, वह जलने लगे और जो जल रहा हो, उसके जलने की स्पीड बढ़ जाए। दाँत पीसने की तरह स्वर चबाकर शैलेश बोला, "अगर ये फाइलें पकड़ी गईं, मुसीबत हो जाएगी।"

मनीषा के हाथ में और भी कई फाइलें थीं। कुछ मोटी, कुछ पतली। डायरियाँ थीं, पोथे भी थे। सभी को जलाना ज़रूरी था। कुछ और भी काग़ज़ात थे, जो कमरे के कोने में पड़े थे। मनीषा ने उनकी ओर इशारा किया, "वह सब भी तो हैं..."

और शैलेश के छक्के छूटने लगे, "अरे, तो क्या सभी कुछ जला दें? याद भी नहीं रहेगा, क्या-क्या जल गया...हे, भगवान!"

कमरे के बाहर से दिव्यांग भी लगातार सलाह दे रहा था, "जलाना नहीं कुछ! दरवाज़ा खोल! शैलेश! अरे, ये दरवाज़ा पीट-पीटकर तोड़ डालेंगे!"

और आकाश दरवाज़ा ठोक-ठोककर चीख़ रहा था, "खोलो! खोलो!"

शैलेश के दिमाग़ में झप्प से बत्ती जल गई। दिव्यांग द्वारा जो एक से अधिक बार कहा गया था, 'जलाना नहीं कुछ...', उसका वास्तविक अर्थ! आह! अवश्य बड़े भइया यह कह रहे हैं, 'कुछ भी करो, मगर जलाओ मत!'

दो फाइलें तो जलाने के लिए पॉट में डाली जा चुकीं। बाक़ी काग़ज़ात को नहीं जलाना है, लेकिन अगर नहीं जलाना है, तो क्या करना है? शैलेश बौखला-बौखला कर देख रहा था अपनी बीवी की ओर।

शयन-कक्ष का बन्द दरवाज़ा बाहर से लगातार भड़भड़ाया जा रहा था। दनादन आकाश की ललकारें सुनाई पड़ रही थीं। शोरगुल के आर-पार, एक बार फिर, दिव्यांग के शब्द शैलेश के कानों तक पहुँचे, "शैलेश! जला तो नहीं रहे? कुछ न जलाना। समझे?"

अन्तिम शब्द 'समझे' के जवाब में शैलेश चिल्लाया, "समझ गया, भाई साहब! कुछ नहीं जला रहा। जलाना कैसा? मैं तो बाथ-रूम कर रहा हूँ।"

सुनकर उतने तनाव में भी शैलेश की बीवी, मनीषा, मन्द-मन्द मुसकरा पड़ी, भले ही पल-दो-पल के लिए। शैलेश उसके कानों के पास अपने होंठ ले आता हुआ बोला, "वाक़ई समझ गया। जलाते नहीं हैं कुछ भी। फेंक देते हैं..."

मनीषा ने फटाफट सहमत हो जाते हुए कहा, "ठीक है! फेंक देते हैं! उठा लेंगे, बाद में!"

फाइलें, पोथे, डायरियाँ आदि, जो मनीषा के हाथों में थमी हुई थीं, अगर पिछवाड़े में फेंक दी जाएँ...जिस पल यह विचार आया, उसी पल मनीषा लपक पड़ी शयन-कक्ष की उस खिड़की की ओर, जो पिछवाड़े में खुलती थी। गिनती के सेकंड्स में सब निबट गया। सब काग़ज़ात खिड़की से बाहर फेंककर मनीषा हाथ झाड़ रही थी। यह देख शैलेश जोश में आ गया। कोने में जो ढेर-से काग़ज़ात और भी रखे थे, उन्हें शैलेश ने ऐसे उठा लिया, जैसे किसी लाड़ले बच्चे को गोद में उठा रहा हो। खिड़की के पास पहुँच उसने सब काग़ज़ात झोंक दिए पिछवाड़े में!

बाहर से दिव्यांग चिल्ला रहा था, "अरे, दरवाज़ा खोल, भाई!"

काग़ज़ात पिछवाड़े में फेंकते-फेंकते शैलेश जवाब दे रहा था, "एक मिनट, भाई साहब! मनीषा कपड़े बदल रही है!"

ये शब्द मनीषा को सचमुच सावधान कर गए। जल्दी-जल्दी उसने नाइटी के ऊपर नाइट-गाउन पहनना शुरू किया। शैलेश ने आँखों-आँखों में सब चेक कर लिया, 'सब सही-सलामत है...'—और शैलेश बढ़ गया, बन्द दरवाज़े की सिटकनी उतारने के लिए।

मनीषा दौड़कर बाथ-रूम में गई, ताकि फ्लश की जंजीर खींच सके। कितनी बड़ी भूल हुई जा रही थी। दोनों मोटी फाइलें, बाथरूम के पॉट में जलकर ख़ाक हो तो चुकी थीं, लेकिन सारी ख़ाक पॉट में ही धरी थीं। आयकर अधिकारी अन्दर आते

ही उस ख़ाक को लेकर भारी हंगामा करते...लेकिन, आह! कितने सही मौक़े पर जंजीर खींचना याद आ गया। भरभराकर फ्लश का पानी चलने लगा था पॉट में! सारी ख़ाक यह जा, वह जा!

परम सन्तोष के साथ मनीषा बाथ-रूम से बाहर निकल आई। बाथ-रूम का दरवाज़ा उसने बाहर से खींचकर बन्द कर दिया।

और शैलेश ने शयन-कक्ष के बन्द दरवाज़े की सिटकनी उतार दी। दरवाज़ा खुला-न-खुला कि आयकर के अनेक कर्मचारी अन्दर की तरफ़ ऐसे लपक पड़े, जैसे मधुछत्ते में पत्थर लग जाने से मधुमक्खियाँ उड़ चली हों...

उधर, पिछवाड़े में जो ड्रामा हुआ था, उसका अनुमान भी शैलेश-मनीषा को कैसे लग सकता था! जिस खिड़की से उन्होंने दो खेपों में काग़ज़ात पिछवाड़े में फेंके थे, उस खिड़की में सलाखें लगी हुई थीं। सलाखों के कारण वे बाहर झाँककर देख नहीं सकते थे कि काग़ज़ात ऐन कहाँ पर गिरे। हाँ, सलाखों के बीच से पार करके काग़ज़ात को बाहर फेंकने में उन्हें कोई परेशानी नहीं हुई थी। काश, वे देख पाते, काग़ज़ात ऐन कहाँ गिरे थे।

आकाश के आदेश का आँख मूँदकर पालन कर रहा जनक बोर हो रहा था। कहाँ तो वह किसी 'हाई एक्शन' की आशा में यहाँ आया था और कहाँ उसे सूने-अकेले पिछवाड़े में खड़ा कर दिया गया था। ग़नीमत थी, पिछवाड़ा साफ़-सुथरा था, अन्यथा मक्खी-मच्छरों की संगत में क्या गत बनती! चौथे माले की खिड़कियों और बाल्कनियों की ओर आख़िर कब तक निरन्तर ताकता रहता जनक? भारी बोरियत का सामना करता हुआ, उस वक़्त, जनक पिछवाड़े की दीवार से टिककर खड़ा था—कि ईश्वर ने दया कर दी। पहले तो जनक को यही लगा, किसी ने ज़ोर से थप्पड़ मारा है उसे—सिर के ठीक ऊपर! अगले ही पल वह समझ गया, दक्षिण में लगातार मौजूद रहने की दक्षिणा मिल गई है! सिर पर किसी का थप्पड़ नहीं गिरा था, बल्कि काग़ज़ात गिरे थे! खोपड़ी पर सीधी और भारी चोट देने के बाद काग़ज़ात जनक के चारों तरफ़ बिखर गए। आश्चर्य और प्रसन्नता के तीव्र आवेग के साथ जनक ने उन्हें उठाना शुरू किया और, साथ-साथ, ऊपर, चौथे माले की ओर नज़र भी उठाई।

देखता क्या है कि काग़ज़ात का एक और ढेर भाँय-भाँय करता नीचे गिर रहा है! 'बचो!' जनक मन-ही-मन चिल्लाया और बन्दर-कुदान सी लगाकर एक तरफ़ हट गया। अगले ही क्षण अनेक फाइलें, पोथे, बहियाँ आदि ज़मीन पर छितरा चुकी थीं। काग़ज़ात की कहीं तीसरी-चौथी खेप तो नहीं गिर रही आसमान से? इस आशंका के साथ जनक बार-बार ऊपर देखता था, मुसकाता जाता था, बिखरे तमाम काग़ज़ात को बिखरे मोतियों की तरह उठा-उठाकर समेटता जाता था...

उधर, चौथे माले पर...

आयकर कर्मचारियों के साथ दिव्यांग ने भी, शैलेश के शयन-कक्ष में, तूफ़ान की तरह प्रवेश किया था। शैलेश से नज़र मिलने के साथ दिव्यांग ने शिकायत की, "इतनी देर? दरवाज़ा खोलने में?"

शैलेश ने तीव्र असहमति के नाटक के साथ कहा, "अरे, तो क्या, भाई साहब! मनीषा कपड़े भी न बदले? मैं बाथ-रूम भी न करूँ?"

तब तक आकाश ने अटैच्ड बाथ-रूम का दरवाज़ा खोल लिया था। एग्ज़ास्ट-फैन घूँऊँ-घूँऊँ करता चल रहा था, भीतर की हवा बाहर फेंकता हुआ, लेकिन पूरे बाथ-रूम में काग़ज़ जलने की जो कसैली बास भरी हुई थी, वह तेज़-से-तेज़ जुकाम से पीड़ित व्यक्ति द्वारा भी पहचानी जा सकती थी। फ्लश अभी-अभी चलाया गया है, इस बात का ऐलान करती, फ्लश की टंकी ख़ाली हो चुकी थी और टंकी के अन्दर का नल चालू होकर छरछरा रहा था। आकाश ने संडास के पॉट की ओर नज़र डाली। जली हुई फाइलों की सारी ख़ाक तो फ्लश हो गई थी, किन्तु टीन की बनी फाइलों की दोनों क्लिपें कहाँ से ख़ाक होतीं! आग ने उन क्लिपों को झुलसाकर ख़राब कर दिया था, लेकिन वे आड़ी-टेढ़ी मुड़कर भी, फ्लश के तेज़ पानी के थपेड़े खाकर भी, मौजूद तो पॉट में ही थीं! पॉट के छेद तक ज़रूर वे धक्के खाकर पहुँच गई थीं, लेकिन जैसे मछली खाने वाले अनाड़ी के गले में काँटा फँस जाता है, वैसे ही दोनों फाइलों की क्लिपें पॉट के छेद में फँसकर रह गई थीं। उन पर नज़र पड़ने के साथ आकाश ने, अपनी मुसकान को रोक लेते हुए, कठोर स्वर में पुकारा, "मिस्टर शैलेश पटेल! ज़रा इधर तो आइए!"

"जी, साहब!" कहता हुआ शैलेश, आकाश के नज़दीक, बाथ-रूम के दरवाज़े पर आ खड़ा हुआ। आकाश ने पॉट के छेद में अटकी दोनों क्लिपों की ओर इशारा करते हुए पूछा, "यह आपने बाथ-रूम किया है? क्यों?"

शैलेश का रंग उड़ गया, "जी...ले...लेकिन मैंने..."

शैलेश समझ नहीं पा रहा था, वाक्य कैसे पूरा करे। यह काम आकाश ने किया, "लेकिन आपने जलाया कुछ नहीं है! यही कहना चाहते हैं न आप? न तो कुछ जलाया, न किसी राख को फ्लश किया। पॉट में जो क्लिपें पड़ी हैं, ये तो यूँ ही पड़ी हैं! हवा में जो...काग़ज़ जलने की तीखी गन्ध है, वह भी...बस, यूँ ही है! मतलब यह कि हम, जो आयकर अधिकारी हैं, हमारे पास अक़ल जैसी कोई चीज़ है ही नहीं! यही राय है न आपकी?"

शैलेश की नज़रें झुक गईं। जब पतिदेव ने नज़रें झुका लीं, तब पत्नीदेवी का भी कर्तव्य था कि नज़रें झुका लें। मनीषा ने निस्संकोच इस कर्तव्य का पालन किया। आकाश तैश में आकर आगे बोला, "काग़ज़ात जलाने की आपकी कोशिश का ही मतलब है, काले धन का न जाने क्या-क्या हिसाब-किताब आपने छिपा रखा था यहाँ!

क्या आपको इतना भी नहीं मालूम कि किसी भी प्रकार के सुबूत को नष्ट करना कितना संगीन जुर्म है?"

कौन-सा जुर्म संगीन है, कौन-सा रंगीन, शैलेश सब जानता था। दिव्यांग भी जानता था। दोनों भाई चुप रहे, क्योंकि वे चुप ही रह सकते थे।

इसी दौर में, फ्लैट के बिलकुल बाहर, चौथे माले पर, लिफ्ट आकर रुक रही थी। लिफ्ट का दरवाज़ा, भीतर का व्यक्ति, आसानी से नहीं खोल पा रहा था, उसके दोनों हाथ अन्यत्र व्यस्त जो थे। अन्यत्र व्यस्त होने का अर्थ यह नहीं कि दोनों हाथों से वह अपनी पीठ खुजा रहा था। दरअसल, दोनों हाथों में वह ढेरमढेर काग़ज़ात थामे हुए था। वह था–जनक।

लिफ्ट के दरवाज़े को जनक ने पैर से ठेलकर खोला। बाहर निकलकर जनक ने लिफ्ट के दरवाज़े को वापस बन्द करने के लिए भी अपने पैरों का ही इस्तेमाल किया। मनुष्य एक बुद्धिमान प्राणी है। कितनी आसानी से वह हाथ से करने के काम पैरों से कर लेता है!

प्रसन्न था जनक। इसीलिए तो वह हौले-हौले सीटी बजा रहा था। सीटी बजाने जैसी हरकत वह आकाश की मौजूदगी में नहीं कर सकता। इसीलिए वह तभी तक सीटी बजाने का आनन्द ले सकता था, जब तक आकाश से आमना-सामना नहीं हुआ था। जनक ने जूते की ठोकर मारकर, दिव्यांग के फ्लैट के अन्दर, अपने शुभ आगमन का ऐलान कर दिया। अन्दर से मिस पंड्या ने पूछा, "कौन?" और जनक ने कुछ इस प्रकार अपना नाम बताया, जैसे जनक न आया हो, सिकन्दर-ए-आज़म का आगमन हो गया हो! आगमन चाहे जिसका भी हुआ था, दरवाज़ा झट से खुल गया और काग़ज़ात थामता, अपनी सीटी पर रोक लगाता जनक फ्लैट में प्रवेश कर गया।

पिछवाड़े की खिड़की के उस पार, जो-कुछ भी फेंका था शैलेश-मनीषा ने, सभी-कुछ वापस आ चुका था, चौथे माले पर शोभायमान, दिव्यांग पटेल के फ्लैट में! और रखा हुआ था, ड्राइंग-रूम के सेंटर-टेबल पर। दिव्यांग और शिल्पा, शैलेश और मनीषा, नौकर और नौकरानी, बूढ़े पिताश्री, पाँच और छह वर्ष के दिव्यांग के दोनों बच्चे–सभी पर मायूसी छाई हुई थी। ठीक विपरीत, आकाश, जनक, मिस पंड्या एवं आयकर के अन्य कर्मचारियों के चेहरों पर गम्भीर प्रसन्नता थिरक रही थी। इन सभी का रुतबा पहले से अधिक हो चुका था। अभी तो यह रुतबा और भी तेज़ होने वाला था...

आकाश ने शैलेश और दिव्यांग, दोनों को, साथ-साथ घूरते हुए कहा, "काग़ज़ात फेंककर आप लोगों ने कोई बहुत बड़ा तीर नहीं मारा। संयोग का सिर्फ़ एक चमत्कार और सारे काग़ज़ात हमारी गोदी में आ गिरे!"

जनक ने भूल-सुधार किया, "नो, सर! गोदी में नहीं गिरे! सिर पर आकर गिरे!"

और जनक ने अपने सिर को ऐसे सहलाया, जैसे अभी तक वहाँ फाइलों, पोथों वग़ैरह का थप्पड़ लगने की सनसनाहट हो रही हो। जनक के मज़ाक से सभी आयकर कर्मचारी मद्धिम-मद्धिम मुसकरा दिए।

आकाश ने अपनी मुसकान को तिलांजलि दे दी और किसी सिद्धपुरुष जैसी मुद्रा पकड़कर अपना सम्भाषण आगे चला दिया, "इनसान की चालाकी को मिट्टी में मिलते देर ही कितनी? ये जो काग़ज़ात पिछवाड़े में पकड़े हुए हैं, इनके ज़ोर पर हम आपके काले धन के लेन-देन की टोह पूरी गहराई से ले लेंगे...किन्तु, मिस्टर दिव्यांग पटेल! यहाँ हम सिर्फ़ नाज़ुक काग़ज़ात की तलाश में नहीं आए हैं। यहाँ तो हम किसी और ही सनसनीख़ेज़ चीज़ की तलाश में आए हैं..."

दिव्यांग थरथराकर बोला, "और...क्या चाहिए आपको?"

आकाश ने ठंडे दिल से कहा, "इसका जवाब आपको तब मिलेगा, जब उस सनसनीख़ेज़ चीज़ को हम ज़ब्त कर रहे होंगे!"

और दिव्यांग के चेहरे पर क्रोधाग्नि भड़क उठी, "अरे! यह कैसा क़ानून है? कि हम कमाते जाएँ और आप ज़ब्त करते जाएँ? तो क्या हम कमाना ही छोड़ दें?"

आकाश ने अविलम्ब उत्तर दिया, "कमाइए न! कमाने से कौन मना करता है आपको? लेकिन जो कमाएँ, खुलकर, सरेआम कमाएँ। छिप-छिपकर, चोरी-चोरी न कमाएँ। छिपकर कमाएँगे, तो काला धन पैदा करेंगे और अगर काला धन पैदा करेंगे—"

तभी दिव्यांग-शिल्पा की नन्ही बच्ची अकुलाकर बोल पड़ी, "मम्मी! बाथ-रूम आया है।"

शिल्पा जैसे सोते से जागी। दोनों बच्चों को ठेलती हुई शिल्पा भीतर ले जाने लगी। कड़वे ढंग से बुदबुदा रही थी शिल्पा, "हाँ, हाँ, बेटी! चल, तैयार हो! चल, बेटे, तू भी चल। दोनों फटाफट तैयार होओ...और स्कूल जाओ! क्या स्कूल भी नहीं जाओगे इनके चक्कर में?"

शिल्पा और दोनों बच्चे परदे के पीछे समा गए।

अचानक परदा हटा और शिल्पा ने ड्राइंग-रूम में झाँका। आर-पार निकल जाए, ऐसी दृष्टि से उसने नौकरानी को घूरा और तड़ातड़ कहा, "छोरी! तू खड़ी-खड़ी क्या देख रही है? यहाँ क्या वीडियो चल रहा है? चल, उठा बोतलें! अभी तक दूध गरम नहीं किया। फट गया न दूध, फिर देखना! क्या गत बनाती हूँ तेरी!"

नौकरानी सिटपिटाकर शिल्पा की दिशा में खिंची चली गई। शिल्पा फिर से परदे की ओट में समा रही थी। इस बार उसकी बड़बड़ाहट गुजराती भाषा में थी, "आजे तो सूरज निकड़ताँ ज कचरो थई गयो!"

परदे की ओट लेने से पहले नौकरानी ने दूध की बोतलें उठा ली थीं।

शिल्पा, नौकरानी और दोनों बच्चों के सहसा चले जाने से ड्राइंग-रूम की आबादी में कमी आ गई। आबादी घटते ही वहाँ चुपचाप बैठे, दिव्यांग के परम वृद्ध पिता का व्यक्तित्व, विशेष ही झलक उठा।

कुछ पलों के तनावपूर्ण सन्नाटे के बाद आकाश ने दिव्यांग से कहा, "हाँ, तो...मिस्टर पटेल! शुरू करें तलाशी?"

दिव्यांग ने व्यंग्य किया, "मुझसे क्यों पूछते हैं?"

"क्योंकि...दरअसल...यह शुरुआत आप ही को करनी है।"

"मतलब?" दिव्यांग की भौंहों पर बल पड़े।

दोनों बच्चों के मुँह धो रही शिल्पा, भीतर, एक-एक शब्द सुन रही थी।

"मतलब यह, मिस्टर पटेल!" आकाश ने जारी किया, "कि हम तब तक तलाशी शुरू नहीं कर सकते, जब तक पंच मौजूद न हों...और इन पंचों को आप ही बुलाएँगे, हम नहीं! इस कारण जब आप चाहेंगे, तभी तलाशी शुरू होगी, क्योंकि पंच तो आप ही के बुलाने से आएँगे।"

"ओह..." दिव्यांग को वास्तव में तसल्ली हुई। अपनी ही पसन्द के, अपने ही पक्ष के व्यक्ति पंच बने हों, फिर तो...

लेकिन इस 'फिर तो...' के बाद की सम्भावनाओं को दिव्यांग ठीक से न समझ सका। उसने सवाल किया, "कितने व्यक्ति बुलाऊँ पंचों के रूप में?"

"दो व्यक्ति...जो आसपड़ोस के हों, समाज में जिनकी प्रतिष्ठा हो और जो यहाँ की पूरी कार्रवाई के दौरान मौजूद रह सकें, इस प्रकार समय निकाल सकते हों..." आकाश ने जवाब दिया, "पूरी कार्रवाई, कई बार, कुछ घंटों में निबट जाती है और कई बार शाम तक, रात तक, आधी-आधी रात तक भी कार्रवाई चलती रहती है..."

दिव्यांग सोच में पड़ गया। आख़िर उसने दो व्यक्ति, मन-ही-मन तय कर लिये और कहा, "ठीक है, मैं फोन कर देता हूँ।"

दिव्यांग ने हाथ बढ़ाया, ताकि रिसीवर उठा सके, किन्तु आकाश उसी क्षण बीच में आ खड़ा हुआ और बोला, "सॉरी, मिस्टर पटेल! आप किसी को फोन नहीं कर सकते।"

"क्यों? मेरा फोन है!"

"बेशक आपका फोन है, लेकिन हमारा क़ानून है कि छापे के दौरान पार्टी किसी को न तो स्वयं फोन कर सकती है और न किसी का फोन रिसीव ही कर सकती है।"

"अरे, लेकिन..."

''ऐसा इसलिए, मिस्टर दिव्यांग पटेल! कि पार्टी अपनी खुफिया भाषा में कब किसको क्या सन्देश दे दे, हम एकाएक नहीं जान सकते। इसीलिए हम कभी रिस्क नहीं लेते। छापे के दौरान आप अपना फोन क़तई इस्तेमाल नहीं कर सकेंगे। सॉरी!''

''तो मैं कैसे बुलाऊँ किसी को? पंचनामे के लिए? गला फाड़कर चिल्लाऊँ?'' कहते-कहते दिव्यांग उत्तेजित-सा हो गया और सचमुच चिल्लाने लगा, ''आओ! आओ! कोई तो आओ! पंचनामा करवाओ!''

जैसे नाटक के मंच पर कोई पात्र एक लम्बा डग भरता हुआ प्रवेश करे, उसी तरह शिल्पा ने ड्राइंग-रूम में प्रवेश किया और पति को डाँटने की तरह पूछा, ''केम, दिव्यांग? केम बराड़ा पाड़े छे?''

दिव्यांग सिर हिला-हिलाकर बोला, ''शिल्पा! मारूँ तो माथूँ फरी जशे, मारूँ तो माथूँ फरी जशे!''

''आपका सिर घूम जाए, ऐसी तो कोई बात है ही नहीं, मिस्टर पटेल!'' मिस पंड्या ने, जो स्वयं गुजरातन थीं, मिस्टर दिव्यांग पटेल की गुजराती भाषा को समझ लेते हुए, जवाब हिन्दी भाषा में दिया, ''पार्टी के सभी संस्थानों पर हम एक समय, एक साथ छापे डालते हैं, और पार्टी के सभी टेलीफोन्स फ़ौरन अपने क़ब्जे में ले लेते हैं, ताकि कोई भी संस्थान किसी दूसरे संस्थान को सावधान न कर सके।''

''आपके हिसाब से, यह बात...ऐसी है ही नहीं कि पार्टी का सिर घूमे! जबकि...टेलीफोन छीन लेने का मतलब तो यह हुआ कि आपने मेरी ज़बान काट ली!'' और दिव्यांग व्याकुल हो गया।

छोटा भाई शैलेश, दिव्यांग के नज़दीक पहुँच, उसके कन्धे पर हाथ रखता हुआ बोला, ''शांत थाओ, मोटा भाई! शांत थाओ!''

शिल्पा के पीछे-पीछे उसके दोनों बच्चों ने भी ड्राइंग-रूम में प्रवेश कर लिया था। संग में थी जवान नौकरानी। दोनों बच्चे स्कूल जाने के लिए शत-प्रतिशत तैयार थे। उनके बस्ते नौकरानी ने उठा रखे थे।

शिल्पा ने बच्चों और नौकरानी को आकाश की ओर लगभग ठेलते हुए कहा, ''इन तीनों की तलाशी अच्छी तरह से लीजिए। पंचनामे का इन्तज़ाम अभी नहीं हुआ है, तो भी...तलाशी की शुरुआत इन तीनों से कर ही लीजिए...क्योंकि मैं बच्चों को स्कूल लेट नहीं भेज सकती।''

आकाश चौकन्ना हो गया, किन्तु केवल भीतर से। बाहर से उसने अपनी घुग्घू मुद्रा को ही स्थिर रखा। अन्तर्प्रेरणा से आकाश जान गया था, शिल्पा ने चमत्कार जैसा कुछ किया ज़रूर है...लेकिन क्या?

शिल्पा झरझर-झरझर बोले जा रही थी, ''नौकरानी रोज़ बच्चों को स्कूल तक छोड़ने जाती है, आज भी जाएगी। हो सकता है, मेरे ये बच्चे, मेरी यह नौकरानी,

अपने कपड़ों में...या अपने बैग्स में...कोई ऐसी चीज़ छिपाकर ले जा रहे हों, जो कई करोड़ की हो...या कई अरब की, कई ख़रब की...''—शिल्पा के स्वर की चुनौती आकाश के आर-पार उतर रही थी!

जो कमज़ोर होता है, वह डरकर, दुबककर, हौले से बोलता है, ऐसा आमतौर पर माना जाता है। मनोवैज्ञानिकों की मान्यता इससे ठीक विपरीत है। उनके अनुसार, हौले से बोलने वाला अकसर कमज़ोर नहीं होता। जिसे अपनी आवाज़ के असर पर यक़ीन नहीं होता, जिसे अपने शब्दों के रुतबे पर गौरव नहीं होता, उसी को अपनी आवाज़ ऊँची करके बोलना पड़ता है, उसी को अपनी बात स्पष्ट करने के लिए दस की जगह सौ शब्दों का इस्तेमाल करना पड़ता है। आत्म-विश्वासी और शक्तिशाली व्यक्ति तो स्वर ऊँचा उठाने की ज़रूरत ही महसूस नहीं करता। जिस बात को दूसरे सौ शब्दों में कहेंगे, उसी बात को वह दस शब्दों में निबटा देगा, क्योंकि उसे अपनी शक्ति मालूम है।

आकाश ने शिल्पा की नज़र से नज़र मिलाकर केवल एक शब्द कहा, ''ज़रूर!'' और इस एक शब्द को भी कहा बिलकुल हौले से, किन्तु वह आकाश का शब्द था! शिल्पा ने उसे सौ शब्दों में चुनौती दी थी कि ले लो तलाशी मेरे दोनों बच्चों की, और मेरी नौकरानी की। आकाश ने उस चुनौती को स्वीकार करने के लिए एक से ज़्यादा शब्दों का इस्तेमाल करने की ज़रूरत नहीं समझी। शिल्पा अपनी बात को लगातार ऊँचे स्वर में प्रस्तुत कर रही थी। आकाश ने जो एकमात्र शब्द कहा, हौले से ही कहा।

आकाश की नज़र शिल्पा पर से हटकर जनक पर ठहरी, ''जनक!''

''सर!''

''दोनों बच्चों के बैग्स...'' आकाश का एक तो स्वर धीमा, ऊपर से वाक्य भी अधूरा! किन्तु कैसा विद्युत जैसा प्रभाव था उसका!

जनक चीते जैसा स्फूर्तिवान हो गया। ''यस, सर!'' बुदबुदाकर वह नौकरानी एवं दोनों बच्चों के सामने जा पहुँचा। नौकरानी के हाथ से दोनों बैग्स लेकर जनक ड्राइंग-रूम के एक कोने में जा बैठा, ताकि बैग्स को खोलकर जब वह तमाम चीज़ें फैला-फैलाकर देखना शुरू करे, तब आते-जाते किसी भी व्यक्ति के लिए बाधा न बने।

पुनः वही धीमा किन्तु कड़क स्वर, ''मिस्टर थत्ते!''

सुनते ही, आयकर अधिकारी मिस्टर थत्ते, आकाश के नज़दीक जा खड़े हुए, ''यस, बॉस!''

''लड़के की तलाशी आप लें।''

''ओके!'' और मिस्टर थत्ते लम्बे डग भरते, शिल्पा के बेटे के पास पहुँच गए, ''आ जा, बेटे! क्या नाम है तेरा?''

लड़का चुप रहा, जैसे उसका कोई नाम ही न हो। मिस्टर थत्ते उसे बड़े ही प्यार से गोद में उठाकर दिव्यांग के शयन-कक्ष में ले गए।

"लड़की को...मिस पंड्या!"

"यस, सर!" और मिस पंड्या ने भी शिल्पा की बेटी को अपनी बेटी बना लिया, "चल, आ, बिटिया! टॉफी खाएगी?"

लड़की उसी तरह चुप रही, जैसे उसका भाई। मिस पंड्या ने उसे गोद में उठाना चाहा, किन्तु उसने अकुलाकर पूरा बदन सिकोड़ लिया। मिस पंड्या ने उसके कन्धे पर हाथ रखा। लड़की पूर्ण आज्ञाकारिता के साथ शैलेश के शयन-कक्ष में चली गई, मिस पंड्या का हाथ अपने कन्धे पर से हटाए बिना। दरवाज़ा पार होते ही मिस पंड्या ने परदा खींच दिया।

शिल्पा के चेहरे पर शुद्ध तिलमिलाहट साँय-साँय करने लगी। उसने सोचा भी न था कि दोनों बच्चों को अलग-अलग कमरों में ले जाकर, एकान्त में उनकी तलाशी ली जाएगी और उस वक़्त बच्चों की प्यारी माँ मौजूद भी नहीं होगी! शिल्पा ने पति-परमेश्वर दिव्यांग की ओर देखा, जैसे वह आँखों-आँखों में पूछ रही थी, 'यह सब क्या हो रहा है?' पति-परमेश्वर नज़र घुमा गए।

मिस्टर थत्ते दिव्यांग के शयन-कक्ष से बाहर निकले! वह लड़के का हाथ थामे हुए थे और गम्भीर थे। बोले, "सर! कुछ नहीं है। जाने दें..."

लगभग साथ-साथ ही मिस पंड्या, शैलेश के शयन-कक्ष का परदा हटाकर ड्राइंग-रूम में आईं और बोलीं, "लड़की भी ख़ाली है। जाने दें..."

इस बार लड़की मिस पंड्या की गोद में उठी हुई थी। मिस पंड्या ने उसे उसके भाई के नज़दीक खड़ा कर दिया। फिर उन्होंने कठोरता से देखा जवान नौकरानी की ओर, "चलो अन्दर।"

नौकरानी हिचक गई, किन्तु बात मान लेने के सिवा कोई चारा नहीं है, यह आत्म-ज्ञान भी उसे तत्काल हो गया। जब वह मिस पंड्या के साथ शैलेश के शयन-कक्ष में जा रही थी, शिल्पा बोल पड़ी, "मैं भी चलती हूँ।"

मिस पंड्या ने न तो हामी भरी, न आपत्ति की। मिस पंड्या, नौकरानी और शिल्पा ने शैलेश के शयन-कक्ष का दरवाज़ा पार किया। इस बार केवल परदा न खींचकर दरवाज़ा अन्दर से बन्द किया गया और यह शुभ कार्य मिस पंड्या नहीं, शिल्पा के हाथों सम्पन्न हुआ।

न जाने क्यों, जनक को ऐसा लगा, जैसे अन्दर जाते-जाते शिल्पा ने उसकी ओर तीखी नज़र डाली थी। जाती हुई शिल्पा की दिशा में जनक ने चेहरा उठाकर देखा नहीं था, शिल्पा की नज़र से जनक की नज़र मिलने का प्रश्न ही नहीं था, इसके बावजूद, जनक की कोई तीसरी आँख खुली हुई थी, जो उसे बता रही थी कि

अन्दर जाते-जाते शिल्पा ने...लेकिन क्यों? जा रही शिल्पा आख़िर क्यों उसे घूरना चाहेगी? क्या इसलिए कि वह दोनों बच्चों के बैग्स में से चीज़ें निकाल-निकालकर जाँच रहा था? जनक के मन-मस्तिष्क में एक-एक कर प्रश्न उभरने और बुझने लगे...

दोनों बैग्स की एक-एक चीज़ निकालकर, खोल-खोलकर देख चुका था जनक। जैसी कि आशा थी ही, कहीं कोई चीज़ ऐसी नहीं थी, जिससे सन्देह जगे। शिल्पा ने जो दनदनाकर चुनौती दी थी कि ले लो तलाशी, उसका राज़ यही हो सकता था कि बच्चे बिलकुल निरापद ढंग से स्कूल जा रहे थे। इसके बावजूद...जाते-जाते शिल्पा ने जनक को घूरने जैसा प्रयास क्यों किया? क्या सचमुच ऐसा प्रयास हुआ था? क्या यह जनक की केवल ग़लतफ़हमी नहीं थी? जनक अपने आपको किसी अदृश्य तराजू पर रखकर तौल रहा था...

और जनक के हाथ में थे दो लंच-बॉक्स, जिन्हें वह खोल चुका था। उसे दो-दो केक-स्लाइस, प्रति लंच-बॉक्स, दिखाई दिए। दोनों लंच-बॉक्सेस में कई-कई टॉफियाँ भी थीं—बड़ी आकृति की, महँगी, चमचम करते रैपर्सवाली, स्वादिष्ट और शायद पौष्टिक भी! 'बड़े घर के बच्चे हैं, भाय!' जनक ने अपने आपसे कहा, 'बड़े घर के बच्चे टॉफियाँ भी बड़ी-बड़ी खाते हैं!

दो-दो केक-स्लाइस का एक-एक जोड़ा...जनक प्रत्येक जोड़े को उघाड़कर देखने की सोच ही रहा था कि महसूस हुआ, कुछ गड़बड़-सी मची है ड्राइंग-रूम में। जनक ने खोजी दृष्टि उठाई, तो पाया, शैलेश के शयन-कक्ष का दरवाज़ा खोलकर शिल्पा वापस ड्राइंग-रूम में आ चुकी है और फूँ-फूँ कर रही है।

ड्राइंग-रूम में मौजूद एक-एक व्यक्ति की नज़र शिल्पा पर ही थी। जनक की भी नज़र उसी पर ठहरी रह गई। शिल्पा के होंठ आवेश से काँप रहे थे। माजरा क्या है? जनक समझा नहीं। क्यों शिल्पा इतने आवेश में है? अभी-अभी, अच्छी-भली, मिस पंड्या के साथ, भीतर गई थी। अभी-अभी ही तो, सुन्दर सहयोगी मुद्रा में, इसी शिल्पा ने दरवाज़ा अन्दर से बन्द किया था। अचानक इतनी तपी हुई क्यों है?

जनक के हाथ लंच-बॉक्सेस की जाँच करते-करते थम गए। उसने आकाश की ओर देखा, लेकिन आकाश की नज़र शिल्पा पर थी और शिल्पा दाँत पीस-पीसकर बोल रही थी, "हलाहल कलजुग आ गया? अरे, एक हद होती है! बेहयाई की भी एक हद होती है! क्या तमाशा है! ऐसे लेते हैं तलाशी? यही तरीक़ा है तलाशी लेने का? नौकरानी भी आख़िर इस घर की एक औरत है! तो क्या आप लोग घर की औरतों को भी नहीं छोड़ेंगे?"

तभी मिस पंड्या ने शैलेश के शयन-कक्ष से निकलकर, नौकरानी के साथ, ड्राइंग-रूम में प्रवेश किया और कहा, "नौकरानी जा सकती है..."

नौकरानी का चेहरा लाल था। बुरी तरह झेंपी हुई लग रही थी वह, नज़र नहीं उठा रही थी। चुपचाप वह दोनों बच्चों के पास जाकर खड़ी हो गई। शिल्पा ने नौकरानी की ओर ऐसे देखा, जैसे कह रही हो, 'हाय, तेरी यह दशा!' एकाएक शिल्पा मिस पंड्या की ओर न केवल मुखातिब हुई, बल्कि कुछ क़दम चलकर आगे भी बढ़ी। स्वर और मुद्रा, दोनों से, शिल्पा घोर आक्रामक हो उठी और चुनौती देती बोली, ''तलाशी तो आप मेरी भी लेंगी! छोड़ेंगी नहीं! सब समझ में आ रहा है! लेकिन क्या इसी तरह...इसी तरह मुझे भी...छी-छी! अरे, क्या इस घर की औरतों की कोई इज़्ज़त नहीं?''

ये सब वाक्य केवल मिस पंड्या के लिए थे, किन्तु इसके बाद के वाक्य मानो सारे संसार के लिए थे। शिल्पा ने ड्राइंग-रूम में मौजूद एक-एक व्यक्ति से अपील करने की तरह घूम-घूमकर, हाथ फैला-फैलाकर कहा, ''मैं प्राण दे दूँगी! हाँ! मगर तलाशी नहीं दूँगी! सुन रहे हैं आप लोग? प्राण दे दूँगी! मगर तलाशी नहीं दूँगी! नहीं दूँगी!''

शिल्पा ने उन्माद में आकर अजीब तरह से झूमना शुरू कर दिया। दिव्यांग जल्दी से उठकर उसके पास पहुँच गया और दोनों हाथों से उसे कसकर थामता हुआ बोला, ''शिल्पा! शिल्पा!''

इस बीच नौकरानी दोनों बच्चों को ठेलती हुई जनक के पास ला चुकी थी। जनक ने दोनों लंच-बॉक्स बन्द कर वापस बैग्स में रख दिए। नौकरानी ने दोनों बैग्स उठाकर अपने कन्धे से लटका लिये। आकाश की नज़र शिल्पा पर। जनक की नज़र शिल्पा पर। नौकरानी और बच्चे फ्लैट से बाहर निकल गए। बच्चों के बैग्स भी फ्लैट से बाहर निकल चुके थे। नौकरानी ने फ्लैट का दरवाज़ा बन्द कर बाहर से खींच लिया। क्लिच! लैच बन्द हो गया। दरवाज़ा बन्द। लैच बन्द। उन्माद चालू! शिल्पा का उन्माद! ज्यों-का-त्यों...

तलाशी का अर्थ सिर में कंघी करना नहीं होता। दुनिया जानती है कि तलाशी में कभी सिर की जूँ की खोज नहीं की जाती। तलाशी में जिन दिव्य पदार्थों के मिल जाने की आशा रखी जाती है, वे तो सम्पूर्ण मानव शरीर के अन्दर-बाहर, ऊपर-नीचे कहीं भी हो सकते हैं, लुके-छिपे, मन्द-मन्द मुसकाते! इसीलिए जब पूरी तलाशी ली जाती है, तब वह अनुभव किसी भजन-मंडली में बैठकर ढोल बजाने जैसा निरापद न तो होता है, न हो सकता है। दुनिया जानती है, वह अनुभव कैसा होता है। इसीलिए, अगर कोई बार-बार तौबा करने लगे कि हाय-हाय और छी-छी! तलाशी क्या ऐसे ली जाती है? तो, यक़ीनन, ऐसे शख़्स की हाय-हाय और छी-छी केवल एक धोखा होती है, केवल बनावट! इसीलिए जब शिल्पा ने अपने आश्चर्य और दुःख को ज़रूरत से ज़्यादा ही फुलाकर सामने रखा, तब मिस पंड्या उसे डाँटे बिना

न रह सकीं, "क्यों इतना ड्रामा कर रही हैं, मिसेज पटेल! ऐसा तो होता है। सब जानते हैं!"

किन्तु शिल्पा अपनी रटन्त छोड़ने को तैयार नहीं थी। पति-परमेश्वर ने आगे बढ़कर जब उसे दोनों हाथों से थाम लिया, तब वह समझ गई कि अब तो और ज़्यादा झूमा जा सकता है। वह और ज़्यादा झूमने लगी और बारम्बार कहने लगी, "हूँ पागल थई गई...हूँ पागल थई गई..."

दिव्यांग पत्नी-परमेश्वरी को व्यर्थ ही समझाना चाहता था, "शिल्पा! शिल्पा! मारी वात सांभड़! मारी वात सांभड़!"

किन्तु उसकी बात सुने, वह शिल्पा कैसी! झूम-झूमकर अब उसने शैलेश की नई-निकोर बीवी मनीषा की ओर इशारे करना शुरू कर दिया और शैलेश को दुनिया की दुष्टता की नई समझ देनी चाही, "शैलेश! शैलेश! तारी बहू ने पण ए छोड़शे नहीं! तारी बहू ने पण ए छोड़शे नहीं!"

शैलेश ने व्याकुल होकर अपने शरीर का पूरा वज़न एक पैर से हटाकर दूसरे पैर पर डाला। फलस्वरूप, शैलेश की मिनि-तोंद में सूक्ष्म हरकत हुई।

आकाश शिल्पा के बरताव का रहस्य ठीक से समझने के लिए ग़ौर से देख रहा था, शिल्पा की ही ओर। झूमती शिल्पा ने, अचानक, इस प्रकार बदन-संचालन किया कि उसकी पीठ घूमकर आकाश की ओर आ गई। वैसे तो...पीठ पर भी मनोभावों का असर होता है, किन्तु कहाँ चेहरा और कहाँ पीठ! शिल्पा ने झूमने के बहाने पीठ घुमाकर आकाश को जैसे ठेंगा दिखा दिया—अब कैसे पकड़ोगे मेरे मनोभावों को!

किन्तु जैसे ही शिल्पा की पीठ घूमी, उसे थाम रहे दिव्य पति दिव्यांग का चेहरा आ गया आकाश के आमने-सामने। आकाश ने दिव्यांग के ही चेहरे को भाँपना शुरू कर दिया—शिल्पा के मनोभावों की छाया शायद दिव्यांग के चेहरे पर आ ही जाए...

दिव्यांग और शिल्पा ने नज़र-से-नज़र मिला रखी थी। दिव्यांग को पता न चल सका, उसके चेहरे को आकाश द्वारा खुली किताब की तरह पढ़ा जा रहा है। आकाश ने महसूस किया, ज़रूर शिल्पा ने आँख के इशारे से दिव्यांग को कुछ समझाया है। दिव्यांग की आँखें कह रही थीं कि शिल्पा की आँखों ने, आँखों-आँखों में, जो भी बताया है, उसे दिव्यांग द्वारा समझ लिया गया है...

शिल्पा की पीठ की तरफ़ खड़े आकाश ने आँकना चाहा, क्या हो सकता है शिल्पा का वह इशारा...और...क्या हो सकता है उसका अर्थ...

मानो उस इशारे के अनुसन्धान में ही कुछ हो रहा हो, इस प्रकार एकाएक शिल्पा अपने पतिदेव की बाँहों में निढाल होने लगी, जैसे बेहोश होने की तैयारी में हो। शिल्पा के शब्द आकाश के दोनों कानों में प्रवेश कर मस्तिष्क तक पहुँच रहे थे, "चक्कर! चक्कर! मने चक्कर आवे छे!"

शिल्पा का शरीर अकेले दिव्यांग से सँभल पाए, इसके लिए सार्वजनिक रूप से दोनों के बीच जितनी शारीरिक आत्मीयता का प्रदर्शन किया जाना अनिवार्य था, उतना प्रदर्शन भारतीय संस्कृति के ख़िलाफ़ होने के कारण दिव्यांग ने कातर दृष्टि से अपने छोटे भाई की बीवी मनीषा की ओर देखा और कहा, "अरे, जो तो! ज़रा संभाड़ तो आने..."

मनीषा ने जेठ के आदेश का पालन तत्काल किया। लपककर मनीषा जब शिल्पा को सँभाल रही थी, तब शैलेश भी लपककर अपनी भाभीश्री को सँभालने में भाईश्री की सहायता करने लगा था। मनीषा, शैलेश और दिव्यांग, शिल्पा को थामकर, अन्दर ले जाने लगे—दिव्यांग के शयन-कक्ष की तरफ़। अन्दर ये तीनों कौन-सा नया गुल खिलाने वाले हैं? आकाश ने मिस पंड्या को अपनी ख़ामोश नज़र से संकेत दिया। मिस पंड्या तुरन्त उन तीनों के साथ हो, दिव्यांग के शयन-कक्ष में प्रवेश कर गईं।

अगले ही क्षण, जनक और आकाश, तीर की तरह एक-दूसरे के नज़दीक आए। जनक ने तपी हुई फुसफुसाहट में कहा, "सर! कोई चाल चली जा रही है!"

आकाश की भौंहों पर बल पड़े, "याद करो, जनक! उस वक़्त तुम क्या कर रहे थे, जब...शिल्पा चिल्लाती हुई इधर वापस आई थी..."

"सर!" जनक ने बताया, "उस वक़्त मैंने...दोनों बच्चों के...लंच-बॉक्स खोल रखे थे। दोनों लंच-बॉक्सेस में केक-स्लाइस थे। बहुत-सी टॉफियाँ भी थीं—बड़ी-बड़ी। मैं सोच ही रहा था कि बड़े घरों के बच्चे बड़ी-बड़ी टॉफियाँ ही तो खाएँगे, छोटी-छोटी टॉफियाँ थोड़े न खाएँगे...कि तभी..."

"कि तभी?"

"शिल्पा चिल्लाती हुई ड्राइंग-रूम में वापस आई। मैं उसकी ओर देखने लगा। बच्चों को स्कूल जाने में देर हो रही थी। नौकरानी और बच्चे मेरे नज़दीक आ खड़े हुए थे। मैंने दोनों लंच-बॉक्स बच्चों के बैग्स में रखे। नौकरानी ने बैग्स मुझसे ले लिये। बच्चों के साथ नौकरानी फ्लैट से बाहर निकल गई...मेरी नज़र तो लगातार शिल्पा पर ही रही।"

"हुँ...जनक! क्या तुम्हें पूरा यक़ीन है कि लंच-बॉक्सेस की तलाशी ठीक से ली जा सकी?"

"नो, सर! क्योंकि शिल्पा का तमाशा बढ़ता जा रहा था और मेरा ध्यान उसी ओर था। मुझे तो लगता है, सर! कि मेरा ध्यान बँटाने के लिए ही यह तमाशा किया गया..."

"मे बी!"

"शिल्पा किस हद तक ड्रामा कर रही थी...प्राण दे दूँगी, तलाशी नहीं दूँगी! आल दैट..."

"तो क्या...बच्चों के लंच-बॉक्सेस में कुछ था? जो इस फ्लैट से बाहर जा चुका है?" आकाश ने अपने आपसे सवाल पूछा और जवाब भी अपने आपसे ही पा लिया, "तर्क और बुद्धि से तो सही साबित होता है..."

सहसा आकाश की बुदबुदाहटें ख़त्म हो गईं। उसने खुलकर, कड़क स्वर में आदेश दिया, "क्विक! जनक! थत्ते! दोनों बच्चे, दोनों बैग्स...और नौकरानी...मुझे वापस चाहिए! फ़ौरन! अभी!"

आदेश देते-देते आकाश ने लम्बे डग भरना शुरू कर दिया था, ताकि दिव्यांग के शयन-कक्ष में जा सके, जहाँ नाटकीय, उन्मादिनी शिल्पा को अभी-अभी ले जाया गया था। आकाश के साथ-साथ, जनक और मिस्टर थत्ते ने भी लम्बे डग भरे। इन तीनों ने, तीन फ़ौजी कमांडरों की तरह, दिव्यांग के शयन-कक्ष में प्रवेश करते ही, वहाँ के पूरे दृश्य को, एक दृष्टिपात में समझ लिया। शिल्पा पलंग पर चित्त पड़ी थी। उसकी आँखें बन्द थीं, मगर सिहरती पलकें बता रही थीं कि पूरा कमरा शिल्पा के ध्यान में है। दिव्यांग और शैलेश सिरहाने खड़े थे। मनीषा सिरहाने बैठी हुई थी, जेठानी जी का मस्तक सहलाती। मिस पंड्या पायताने खड़ी थीं, बहुत चौकन्नी। आकाश व साथियों का प्रवेश हुआ होने पर भी मिस पंड्या ने शिल्पा पर से अपनी नज़र हटने न दी।

शैलेश ने तो नहीं, दिव्यांग ने सीधी नज़र से देखा आकाश की ओर। आकाश ने गूँजती आवाज़ में पूछा, "मिस्टर पटेल! जल्दी बताइए, आपके बच्चे कौन-से स्कूल में पढ़ते हैं? स्कूल का पूरा नाम, पता..."

दिव्यांग ख़ामोशी से देखता रह गया। आकाश एकदम उसके नज़दीक जाकर भिड़-सा गया, "बोलिए फटाफट!"

दिव्यांग न बोला। वह समय बिता रहा था—एक-एक पल।

इस बार आकाश ने अपना गुस्सा बिलकुल न छिपाया, "बोलते क्यों नहीं? बोलिए! वरना बुलाऊँ पुलिस? इतनी-सी बात के लिए?"

पुलिस बुलाना आकाश की अधिकार-सीमा में था या नहीं, दिव्यांग नहीं जानता था, किन्तु 'पुलिस' शब्द ही काफ़ी रहा, उसकी जीभ परिचालित कर देने के लिए। उसने झटपट बताना शुरू कर दिया, "सेंट फ्रान्सिस हायर सेकंड्री स्कूल...सोसायटी के गेट से निकलते ही, दाहिनी तरफ़...दसेक मिनट के पैदल रास्ते पर..."

आकाश ने चुटकी बजाई, "दोनों बच्चों के नाम? क्लास? सेक्शन?"

"रूपाली पटेल, फर्स्ट ए। हिमांशु पटेल, सेकंड सी..."

आकाश ने जनक और थत्ते की ओर घूमकर कहा, "लपको!"

जनक और थत्ते एक चौंध की तरह शयन-कक्ष से बाहर निकल गए।

आकाश ने गहरी साँस ली। लपकने का आदेश देता आकाश दिव्यांग से ज़रा परे हट गया था। यह दूरी दिव्यांग से मानो सही नहीं गई। आकाश को पता न चला,

दिव्यांग कब उसके नज़दीक आ खड़ा हुआ, आकाश की नज़र दरवाज़े पर होने के कारण। दिव्यांग एक धीमी, चालाक, खिसियानी हँसी हँसा। तब आकाश ने सिर घुमाकर देखा उसकी ओर। क्यों हँस रहा था दिव्यांग? क्या स्कूल का नाम-पता झट से बता देने के पीछे भी उसकी कोई चाल थी? आकाश सहसा न समझ पाया...

अपनी धीमी हँसी को दिव्यांग ने ज़रा और धीमा कर लिया, किन्तु पूरी तरह रोका नहीं। यह हँसी आकाश को सख़्त नागवार गुज़र रही थी। 'क्या किसी तरह दिव्यांग के होंठों को आपस में भिड़ाकर सिलाई नहीं की जा सकती?' आकाश ने सोचा। अपनी इस कल्पना पर वह मुसकराए बिना न रह सका। दिव्यांग ने समझा, आकाश उसकी धीमी हँसी के जवाब में मुसकरा रहा है। उत्साहित होकर दिव्यांग ने कहा, "साहब! आपको हमारे बच्चों से क्या काम है?"

हवा के झोंके से जैसे कोई मोमबत्ती अचानक बुझ जाए, उसी तरह दिव्यांग के इस सवाल ने आकाश की मुसकान को बुझा दिया। वह रूखे स्वर में बोला, "यह सवाल आप मुझसे नहीं, अपने आपसे पूछिए।"

"लेकिन, साहब! मैं कैसे जान सकता हूँ कि मेरे बच्चों से आपको क्या काम है?"

"तो जाइए, अपनी बीवी से पूछिए।"

"फिर भी...आप कुछ तो कहें..."

आकाश ने फ़ौरन बात काट दी और याद दिलाते हुए कहा, "आप किन्हीं दो पड़ोसियों को फोन करने वाले थे न? पंचनामे के लिए?"

दिव्यांग ने उलाहना दिया, "कहाँ...आपने तो फोन को छूने भी नहीं दिया था..."

"आइए मेरे साथ!" और आकाश ने दिव्यांग की बाँह पकड़ ली। उसे ज़बरन ठेलता हुआ-सा आकाश ड्राइंग-रूम में ले आया, जिधर फोन रखा था।

"फोन आप नहीं कर सकते, लेकिन आपकी तरफ़ से मैं ज़रूर कर सकता हूँ!" आकाश ने रिसीवर उठा लिया, "बोलिए दिव्यांग जी! नाम...नम्बर..."

दिव्यांग मानो अपनी हकलाहट को रोकता हुआ बोला, "जी...वो...मिस्टर कुलकर्णी...890 4337 और...मिसेज तिवारी...890 1230..."

आकाश ने डायल घुमाना शुरू करते हुए, दोनों नम्बरों को बुदबुदाहट में दोहराया, "890 4337 और...890 1230..."

आ पहुँचे थे पंच! मिस्टर कुलकर्णी और मिसेज तिवारी। दोनों साठ-साठ बरस के लग रहे थे। आते ही उन्होंने प्रसन्नता ज़ाहिर की कि उन्हें पंच बनाया गया। सच पूछें, तो वे रोमांचित ही थे। आयकर के छापे में पंच बनने का उनके लिए यह पहला

अनुभव था। आते ही उन्होंने बयान करना शुरू कर दिया कि बुढ़ापे में वक़्त काटना कितनी बड़ी समस्या होती है। पंच बनकर आज का एक दिन तो वे अच्छे से गुज़ार ही लेंगे, उन्हें यक़ीन था। दिव्यांग को उनकी बातें अच्छी नहीं लग रही थीं। दिव्यांग ने उन्हें इसलिए बुलाया था कि वे पड़ोस में रहते थे और दिव्यांग को बेटे जैसा मानते थे। बेटे को छत्रच्छाया देने के बजाय वे तो अपना वक़्त काटने आए थे!

आकाश ने दोनों बुजुर्गों को हार्दिक धन्यवाद दिया। वे न देते अपना वक़्त, तो इस छापे को शुरू ही न किया जा सकता। आकाश की बात सुनकर मिस्टर कुलकर्णी और मिसेज तिवारी मन्द-मन्द मुसकराने लगे।

दिव्यांग ने मरी-मरी आवाज़ में कहा, "शिल्पा की तबीयत बहुत ख़राब है।"

मिसेज तिवारी ने जानना चाहा, "अच्छा? क्या हुआ?"

"यही...अचानक छापा पड़ने से...शॉक लग गया। अन्दर लेटी है।"

"देखूँ..." कहतीं मिसेज तिवारी ने अन्दर जाना चाहा, किन्तु आकाश ने इन शब्दों के साथ टोक दिया, "प्लीज़! मिसेज तिवारी! पहले आप ज़रा इस सर्च-वारंट पर दस्तख़त कर दीजिए।"

"हाँ-हाँ, ज़रूर..." और मिसेज तिवारी ने आकाश द्वारा प्रस्तुत सर्च-वारंट पर दस्तख़त कर दिए। आकाश ने जब कहा कि साथ में पूरा नाम और पूरा पता भी लिख दें, तो उन्होंने पूरा नाम और पूरा पता भी लिख दिया।

"थैंक्यू, मैडम!" आकाश बोला, "अब आप अन्दर जा सकती हैं।"

लगे हाथ आकाश ने यह भी कह दिया, "वहाँ आपकी भेंट मिस पंड्या से भी होगी, जो आयकर विभाग में ऑफिसर हैं..."

आकाश ने ऐसा इसलिए कहा कि मिसेज तिवारी यदि कल्पना कर रही हों कि अन्दर जाकर वह अपनी प्यारी शिल्पा की कुछ सहायता करेंगी, तो इस ख़याल को वह मन से निकाल दें। पंच का काम है गवाह बनना, न कि सहायता करना, किन्तु प्यारे पड़ोसी होने के कारण पंच, कभी-कभी, सहायता करने की भी सोचने लगते हैं। यदि शिल्पा की सहायता मिसेज तिवारी ने की, तो मिस पंड्या के सुन्दर नेत्र इस सुन्दर कार्य को अवश्य देख लेंगे...सहायता यों की जा सकती थी कि शिल्पा चुपके से कोई हीरा मिसेज तिवारी को दे दे, जिसे मिसेज तिवारी अपने वस्त्रों में कहीं छिपा लें। पंच होने के कारण मिसेज तिवारी पर किसी का सन्देह जाएगा भी नहीं...लेकिन नहीं! आयकर अधिकारी मिस पंड्या को दो-दो सुन्दर नेत्रों के साथ शिल्पा के आसपास मौजूद इसीलिए रखा गया था कि जब एक मनुष्य दूसरे मनुष्य की सहायता करे, तब तीसरे मनुष्य को पता चल जाए!

मिसेज तिवारी दिव्यांग के शयन-कक्ष में समा चुकी थीं, जहाँ शिल्पा शयन कर रही थी। दिव्यांग ड्राइंग-रूम में ही, आकाश के नज़दीक रुका रह गया था। आकाश

मिस्टर कुलकर्णी से सर्च-वारंट पर दस्तख़त करवाकर, पूरा नाम, पूरा पता लिखवा रहा था। सर्च-वारंट मिस्टर कुलकर्णी से वापस लेकर आकाश ने अपने ब्रीफकेस में रखा और लॉक लगा दिया।

"थैंक्यू, मिस्टर कुलकर्णी!" आकाश मुसकरा दिया, "अब हम यहाँ की तलाशी शुरू कर सकते हैं।"

"मैं भी ज़रा शिल्पा का हालचाल पूछ लूँ।" मिस्टर कुलकर्णी ने अपनी मनोकामना सामने रखी।

"क्यों नहीं!" आकाश ने कहा, "शौक से पूछिए शिल्पा जी का हालचाल!" फिर जैसे एकाएक याद आया, "और हाँ...तलाशी पूरी होने पर, पंचनामे पर भी आप दोनों के दस्तख़त लगेंगे।"

"श्योर! श्योर! ज़रूर ..." और मिस्टर कुलकर्णी, दिव्यांग के शयन-कक्ष में प्रवेश कर गए।

दिव्यांग अभी भी आकाश के नज़दीक ही खड़ा था। फलस्वरूप, दिव्यांग के ही साथ बातचीत का नया मोर्चा खुल जाता शायद...किन्तु तभी टेलीफोन ने घनघनाना शुरू कर दिया।

आकाश ने रिसीवर उठाया, "हैलो?"

आकाश ने किरकिराती आवाज़ सुनी, "सर! मैं—जनक!"

"हाँ, जनक! बोलो!"

"सर! बच्चे स्कूल पहुँचे ही नहीं हैं!"

"ओह! नो!" आकाश बोल पड़ा! अब आकाश को समझ में आया, बच्चों के स्कूल का नाम-पता बताने के बाद दिव्यांग क्यों अपनी धीमी, चालाकीपूर्ण हँसी को रोक नहीं पा रहा था।

फोन पर जनक का किरकिराता स्वर जारी था, "ज़ाहिर है, सर! कि ख़ुद नौकरानी ने ही बच्चों को स्कूल नहीं पहुँचाया है। वह उन्हें कहीं और ले गई है।"

आकाश रिसीवर के माउथ-पीस में बुदबुदाया, "एक मिनट..." फिर उसने दिव्यांग पर तीखी नज़र डाली, "मिस्टर पटेल! आपके बच्चे कहाँ हैं?"

"स्कूल में हैं। और कहाँ हो सकते हैं?" दिव्यांग ने रेडीमेड उत्तर दिया।

"नहीं हैं स्कूल में। जल्दी बताइए, कहाँ हैं?"

"अरे, लेकिन अभी आपके सामने ही तो गए हैं स्कूल!"

"प्लीज़, मिस्टर पटेल! आपको अच्छी तरह मालूम है, बच्चे कहाँ हैं।"

"मैं तो...बच्चे जा रहे थे, तब आप ही के पास खड़ा था। सच कहता हूँ, मुझे कुछ नहीं मालूम।"

"तो जिसे मालूम है, उससे पूछकर आइए। यानी, अपनी बीवी से।"

दिव्यांग हड़बड़ाता हुआ अपने शयन-कक्ष की ओर जाने लगा। आकाश ने उसे रोककर सावधान किया, "सुनिए! काला धन छिपाने के लिए अपने मासूम बच्चों को इस्तेमाल करना बहुत ही गन्दी बात है। बेहतर हो, आप अपने ही मुँह से अपनी सारी ब्लैक-मनी के रहस्य खोल दें—तलाशी शुरू होने से पहले ही। ऐसी सूरत में हम आपसे पेनाल्टी बिलकुल नहीं लेंगे। स्लैब के हिसाब से सिर्फ़ टैक्स ही लेंगे।"

दिव्यांग ज़रा चिढ़कर बोला, "जी, मुझे यह मालूम है!"

जिसके जवाब में आकाश ने सख़्त होकर कहा, "मालूम तो है, लेकिन याद नहीं है! इसीलिए याद दिला रहा हूँ कि ऊँचे-ऊँचे स्लैब में भी आपसे पचास प्रतिशत से ज़्यादा टैक्स नहीं लिया जाएगा, लेकिन...अगर हमने पेनाल्टी लगाई...आपको लेने के देने पड़ जाएँगे।"

"जी, मैं पूछकर आता हूँ! प्लीज़!" दिव्यांग अकुलाकर जाने लगा, किन्तु आकाश ने फिर से टोका, "याद तो है न, मिस्टर पटेल! अपनी बीवी से आपको क्या पूछना है? कहाँ हैं दोनों बच्चे?"

आकाश के व्यंग्य ने दिव्यांग को बींध डाला। वह जल्दी से अपने शयन-कक्ष में समा गया। आकाश रिसीवर से मुख़ातिब हुआ, "हैलो, जनक! सुनो...मुझे बिलकुल आशा नहीं है कि मिस्टर या मिसेज पटेल अपने बच्चों का अता-पता बताएँगे! फिर भी, लाइन होल्ड करो।"

आकाश के इस आदेश के जवाब में जनक ने यही कहा, "यस, सर!"

पन्द्रह सेकंड तक, टेलीफोन पर, जब आकाश का स्वर सुनाई न दिया, तब जनक अकुलाकर बोला, "सर!"

"हाँ, जनक!"

"सर! आप चिन्ता न करें। बच्चे आसपास की ही किसी सोसायटी में होंगे। कहीं दूर नहीं ले जाए गए होंगे। सिक्योरिटी गार्ड से पता चल जाएगा। वह मिस्टर पटेल के दोस्तों वग़ैरह को ज़रूर जानता होगा।"

"या! दैट्स करैक्ट!" आकाश ने सहमति दर्शाई, फिर आदेश दिया, "सुनो, जनक! अगर बच्चों की खोज तुम्हीं दोनों को करनी पड़ गई, तो...तुम और थत्ते अलग-अलग दिशाओं में दौड़ोगे।"

जनक का स्वर, फोन पर, बहुत ही साफ़ सुनाई दे रहा था, "यस, सर!"

"एक मिनट...होल्ड करो!" आकाश ने कहा, "मिस्टर पटेल अपने कमरे से निकल रहे हैं..."

फिर, ड्राइंग-रूम में प्रवेश कर रहे दिव्यांग से मुख़ातिब होते आकाश ने कठोरता से पूछा, "यस, मिस्टर पटेल! कहाँ हैं बच्चे?"

दिव्यांग ने भरपूर आत्म-विश्वास के साथ झूठ परोस दिया, "ऐसा है, साहब! शिल्पा बिलकुल होश में नहीं है। उसे तो समझ में ही नहीं आ रहा है कि मैं क्या पूछ रहा हूँ।"

"ओके! फाइन! मैं अभी डॉक्टर बुलवाता हूँ!" आकाश ने बिना मुसकराए कहा, फिर रिसीवर के माउथ-पीस में पुकारा, "हैलो, जनक?"

जनक का किरकिराता स्वर अकेला आकाश सुन रहा था, "यस, सर!"

आकाश ने सूचना दी, "मिस्टर पटेल अपने बच्चों का ठिकाना नहीं जानते! इस ठिकाने की तलाश अब तुम्हीं दोनों को करनी होगी।"

"नो प्रॉब्लम, सर! बच्चों को अभी हाज़िर करते हैं!" और जनक ने अपने छोर का रिसीवर रख दिया।

अब आकाश ने किसी और नम्बर पर डायल घुमाना शुरू किया। दिव्यांग की ओर आकाश चुनौती की नज़र से देख रहा था। बोला, "मैं इन्कम-टैक्स के पैनल-डॉक्टर को बुला रहा हूँ।"

स्कूल का नाम-पता बताने के बाद दिव्यांग जिस तरह नज़दीक आकर खड़ा हुआ था, जिस तरह मन्द-मन्द हँसा था, ठीक उसी तरह, एक बार फिर वह आकाश के नज़दीक आ खड़ा हुआ और मन्द-मन्द हँसता पूछने लगा, "क्या, साहब! क्यों इतने कड़क हो रहे हैं!"

यहाँ दिव्यांग ने अपने हास्य पर पूर्ण-विराम लगाया और बुदबुदाकर कहा, "कुछ ऐसा करिए कि हम भी खुश और आप भी खुश!"

आकाश ने आँखें तरेरकर देखा दिव्यांग की ओर, "मुझे मालूम था, मिस्टर पटेल, यह बात आप ज़रूर कहेंगे! दुबारा न कहिएगा! पहली बार मैं माफ़ कर देता हूँ!"

पैनल-डॉक्टर के फोन-नम्बर का एक-एक डिजिट मिलता जा रहा था। अब, दूसरे छोर पर ट्रिन-ट्रिन हो रही थी और रिसीवर किसी भी क्षण उठाया जा सकता था। रिसीवर उठाया जाए, तब तक के समय का इस्तेमाल करने के लिए आकाश ने दिव्यांग पर फिर एक बार वेधक दृष्टिपात किया और कहा, "आप जैसों ने ही इस देश का बेड़ा ग़र्क़ कर रखा है, मिस्टर दिव्यांग पटेल!"

दिव्यांग नामक चिकने घड़े पर से पानी जिस पल गिरा, उसी पल बह गया। सुचिक्कण घड़ा फिर से चमचमाने लगा। दिव्यांग ने जो जवाब दिया, वह लाजवाब ही था, "देश का क्या है, साहब! देश तो चलता रहता है!"

सीधा-सरल जवाब! किसी भी विवेकशील व्यक्ति को तिलमिला दे और ख़ामोश भी कर दे, ऐसा जवाब!

किन्तु दूसरों के जवाबों से ख़ामोश हो जाना आकाश ने कभी नहीं सीखा। हाँ, अपनी इच्छा से वह चुप्पी साध जाए, यह अलग बात है। दिव्यांग को उसने सिर से

पैर तक देखा, जैसे उसे इसी बात पर सन्देह हो कि दिव्यांग मानव है या नहीं। फिर अपने हर शब्द को साफ़-साफ़, जुदा-जुदा उच्चारित किया आकाश ने, "ऐसा है, मिस्टर पटेल! चूहे हर जहाज़ में होते हैं, लेकिन चूहे इतने नहीं बढ़ जाने चाहिए कि उनके वज़न से जहाज़ ही डूब जाए!"

दिव्यांग में इतना बूता नहीं था कि आकाश की बात की ऊँचाई नाप सके, समझ सके। बात वह आधी समझा, लेकिन मुसकराया इस प्रकार, जैसे पूरी समझ गया हो। आकाश ने उसकी मुसकान को देखने लायक भी न समझा।

फोन की ट्रिन-ट्रिन, जो दूसरे छोर पर हो रही थी, रुक गई। ज़ाहिर था, रिसीवर उठाया जा चुका था। आकाश के कानों तक किरकिराता स्वर पहुँचा, "डॉक्टर चांडक हियर!"

आकाश ने रिसीवर में कहा, "हैलो, डॉक्टर!" फिर, रिसीवर के माउथ-पीस को हथेली से ढाँकते हुए, दिव्यांग से कहा, "क्या आप चाहते हैं, मिस्टर पटेल, कि भारत देश का जहाज़ चूहों के वज़न से डूब जाए? चूहों के वज़न से?" दिव्यांग के उत्तर की परवाह किए बग़ैर, माउथ-पीस पर से हथेली हटाते हुए आकाश ने कहना जारी किया, "हैलो, डॉक्टर चांडक! आकाश हियर..."

डॉक्टर चांडक का किरकिराता स्वर, "हैलो, माय डियर लाइट-हाउस! हाऊ आर यू?"

"आय एम फाइन, डॉक्टर! थैंक्स फॉर द कॉम्प्लीमेंट! एक पता नोट करिए, डॉक्टर साहब! यहाँ रेड चल रही है और आपको यहाँ आना है—फ़ौरन! लिखिए पता..."

आ चुके थे डॉक्टर चांडक। एकदम छरहरे, लम्बे थे वह, किन्तु जर्जर नहीं। लेटी पड़ी शिल्पा की जाँच भी उन्होंने कर ली थी। आयकर के पैनल-डॉक्टर होने के नाते उनके नाम बुलौवा तो कभी भी, कहीं से भी आ जाता था। ज़्यादातर मामलों में उन्होंने यही देखा था, लोग सचमुच घबरा जाते हैं। काला धन इकट्ठा करते, छिपाते वक़्त लोग यही सोचकर चलते हैं कि आयकर का छापा दूसरों पर पड़ सकता है, हम पर नहीं, किन्तु जब उन्हीं पर छापा अचानक पड़ता है, तब वे हताश और हक्के-बक्के हो जाते हैं, इस हद तक कि लोगों पर दिल के दौरे पड़ते भी देखे गए हैं। आयकर अधिकारी, ऐसी नाजुक स्थिति में, छापा रोक देते हैं, सन्देहास्पद स्थानों को केवल सील करके चले जाते हैं, जल्द ही दुबारा आने के लिए। दिल के दौरे जैसी चरम सीमा की प्रतिक्रिया यदि 'पार्टी' पर नहीं हुई है, तो वे, अपने पैनल-डॉक्टर की सलाह लेते हुए, प्रयास यही करते हैं कि छापे की कार्रवाई रोकनी न पड़े। अगर किसी पर दिल

का दौरा पड़ ही गया हो, तो ऐसे व्यक्ति की सुरक्षा का पूरा इन्तज़ाम हो जाने के बाद ही आयकर अधिकारी विदा लेते हैं।

दूसरी ओर, एक सच्चाई यह भी है कि छापा पड़ते ही, उसे टालने के लिए लोग तुरन्त बीमार पड़ जाते हैं, यानी, बीमारी का सुन्दर अभिनय करने लगते हैं। ऐसे अभिनय को पहचानना मुश्किल तो नहीं, किन्तु डॉक्टर बुलाए बिना गुज़ारा भी कैसे हो!

दिव्यांग और शैलेश खड़े थे। मनीषा और मिस पंड्या खड़ी थीं। दोनों पंच, मिस्टर कुलकर्णी और मिसेज तिवारी, खड़े थे। आकाश खड़ा था और डॉक्टर चांडक भी, जो शिल्पा की जाँच करने के लिए बैठ गए थे, अब उठकर खड़े हो रहे थे। एक अकेली शिल्पा थी, जो लेटी हुई थी, बाक़ी सब खड़े थे। डॉक्टर चांडक ने आकाश की ओर एक सार्थक नज़र डाली। उस सूक्ष्म नज़र को केवल आकाश ही पहचानता था। बहुत गम्भीर नज़र, किन्तु भीतर-ही-भीतर हँसती हुई। बीमार पड़ने के सुन्दर ढोंग का एक और नायाब नमूना! डॉक्टर चांडक ने उठकर, एक पल चुप रहकर, फिर से आकाश पर ही सूक्ष्म नज़र फेंककर, आख़िर अपना फ़ैसला सुना दिया, "मिसेज पटेल को शॉक तो लगा है, लेकिन वह एक दिलेर महिला हैं। उन्हें ऐसा कुछ नहीं हुआ है, जिससे हमें आज के छापे को रोकना पड़ जाए।"

शिल्पा तीखी होकर बोली, "अरे, यह कैसा डॉक्टर है! हमारे फैमिली डॉक्टर को बुलाइए।"

इस बार, न जाने कैसे, दिव्यांग ने झिड़क दिया शिल्पा को, "पड़ी रे चुपचाप! बहू थयूँ!" फिर डॉक्टर से कहा, "आप इसे कुछ गोली-वोली दे दें।"

डॉक्टर चांडक ने परम सेवा भाव से कुछ गोलियाँ शिल्पा को अपने हाथ से, गरम पानी से, निगलवाईं। आकाश ने मन-ही-मन कहा, 'शायद ये सिर्फ़ कैल्सियम की गोलियाँ हैं।' जाते-जाते डॉक्टर ने दो-दो घंटे में तीन-तीन की दर से लेने के लिए अनेक गोलियाँ बैग से निकालकर शिल्पा की सेवा में धर दीं। शिल्पा का कन्धा थपथपाकर वह बोले, "रिलैक्स! रिलैक्स!"

आकाश ने मन-ही-मन इसका हिन्दी अनुवाद किया, 'पड़ी रह! पड़ी रह!'

लेकिन चेहरे से तो आकाश वही धीर-गम्भीर! डॉक्टर चांडक ने भी धीर-धीर, गम्भीर-गम्भीर मुद्रा में विदा ली, "मैं चलूँ..." इन शब्दों के साथ।

ट्रिन-ट्रिन! बजता टेलीफोन। आकाश का रिसीवर उठाना, "हैलो?"

और उधर से जनक की किलकती आवाज़, "सर! बच्चे मिल गए!"

आकाश के गले में जैसे उस किलक की प्रतिध्वनि उठी, "रियली, जनक?"

'यस, सर!''—''वापस ले आओ तीनों को! गुड जॉब!''—आकाश ने गद्‌गद होकर कहा। फिर दिव्यांग को बताया, ''बधाई, मिस्टर पटेल! आपके बच्चे मिल गए!''—सुनते ही दिव्यांग का चेहरा काग़ज़ जैसा सफ़ेद हो गया।

दिव्यांग को सूझा नहीं, अब वह क्या करे। संसार का नियम है, परेशान बच्चा माँ की तरफ़ और परेशान पति पत्नी की तरफ़ भागता है। इसी नियम का पालन करते दिव्यांग के क़दम, अपने आप, शयन-कक्ष की ओर उठ गए, जहाँ पत्नी-परमेश्वरी शिल्पा पलंग पर शोभायमान, चित्त पड़ी थी। दिव्यांग के होंठों पर गुजराती भाषा के ये शब्द थे, ''शिल्पा! बच्चाँ आवी रह्याँ छे!'' जैसे कातर ढंग से दिव्यांग पटेल ने अपनी पटेलानी की शरण लेनी चाही थी, उसे देख आकाश को अनायास अपनी अर्द्धांगिनी याद आ गई—शालिनी! घर में शालिनी अभी क्या कर रही होगी? आकाश ने अन्दाज़ा लगाना चाहा। वह अन्दाज़ा न लगा सका, क्योंकि न चाहते हुए भी उसका ध्यान टेलीफोन के डायल की ओर खिंचा जा रहा था। डायल...कौन घुमा रहा है डायल? स्वयं आकाश! कौन-सा नम्बर घुमा रहा था आकाश? शालिनी को स्मृति की डिबिया में बन्द कर आकाश ने ग़ौर करना, समझना चाहा, कौन-सा नम्बर घुमा रही थीं उसकी उँगलियाँ? ओह! आकाश को खुलकर हँसने का मन हुआ, क्योंकि अन्यमनस्क होते हुए भी वह, यन्त्रवत्, कंट्रोल-रूम का नम्बर घुमा रहा था...

आयकर विभाग का कंट्रोल-रूम...जहाँ पाँचों छापों का सूचना-केन्द्र था...जहाँ से, छापों के दौरान, किसी भी तरह की सलाह ली जा सकती थी, किसी भी तरह की सहायता भी पाई जा सकती थी...दिव्यांग पटेल के फ्लैट में घुसने के साथ घटनाचक्र ऐसी तेज़ी के साथ घूमा था कि आकाश को याद ही नहीं रहा था, कंट्रोल-रूम के साथ बात करना...अपनी सब सूचनाएँ कंट्रोल-रूम को देना और दूसरों की सब सूचनाएँ वहाँ से प्राप्त करना...

किन्तु आकाश की उँगलियों ने, कम्प्यूटर की तरह, स्वयं संचालित होकर, अपना काम कर दिखाया था—एक सही नम्बर पर डायल घुमाकर! टेलीफोन के दूसरे छोर पर होती ट्रिन-ट्रिन जब आकाश ने सुनी, तब उसे पक्का यक़ीन था कि ट्रिन-ट्रिन किसी रांग-नम्बर पर नहीं, बल्कि कंट्रोल-रूम में ही हो रही थी...

उस ओर, रिसीवर उठाया जाते ही ट्रिन-ट्रिन रुक गई और एक रोबीले पुरुष स्वर ने कहा, ''हैलो?''

आकाश ने संवाद शुरू किया, ''हैलो! कंट्रोल-रूम?''

''यस!''

''आकाश स्पीकिंग!''

''शूट!''

"छापे की शुरुआत ठीक छह-पैंतीस पर। गृह-प्रवेश में ख़ास तक़लीफ़ नहीं। पार्टी होस्टाइल। पंचनामा डन। सर्च शुरू कर रहे हैं।"

"ब्रेवो!"

"दूसरे छापों की पोज़ीशन?"

"सभी छापे एक साथ, एक समय पड़े—छह-पैंतीस पर। सभी जगह सर्च शुरू।"

"दैट्स फाइन!"

सहसा कंट्रोल-रूम में बैठे ऑफिसर का लहजा बदल गया। उसने हलकी बेताबी से कहा, "सुनिए, आकाश जी!"

"हँ...हँ..."

"वार्डन रोड का छापा मिसेज अग्रवाल सँभाल रही हैं न? उन्हें लगातार आपका फोन एंगेज़्ड मिल रहा है। वह आपसे ज़रूरी बात करना चाहती हैं।"

"ओके!" आकाश ने बात ध्यान में रख ली, "मैं ही उन्हें अपनी ओर से फोन कर लूँगा। बस, थोड़ी देर में। लगता है, मिसेज अग्रवाल किसी उलझन में फँस गई हैं..."

उलझन, सच पूछें तो, बस, इतनी थी कि मिसेज अग्रवाल का दिल नहीं मान रहा था। वार्डन रोड के उस फ्लैट की एक-एक चीज़ उन्होंने हटाकर देखी थी। सजावटी फाल्स-सीलिंग उन्होंने जगह-जगह तोड़ दी थी। फ़र्श उखाड़ डाला था। दीवारों को जगह-जगह फोड़ दिया था। जहाँ भी रंचमात्र भी सन्देह हुआ था, उन्होंने कसकर तलाशी ली थी। गृह-स्वामी का भी जवाब नहीं था। पूरा सहयोग मिल रहा था उसकी ओर से। किसी भी तोड़फोड़ का विरोध नहीं किया था उसने। किसी भी चीज़ को हटाने, सरकाने, खोलकर या तोड़कर दिखाने के आदेश का अनादर नहीं किया था उसने। वह गम्भीर अवश्य था, खिन्न भी था, किन्तु असहयोगी एक क्षण के लिए भी नहीं।

कहाँ तो आशा थी चमचमाते हीरों की और कहाँ पीतल का चम्मच भी नहीं मिल रहा था, ऐसा कि जिसे ज़ब्त किया जा सकता। ऐसा नहीं कि फ्लैट में क़ीमती चीज़ें नहीं थीं। निस्सन्देह वह एक अमीर और शौकीन आदमी का फ्लैट था और वहाँ जो कुछ था, क़ीमती ही था, किन्तु हर चीज़ की ख़रीद से सम्बन्धित काग़ज़ात गृह-स्वामी ने मृदु मुसकान के साथ प्रस्तुत कर दिए थे। वहाँ सभी कुछ 'डिक्लेयर्ड' था, 'व्हाइट' था, 'ब्लैक' कुछ नहीं था...

लेकिन क्या सचमुच ऐसा हो सकता है? वैसे, इस संसार में असम्भव तो कुछ नहीं है, किन्तु आज के ज़माने को देखते हुए...और फिर, आकाश का जो विशेष

सूत्र था—'आकाशवाणी'—उसके कथन को देखते हुए...'पार्टी' क़तई दूध की धुली नहीं है। मुमकिन है, 'पार्टी' के पाँच फ्लैटों में से केवल यहाँ का फ्लैट दूध से धोकर रखा गया हो, काले धन की परछाईं को भी यहाँ प्रवेश न करने दिया गया हो, किन्तु...

मिसेज अग्रवाल का दिल मानता, तब न! 'कहीं कोई चाल ज़रूर है...' वह बार-बार अपने आपको सावधान कर रही थीं।

गृह-स्वामी की वृद्धा माँ से, जो कुछ भी वहाँ हो रहा था, या हो चुका था, देखा नहीं जा रहा था। एक-एक क़ीमती सामान तितर-बितर! कौन से अपराध की सज़ा थी यह? लगभग नब्बे बरस की वह वृद्धा, मिसेज अग्रवाल का मूल्यांकन, केवल एक खलनायिका के रूप में ही कर सकती थी। वृद्धा के अनुसार, ईश्वर इस निर्मम खलनायिका को, कभी-न-कभी, कड़ी से-कड़ी सज़ा ज़रूर देगा! मिसेज अग्रवाल ने वृद्धा को समझाने का पूरा प्रयास किया था कि फ़ाल्स-सीलिंग या दीवारों आदि में जो तोड़-फोड़ हुई है, उसकी मरम्मत आयकर विभाग की ओर से करवा दी जाएगी, किन्तु वृद्धा के होंठों से बार-बार एक ही वाक्य फूट रहा था, "भगवान सब देख रहा है! भगवान सब देख रहा है!"

शुरू में तो वृद्धा थोड़ी-बहुत, इधर-उधर, चलती-फिरती दिखाई दी थी, किन्तु ज्यों-ज्यों आयकर विभाग ने तलाशी आगे चलाई थी और फ्लैट का हर सामान इधर-उधर होने लगा था, त्यों-त्यों वृद्धा को मर्मांतक चोट लगती गई थी और उसने सचमुच भगवान की मूर्तियों के सामने नत-मस्तक होकर बैठ जाने में ही ग़नीमत देखी थी। वृद्धा कभी तो विष्णु जी के सामने मस्तक झुका रही है, कभी लक्ष्मी जी के सामने और कभी सरस्वती जी के सामने...बार-बार वृद्धा के मुँह से वही वाक्य फूट रहा है, "भगवान सब देख रहा है!"

भगवान का देखना...सब-कुछ देखना...ज़रूर भगवान के देखने में, भगवान की आँखों में चमत्कार है...मिसेज अग्रवाल ने तर्क लड़ाया था। काला धन छिपाने के लिए पवित्र मूर्तियों का भी इस्तेमाल करने से चूकते नहीं हैं लोग! पवित्र मूर्तियों की आँखों में क़ीमती हीरे जड़े मिल जाते हैं, यह कोई अजूबा नहीं है...तो क्या... वृद्धा के उस...तोता-रटन्त वाक्य के पीछे...इसी तरह का कोई रहस्य छिपा है? मिसेज अग्रवाल ने गृह-स्वामी से, और उसकी वृद्धा माँ से, भारी क्षमा-याचना करने के बाद, उन तीनों ईश्वरीय मूर्तियों की सूक्ष्म जाँच की थी। मिसेज अग्रवाल अपने साथ जिस जौहरी को लेकर आई थीं—वैल्यूअर के रूप में—उसने तीनों मूर्तियों की छहों आँखों को भली-भाँति देखा-परखा था और गम्भीरता से कह दिया था, "आँखों में मामूली काँच ही जड़े हैं। कहीं कोई हीरा, माणिक, मोती नहीं जड़ा है..."

वे तीनों मूर्तियाँ डेढ़-डेढ़ फीट की थीं। कितनी सौम्य, सुन्दर, नाजुक, पवित्र! उन पर सन्देह करना ही अनैतिक लग रहा था। एक ही कतार में स्थापित थीं तीनों। भगवान विष्णु समस्त संसार का सुन्दर-सुचारु लालन-पालन करने का वचन देते, महा-सर्प शेषनाग के महा-कुंडलों पर शयन कर रहे थे। देवी लक्ष्मी अधिकतम उदारता से धन की वर्षा करती खड़ी थीं, अपने प्रिय वाहन उलूक पर आरूढ़ होकर। देवी सरस्वती ज्ञान और गरिमा के महा-सागर सी लग रही थीं। वह सवार थीं लम्बी-लहरीली गर्दन वाले, सुन्दर, सुकोमल, सफ़ेद हंस पर।

तीनों के छहों नेत्रों की सूक्ष्म जाँच हो जाने के बाद, मिसेज अग्रवाल ज्यों ही सामने से हटीं, वृद्धा ने परम और चरम भक्ति-भाव से, तीनों मूर्तियों के सामने झुक-झुककर, फिर वही रटन्त शुरू कर दी, ''भगवान सब देख रहा है!''

मिसेज अग्रवाल ने वृद्धा की पीठ स्नेह से सहलाकर कहा, ''हाँ, हाँ, माता जी! भगवान सब देख रहा है। अगर हमने कोई भूल की है, तो भगवान हमें अवश्य दंड देगा। अब आप उठिए और भीतर आराम से लेटिए।''

वृद्धा न तो उठने को तैयार, न बड़बड़ाहट छोड़ने को तैयार, ''भगवान सब...''

उधर, दिव्यांग के फ्लैट में, दोनों बच्चों और एक अदद नौकरानी की तीव्र प्रतीक्षा की जा रही थी। डोर-बेल ज्यों ही बजी, मिस पंड्या ने दरवाज़ा खोल दिया और बच्चों को सामने देखते ही कहा, ''पधारिए!''

बच्चे दौड़कर फ्लैट में घुसे। उनके बैग्स उठाए नौकरानी हताश और थकी हुई लग रही थी। चेहरे पर अपराध भावना पोते नौकरानी ने बेमन से फ्लैट में क़दम रखे। पीछे-पीछे जनक और मि. थत्ते अन्दर आए। मि. थत्ते ने आते ही खटाक् से दरवाज़ा बन्द कर दिया।

दोनों बच्चे बुरी तरह नर्वस थे। दिव्यांग के पैरों से दोनों एक-साथ लिपट पड़े और रुआँसे होकर बोले, ''पप्पा!''

दिव्यांग ने गहरी साँस लेकर उन्हें थपथपाया।

तब तक जनक ने लपककर दोनों बच्चों के स्कूल-बैग्स नौकरानी के कन्धे से उतारकर अपने क़ब्ज़े में ले लिये थे। जनक जल्दी-जल्दी दोनों बैग्स खोलने लगा।

एक बारगी तो आकाश की भी धड़कन तेज़ हो गई। क्या निकलने जा रहा था इन स्कूल-बैग्स में से? कितने करोड़ का हीरा? हीरा या हीरे?

अन्दाज़े के अनुसार ही, बच्चे ज़्यादा दूर नहीं ले जाए गए थे। वे केवल चार इमारतों के फ़ासले पर, दिव्यांग के एक दोस्त के फ्लैट में से बरामद हुए। सिक्योरिटी गार्ड को बहलाकर जनक और मि. थत्ते ने सहज ही मालूम कर लिया था कि आसपास

के किन-किन फ्लैटों, कोठियों में दिव्यांग का पारिवारिक आना-जाना था। ऐसे सभी ठिकानों की जाँच, जनक और मि. थत्ते, फटाफट करते चले थे। गिनती के ही मिनटों में वे दोनों बच्चों एवं एक अदद नौकरानी के आमने-सामने खड़े थे। नौकरानी उन्हें देखते ही चकरा गई थीं। बेचारी ने सोचा होगा, कहीं मेरी पूरी तलाशी फिर से न ली जाए! उसने झट से स्वीकार कर लिया था कि 'मालिकों' का आदेश होने के ही कारण वह बच्चों को स्कूल के बजाय यहाँ ले आई थी...

दिव्यांग के फ्लैट में, बच्चों के दोनों स्कूल-बैग्स खोल रहा जनक, यही याद कर रहा था कि उसे और मि. थत्ते को अचानक सामने देखकर नौकरानी का रंग किस बुरी तरह उड़ा था...

दोनों लंच-बॉक्स, स्कूल-बैग्स में से, बाहर निकाले जा चुके थे। जनक ने एक लंच-बॉक्स हाथ में लेकर खोलना चाहा कि–

"ठहरो, जनक!" यह आदेश आकाश का था। जनक के हाथ रुक गए। उसने अचरज से देखा अपने उच्च अधिकारी की ओर। लंच-बॉक्स खोलने से मना क्यों कर रहा था आकाश?

आकाश की दृष्टि दिव्यांग पर थी, "मिस्टर पटेल! ध्यान रहे! लंच-बॉक्स खुलने के साथ हमारी तलाशी शुरू मानी जाएगी। हम आपको एक मौक़ा और देते हैं। अगर इन दोनों लंच-बॉक्सेस को हम नहीं, आप खोलें और इनमें जो भी चीज़ छिपी है, उसे अपने हाथों से निकालकर हमारे सामने रख दें, तो हम यही मानकर चलेंगे कि आपने काले धन को अपनी इच्छा से हमारे सामने डिक्लेयर कर दिया। ऐसी सूरत में हम आप पर बिलकुल भी पेनाल्टी नहीं लगाएँगे...हम आपके दोस्त हैं, मिस्टर पटेल! हम बिलकुल नहीं चाहते, आप पर पेनाल्टी लगे..."

आकाश का इशारा पाकर जनक ने दोनों लंच-बॉक्स आकाश के हाथ में रख दिए। दोनों लंच-बॉक्स दिव्यांग के सामने प्रस्तुत-सा करता आकाश, दिव्यांग की ओर क़दम उठाने लगा। दिव्यांग पटेल के लिए यह भारी कशमकश की घड़ी थी। आकाश को वह अपना हितैषी कैसे मान ले एकाएक? आकाश तो उसकी 'मेहनत की कमाई' पर 'डाका' डालने आया था! लेकिन यही आकाश उसे पेनाल्टी से बचाना चाहता है! क्या सचमुच ऐसा हो सकता है? ज़रूर इसमें कोई धोखा होना चाहिए...

दिव्यांग कुछ फ़ैसला कर सके, इससे पहले, उसकी महा-पत्नी शिल्पा, बिफरती हुई वहाँ प्रवेश कर चुकी थी। जो शिल्पा चक्कर खा-खाकर, पलंग पर एकदम चित्त पड़ी थी, वही उस वक़्त बिना कोई चक्कर खाए, कुछ इस तरह प्रकट हो रही थी कि यदि उसने अपने पति-परमेश्वर की सहायता न की, तो नैया डूब जाएगी। दूसरी ओर, शिल्पा यह भी समझ चुकी थी कि अब नैया को डूबने से नहीं बचाया जा सकेगा। इसीलिए उसके मुँह से जो वाक्य बार-बार फूट रहा था, वह एक डरी हुई

और नाराज़ सन्नारी का वाक्य था। वह किसी की नैया के तारणहार का आत्म-विश्वासी वाक्य नहीं था। शिल्पा का सुन्दर चेहरा ज़रा विकृत हो गया था, जब वह कह रही थी, "लूट लिया! लूट लिया हमको!"

आकाश ने शिल्पा की उपेक्षा की, जैसे शिल्पा थी ही नहीं, और केवल दिव्यांग पर नज़र जमाकर पूछा, "बोलिए, मिस्टर पटेल! क्या कहते हैं?"

दिव्यांग ने दीन-हीन होकर अपनी महा-पत्नी से पूछा, "शिल्पा! हूँ शूँ बोलूँ, शिल्पा?"

अब आकाश मानो एक-एक पल की बचत करता हुआ आगे बढ़ना चाहता था। उसका हर शब्द ड्राइंग-रूम में थर्राहट-सी पैदा कर रहा था, "मैं सिर्फ़ तीन तक गिनती गिनूँगा और फिर...लंच-बॉक्स खुद खोल लूँगा! एक!"

कहाँ तो शिल्पा दिव्यांग को सहारा देने आई थी और कहाँ वह स्वयं ही दिव्यांग का सहारा लेती सिहरने लगी। बोली, "कुछ नहीं है, साहब! इनमें कुछ नहीं है!"

दोनों बच्चे अब दिव्यांग को छोड़कर शिल्पा के पैरों से लिपट पड़े, "मम्मी! मम्मी!"

दिव्यांग के स्वर में विलाप का स्पर्श था, "शिल्पा! तारो लंच-बॉक्स नो चमत्कार गयो पाणी माँ!"

आकाश ने ऐलान किया, "दो!"

दिव्यांग शिल्पा को मना रहा था, "डिक्लेयर करी दे, पगली!"

शिल्पा के नेत्र और स्वर, दोनों विस्फारित थे, "नहीं...नहीं..."

'तीन' बोलने से पहले आकाश ने कहा, "होशियार!"

फिर, आकाश 'तीन' बोलने जा ही रहा था कि शिल्पा बोल पड़ी, "ठहरिए!"

आकाश ठहर गया। शिल्पा उसकी ओर बढ़ने लगी। जब वह दोनों लंच-बॉक्स आकाश से ले रही थी, अपने हाथों का लरजना वह छिपा नहीं पा रही थी। उसने लंच-बॉक्स खोलने शुरू किए। उसका धैर्य एकदम ही छूट जाने लगा और वह भहराकर बैठ गई।

आख़िर शिल्पा ने दोनों लंच-बॉक्स खोल लिये। आकाश ने देखा, वह लंच-बॉक्सेस में भरी अनेक टॉफियाँ अपने हाथों में ले रही थी। शिल्पा उठी। मुश्किल से ही उठ पाई वह। सभी टॉफियाँ उसने अंजलि में भर ली थीं। जैसे श्रद्धा-पुष्प अर्पित कर रही हो, इस तरह उसने तमाम टॉफियाँ आकाश को दे दीं और कहा, "लीजिए! और खुश रहिए!"

आकाश ने टॉफियाँ ले लीं, किन्तु शिल्पा ने जो व्यंग्य किया था, उसका जवाब देना निहायत ज़रूरी था। वह बोला, "आप तो ऐसे कह रही हैं, शिल्पा जी, जैसे मैं यह सब अपने घर ले जा रहा होऊँ! देवी जी! जो भी चीज़ आपके यहाँ से ज़ब्त

होगी, आयकर कार्यालय में जमा की जाएगी। टैक्स भरिए, छुड़ाकर ले जाइए। ज्यों ही आप टैक्स भरकर, छुड़ाकर ले जाएँगी, यह ब्लैक मनी व्हाइट मनी बन जाएगी और आप इसका खुलकर इस्तेमाल कर सकेंगी!''

शिल्पा तिलमिलाकर बोली, ''साथ में यह भी कह दीजिए कि आप कितने दयावान हैं! क्योंकि आप ही ने हमें पेनाल्टी से बचाया है! लेकिन मैं सिर्फ़ इतना कहूँगी–ले जाइए! ले जाइए!''

और शिल्पा वहाँ खड़ी न रह सकी। पैरों से लिपटते बच्चों को अलग कर वह दौड़ पड़ी, ताकि वापस अपने शयन-कक्ष में समा सके। इस बार वह अपने पलंग में ऐसी चित्त गिरने वाली थी कि जिसे संसार का कोई डॉक्टर ढोंग कहकर टाल न सके।

माँ से जुदा हुए बच्चे सकते में आ गए थे। उनसे ड्राइंग-रूम में खड़ा नहीं रहा जा रहा था, किन्तु माँ के पीछे-पीछे, शयन-कक्ष में जाने का साहस भी वे नहीं बटोर पा रहे थे। बच्चों ने एक-दूसरे के हाथ पकड़ लिये और अपने पिता दिव्यांग पटेल की ओर ताकना शुरू कर दिया।

आकाश, जनक, मिस्टर थत्ते, मिस पंड्या एवं आयकर विभाग के सभी कर्मचारियों का ध्यान अब उन टॉफियों पर केन्द्रित था, जो आकाश की हथेलियों में थमी थीं। आकाश उन्हें हौले-हौले उछाल रहा था। जनक ने बेताबी से कहा, ''सर! ये टॉफियाँ देखने में ही इतनी स्वादिष्ट लग रही हैं कि खुलने के बाद तो ये...''

आकाश बुदबुदाया, ''खोलते हैं...खोलते हैं...''

अब, आकाश की उँगलियाँ टॉफियों के रैपर उतार रही थीं। वे बड़े आकार की टॉफियाँ थीं, जिनके बीच में मावा भरा होता है। रैपर उतरने के बाद आकाश के हाथ में जो आया, वह टॉफियाँ ही थीं, किन्तु बारीकी से देखने पर राज़ खुला कि कुछ टॉफियाँ बीच से कटी हुई हैं!

जैसे डिबिया खुल जाए, वैसे ही वे टॉफियाँ बीच से खुल गईं! उनके बीच का मावा खुरचकर निकाला जा चुका था। इससे भीतर जो पोल बन गई थी, वहाँ फिट कर दिया गया था–चमचमाता हीरा! ऐसे कुल चार हीरे बरामद हुए।

आकाश बेसाख़्ता बोल पड़ा, ''वाह! क्या बात है! फैंटास्टिक! ग़ज़ब!''

चार-चार हीरे आकाश की हथेली पर चमचमा रहे थे कि–

फ्लैट के बन्द दरवाज़े की घंटी टन्न से बजी। मिस पंड्या ने हाथ बढ़ाकर दरवाज़ा खोल दिया। खुलते दरवाज़े के साथ-साथ मिस पंड्या किनारे भी हटती गईं। फलस्वरूप, वह लगातार दरवाज़े की ओट में बनी रहीं। जिन महाशय का शुभ आगमन हुआ था, वह न देख सके कि दरवाज़ा किसने खोला। उन्होंने तो प्रवेश करते ही, अपनी ही धुन में बोलना शुरू कर दिया, ''पटेल साहब! आ गया मैं! जड़ी-बूटी लेने!''

ये सारे शब्द आगन्तुक ने काफ़ी ऊँचे स्वर में बोले, ताकि 'पटेल साहब' फ्लैट की चाहे जिस गहराई में होते, उन्हें सुनाई पड़ ही जाता। ऊँचे स्वर के कारण आगन्तुक का भारी उत्साह भी प्रकट हुआ जा रहा था, किन्तु...तभी आगन्तुक का ध्यान आयकर विभाग के उन तमाम कर्मचारियों पर गया, जो ड्राइंग-रूम में चारों तरफ़ फैले खड़े थे और पैनी नज़रों से आगन्तुक को ही देखे जा रहे थे। आगन्तुक की बोलती बन्द हो गई। बोलती जब खुली, वह इतना ही बुदबुदा सका, "मैं...ग़लत जगह तो नहीं आ गया?"

आकाश हँसा, "जी नहीं! आप बिलकुल सही जगह आए हैं। पधारिए! आप ही का इन्तज़ार था! आप इसी जड़ी-बूटी को लेने आए हैं न?"—और आकाश अपनी हथेली के हीरों को हौले-हौले उछालने लगा। वे उछलते हीरे आपस में टकराकर कितने सनसनीख़ेज़ ढंग से बज रहे थे।

न केवल आकाश ने, बल्कि फ्लैट में मौजूद सभी आयकर अधिकारियों ने एक नज़र में पहचान लिया था, कौन था वह आगन्तुक। पाँचों फ्लैट्स पर छापे सुबह की पहली किरण फूटने के साथ शुरू कर देने की जो योजना बनानी पड़ी थी, उसके वास्तविक सूत्रधार यही आगन्तुक महोदय ही तो थे! 'पार्टी' का कोई 'बहुत भरोसे का आदमी' सुबह आठ बजे के आसपास, पाँच में से किसी एक फ्लैट पर आने वाला था, ताकि हीरों को हासिल करे और फिर ले जाकर कहीं छिपा दे। इस आदमी के आगमन से बहुत पहले ही, यानी सूर्योदय के साथ ही, पाँचों छापे एक साथ मार देने की योजना बनती ही नहीं, अगर 'बहुत भरोसे का यह आदमी' सुबह आठ बजे नहीं, दोपहर बारह बजे आने वाला होता। धन्यवाद, प्रिय आगन्तुक! तेरे दबाव के कारण ही सबको अपने टीम-वर्क का परिचय देने का मौक़ा मिला।

आकाश आगन्तुक के एकदम नज़दीक आ खड़ा हुआ था। उसके कन्धे पर हाथ रख आकाश ने पूछा, "क्या नाम है आपका?"

आगन्तुक ऐसा सन्न रह गया था कि कन्धे पर से आकाश का हाथ हटाने तक का होश नहीं था उसे। नाम-वाम भला वह क्या बताता! आकाश ने उसके कन्धे को दो-तीन बार थपथपा दिया। फिर कहा, "हमें मालूम था, आप यहाँ सुबह-सुबह आने वाले हैं। 'जड़ी-बूटी' लेने! हीरों के लिए यह कोड-नेम अच्छा बनाया है आपने! यह सूझबूझ आप ही की है न? या किसी और की? 'जड़ी-बूटी' को आप किस आश्रम में घिसने वाले थे, प्यारे भाई?"

आगन्तुक ने अपने सूखे गले को तर करने के लिए थूक निगला। अस्फुट-सा वह इतना बोल सका, "जी, ले...लेकिन..."

"मेरा ख़याल है, आपके पास और भी कई पार्टियाँ होंगी, जिनके काले धन को आप डाकिए की तरह इधर-से-उधर ले जाते होंगे। बताइए, क्या नाम हैं उन पार्टियों के?" आकाश ने आगन्तुक की आँखों में आँखें डालकर पूछा।

किन्तु आगन्तुक की ज़बान मानो उसके मुँह के ही अन्दर घुलकर ग़ायब हो गई थी। आकाश से नज़र चुराने की लाख कोशिश वह कर रहा था, लेकिन आकाश एक साथ न जाने कितनी दिशाओं से घूर रहा था उसे! बारम्बार उसकी नज़र आकाश से भिड़ ही जाती।

तभी आगन्तुक को दिव्यांग दिखाई दे गया। कैसा कमाल था कि वह सामने ही खड़ा था, किन्तु नज़र अब आ रहा था! हताश दिव्यांग से आगन्तुक ने आँखों-आँखों में पूछा, 'माजरा क्या है?'

दिव्यांग ने अपने गले पर इस संकेत में उँगली फेरी कि गला कट गया है।

अब तो स्वयं आगन्तुक ने भी अपना गला कटा हुआ महसूस किया। आकाश ने उसे एक कोने में, स्टूल पर, बिठा दिया था। मुसकराते आकाश के स्वच्छ दाँत चमक रहे थे और चमक रही थीं आँखें भी।

"फ़िलहाल हम आपका नाम मिस्टर डा रख देते हैं!" आकाश ने कहा, "डा यानी डाकिया! हाँ, तो...मिस्टर डा साहब! जब तक हम यहाँ हैं, आप यहीं बैठेंगे और जब हम यहाँ से जाएँगे, आप हमारे साथ चलेंगे—इन्कम-टैक्स ऑफिस! बात आई समझ में? वहाँ आपके साथ हम थोड़ा...प्रेमालाप करेंगे। हम जो भी जानना चाहेंगे, सब आपको उगल देना होगा हमारे सामने! थैंक्यू, मिस्टर डा अचानक प्रकट होने के लिए!"

वार्डन रोड के फ्लैट में, मिसेज अग्रवाल की उलझन जस-की-तस बनी हुई थी। वह वृद्धा अभी तक विष्णु-लक्ष्मी-सरस्वती की पवित्र मूर्तियों के सामने डटी बैठी थी, अपनी उसी रटन्त को जारी रखे हुए, "भगवान सब देख रहा है!"

मिसेज अग्रवाल ने गृह-स्वामी से कहा, "मेरी अब भी यही राय है कि डॉक्टर बुला लें। हमारा छापा अचानक पड़ने से आपकी माता जी को शॉक लग गया है। तभी तो वह लगातार एक ही वाक्य रटे जा रही हैं।"

गृह-स्वामी ने विनम्रता से कहा, "डॉक्टर बुलाने से मैं मना तो नहीं कर रहा, लेकिन उसकी ज़रूरत नहीं है। बरसों से मेरी माता जी की मनोदशा ऐसी ही चल रही है। सुबह से किसी एक बात को लेकर बैठ जाएँगी और फिर...उसी बात को सारा दिन रटती रहेंगी..."

मिसेज अग्रवाल दुःख के स्वर में बोलीं, "हमारे छापे ने आपके पूरे फ्लैट का हुलिया बदल दिया। सोफे और क़ालीन को भी नहीं छोड़ा हमने! उन्हें भी उधेड़कर, चीरकर देखा! इन तीन मूर्तियों को भी हम कितनी बारीकी से जाँच-परख चुके, लेकिन..."

मिसेज अग्रवाल के अधूरे वाक्य को गृह-स्वामी ने पूरा किया, ''लेकिन कहीं भी काला धन पकड़ में न आया! दरअसल, इस फ्लैट में काला धन है ही नहीं। यह बात मैं शुरू से कह रहा हूँ और तलाशी में आपको पूरा सहयोग भी दे रहा हूँ।''

मिसेज अग्रवाल ने स्वीकारा, ''मैं आपकी सहयोग भावना की वास्तव में प्रशंसा करती हूँ।''

''तो...मैडम! क्या मैं मानकर चलूँ कि आपके छापे की कार्रवाई पूरी हो चुकी?'' गृह-स्वामी ने भोली मुद्रा में प्रश्न किया, जिसके जवाब में मिसेज अग्रवाल ने कठोरता से केवल एक शब्द कहा, ''नहीं!''

आकाश से मशवरा किए बग़ैर वह इस छापे को ख़त्म किसी सूरत में नहीं कर सकती थीं। उन्होंने कंट्रोल-रूम को बता दिया था कि आकाश का फोन-नम्बर उन्हें लगातार एंगेज़्ड मिल रहा था। कंट्रोल-रूम ने भी उन्हें सूचित कर दिया था कि यह बात आकाश जी तक पहुँचाई जा चुकी है और शीघ्र ही आकाश जी स्वयं ही आपसे फोन-सम्पर्क करेंगे।

आ पहुँचा आकाश का फोन। मिसेज अग्रवाल ने एक-एक व्यक्ति को कमरे से बाहर निकाला, दरवाज़ा भीतर से अच्छी तरह बन्द किया, फिर रिसीवर दुबारा हाथ में लेकर कहा, ''सॉरी, आकाश जी! आपको ज़रा रुकना पड़ा। मैं, दरअसल, बड़ी बेताबी से आपके फोन का इन्तज़ार कर रही थी। एनी वे...पहले आप अपनी सुनाइए।''

''सबसे पहले तो मैं आपसे माफ़ी माँगना चाहूँगा, क्योंकि मैं काफ़ी देर बाद फोन कर पा रहा हूँ।'' आकाश का स्वर, टेलीफोन पर भी, उत्साह और उमंग से ओतप्रोत लग रहा था, ''एक महान ख़बर है मेरे पास!''

मिसेज अग्रवाल ने कौतूहल से पूछा, ''महान ख़बर? फिर तो बता दीजिए जल्दी से!''

''हमने चार शानदार हीरे ज़ब्त किए हैं। वैल्युअर का कहना है, कम-से-कम आधे करोड़ के हीरे हैं ये!''

''बधाई हो, आकाश जी को बधाई हो!''

''थैंक्स, मिसेज अग्रवाल! अब आप...मुझसे जो मशवरा करना चाहती हैं...''

मिसेज अग्रवाल ने शुरू किया, ''मेरा ख़याल है, हीरे केवल एक फ्लैट में मिलेंगे, इस थ्योरी को हम छोड़ सकते हैं।''

''क्यों नहीं! अरे, हम तो चाहते हैं कि हीरे पाँचों फ्लैट्स में बरामद हों और ज़ब्त भी हों! क्यों, क्या आप भी हीरों के नज़दीक पहुँच रही हैं?''

''अभी तक हमें ऐसा कुछ भी नहीं मिला, जो ज़ब्त करने लायक़ हो, लेकिन...'' और मिसेज अग्रवल ने उस वृद्धा की रहस्यमय रटन्त का पूरा ब्योरा

आकाश को सुना दिया। फिर पूछा, "मूर्तियों की आँखों में तो मामूली काँच ही लगे हैं। सवाल है कि फिर...भगवान कैसे सब देख रहा है?"

आकाश गम्भीरता से बोला, "इतनी दूर से मैं सिर्फ़ इतना कह सकता हूँ, मिसेज अग्रवाल...कि कई बार केवल एक तिनका, बस, एक मामूली तिनका ही होता है, जिसकी ओट में छिपकर...सच्चाई मुसकरा रही होती है। मुझे यक़ीन है, आप उस तिनके को ज़रूर पहचान सकती हैं..."

ग़ौर से देख रही थीं मिसेज अग्रवाल, विष्णु-लक्ष्मी-सरस्वती की तीनों मूर्तियों की छहों आँखों को। आकाश के शब्द उनके कानों में गूँज रहे थे, 'आप उस तिनके को ज़रूर पहचान सकती हैं...ज़रूर पहचान सकती हैं...'—और सचमुच वह तिनका, मामूली-सा वह तिनका, मिसेज अग्रवाल द्वारा पहचान लिया गया। निस्सन्देह भगवान विष्णु की मूर्ति की आँखें साधारण काँच से बनी थीं, किन्तु जिस शेषनाग पर विष्णु जी सवारी कर रहे थे, उसकी आँखें? माना, लक्ष्मी जी की मूर्ति की आँखों में मामूली काँच ही लगे थे, किन्तु उनके प्रिय वाहन उल्लू की आँखों में? देवी सरस्वती के सुन्दर-सलोने, लम्बी गर्दन वाले वाहन इस हंस की आँखों में जो चमक है, क्या ऐसी चमक मामूली काँच में हो सकती है? मिसेज अग्रवाल ने अपने जौहरी को नज़दीक बुलाया और...सन्न रह गया जौहरी!

ट्रिन-ट्रिन! ट्रिन-ट्रिन! कितनी बेताबी से बज रहा था टेलीफोन! आकाश ने रिसीवर उठाया, "हैलो!" और मिसेज अग्रवाल का ऐसा स्वर सुनाई दिया, जिससे फ़ौरन 'झनक-झनक पायल बाजे' फिल्म की याद आ जाए! शुभ समाचार सुनते ही आकाश बोल पड़ा, "क्या कहती हैं, मिसेज अग्रवाल!"

"जी हाँ, आकाश जी! ज़रा सोचिए! सब-कुछ कितना आमने-सामने था, मगर दिख नहीं रहा था! आपने जो हिप्नोटिक सजेशन दिया, उसके लिए बहुत-बहुत धन्यवाद! इसी सजेशन के कारण मैं देख सकी—शेषनाग की आँखों में दो हीरे! उल्लू की आँखों में तो दो बड़े-बड़े हीरे! हंस की आँखों में भी दो चमचमाते हीरे! सबकी कम-से कम क़ीमत तीन करोड़ रुपए!" बताते-बताते मिसेज अग्रवाल की साँस भर आई।

आकाश ने उन्मुक्त हास्य के साथ कहा, "हा-हा! मिलाइए हाथ!"—और सचमुच आकाश ने ऐसे हाथ बढ़ा दिया, जैसे मिसेज अग्रवाल दूर...वार्डन रोड से फोन न कर रही हों, बल्कि आमने-सामने ही खड़ी हों!

"अरे, मामाज्जी!" दरवाज़ा खोलते ही श्वेता किलक उठी। 'नमस्कार' बोल सकती, इससे पहले ही मामा ने उसके दोनों गाल अपनी एक-एक मुट्ठी में कसकर भर लिये और दाएँ-बाएँ ऐसे खींचे कि श्वेता का सुन्दर मुखड़ा वानर जाति की याद दिलाने लगा। हर्ष और आश्चर्य से श्वेता की किलक एक तीखी चीख़ में बदल गई।

प्रतीक दौड़ता आया, चेहरे पर 'क्या हुआ, दीदी?' का भाव लिये। मामा को अचानक सामने पाकर प्रतीक अभी ठीक से चकरा भी न पाया था कि धर दबोचा गया। श्वेता को तत्काल छोड़कर मामा ने प्रतीक को बाँहों के शिकंजे में कसकर गोल-गोल घुमाना शुरू कर दिया। प्रतीक मुँह फाड़कर हँसने लगा।

ऐसे खिलन्दड़े हैं मामा। लेकिन सबके साथ नहीं। श्वेता और प्रतीक के लिए उनके दिल में शुरू से ही विकट प्रेम रहा है।

खिलन्दड़े मामा कभी जब नाजुक मसलों पर आते हैं, तब इतने गुरु-गम्भीर हो जाते हैं कि सहसा यक़ीन ही न हो, क्या यह मामा वही वाले मामा हैं? रिश्ते-नातों के हर परिवार में मामा की हर राय गम्भीरता से सुनी जाती है। दूर-दूर तक रिश्तेदारी में कोई शादी बिना मामा की सहमति लिये तय नहीं की जाती...

इतवार का दिन। आकाश घर पर ही था। श्वेता और प्रतीक की किलकारियाँ सुन आकाश और शालिनी लपककर ड्राइंग-रूम में आए। मामा की मौजूदगी में सारी औपचारिकताएँ ख़त्म हो जाती हैं। कोई किसी को नमस्ते कर पाए, इसकी गुंजाइश ही कहाँ छोड़ते हैं मामा।

शालिनी अपने भइया को देख एकदम खिल गई। आकाश का भी जैसे वज़न बढ़ गया। प्रतीक को मामा के शिकंजे से छुड़ाती हुई शालिनी कहने लगी, "उतारो भी। छोटा नहीं रहा अब। भारी है।"

शिकंजे से छूटते ही प्रतीक अपनी पसलियाँ सहलाता, हाय-हाय करता भागा। श्वेता ने अपने दोनों गाल शालिनी को दिखाए, "कैसे नोच डाले। देख, मॉम!"

मामा मुसकराए, "जा। बर्फ़ घिस बर्फ़।"

श्वेता झूठी ऊँ-ऊँ करती खिसक गई।

दोपहर के भोजन के बाद प्रतीक चला गया दोस्तों के संग क्रिकेट खेलने और श्वेता ने राह पकड़ी एक सहेली के घर की। अब मामाजी ने शालिनी और आकाश को घेरा, "श्वेता के ब्याह के बारे में क्या सोचा है?"

शालिनी और आकाश अकबकाकर एक-दूसरे के चेहरे ताकने लगे, जैसे उन्हें पहली बार नींद से जगाकर बताया गया हो कि श्वेता तो पराया धन ठहरी...

"अभी तो बी. कॉम का ही फाइनल ईयर है। फिर एम. कॉम करना चाहती है। साथ में...कम्प्यूटर का कोई एक्स्टेन्सिव कोर्स..." शालिनी ने कमज़ोर स्वर में कहा, "फिर, जब तक ढंग की नौकरी न लगे, श्वेता नहीं चाहती कि..."

"श्वेता की छोड़ो। तुम क्या चाहती हो?" मामा ने सीधी नज़र से देखा शालिनी की ओर।

"आजकल तो बच्चों की मरज़ी से चलना पड़ता है।" आकाश ने पत्नी को सहारा देने की गरज़ से कहा।

"अच्छा घर और अच्छा वर अगर मिल रहा हो, तो शादी करने से हिचकना नहीं चाहिए। पढ़ाई और नौकरी बाद में भी हो सकती है। सही अवसर बार-बार नहीं आते सामने..." और मामा जी ने विस्तार से बताया उस लड़के के बारे में, जिसे वह श्वेता के लिए ध्यान में रखे हुए थे।

.

आयकर भवन के अपने कमरे में आकर आकाश ने कुर्सी सँभाली ही थी कि उसकी सेक्रेटरी मिसेज जो ने उत्साहित स्वर में वह महान समाचार दिया।

"ओह!" आकाश अस्फुट बोल पड़ा, "थैंक्स, मिसेज जो। थैंक्स फॉर द बिग न्यूज़।"

उस महान समाचार में अनहोनी जैसा कोई तत्त्व तो था नहीं। फिर भी, आकाश की धड़कन कुछ बढ़ कैसे गई? स्वयं आकाश को आश्चर्य हुआ। स्वस्थ होने के लिए उसे बाक़ायदा चेष्टा करनी पड़ी।

"ज़रा...शालिनी से बात करा दीजिए।" आकाश ने मिसेज जो से कुछ इस प्रकार कहा, मानो मिसेज जो ने अगर घर का फोन-नम्बर मिलाकर न दिया, तो आकाश स्वयं तो वह नम्बर मिला ही नहीं सकता था। मिसेज जो ने तत्काल घर का नम्बर मिलाकर, रिसीवर आकाश को थमा दिया।

"हैलो, शालिनी।" आकाश ने शुरू किया। वह समझ नहीं पा रहा था, मुसकराकर बात करे या गम्भीर बने रहकर।

बात मुसकराने की थी, क्योंकि आकाश के नाम पर सरकारी फ्लैट आवंटित हो गया था और बात गम्भीर हो जाने की भी थी, क्योंकि अब श्रीगोपाल का पड़ोस छूट जाएगा और मौक़ा सामने होगा—श्रीगोपाल पर आयकर का छापा मारने का।

"हैलो?" शालिनी का स्वर सुनते ही आकाश ने बेताबी से उसे महान समाचार दे दिया। "सच?" शालिनी एकदम पुलकित हो गई, "कब जाएँगे अपने फ्लैट में?"

आकाश हँसा, "फ्लैट अपना नहीं, पगली, सरकार का है। इन्कम-टैक्स कॉलोनी में, तीसरे माले पर..."

आकाश का वाक्य बीच में ही काटकर शालिनी बोली, "अरे, बहुत मज़ा रहेगा।"

तीसरे ही दिन आकाश, शालिनी, श्वेता और प्रतीक, प्राइवेट कॉलोनी के उस मनहूस माहौल से निकलकर, श्रीगोपाल का तनावपूर्ण पड़ोस छोड़कर, सुदूर... इन्कम-टैक्स कॉलोनी के 'अपने' यानी कि सरकारी फ्लैट में पहुँच चुके थे। मकान बदलने की थकान उन्हें छू भी नहीं सकी थी।

आकाश श्रीगोपाल वर्मा को सँभलने का मौक़ा नहीं देना चाहता था। आकाश को पड़ोस से जाते देखते ही श्रीगोपाल सावधान हो सकता था कि अब कहीं छापा न पड़ जाए, पड़ोस का लिहाज़ अब थोड़े ही रखा जाएगा...और श्रीगोपाल अपना 'माल' इधर-से-उधर कर सकता था। इसीलिए जिस दिन आकाश ने श्रीगोपाल का पड़ोस छोड़ा, ऐन उसी दिन, ऐन उसी दौरान, श्रीगोपाल की तिरालीस दुकानों पर और मिठाइयों की फैक्टरी पर भी, एक साथ, एक समय, छापे मारे जा चुके थे।

ये छापे आकाश द्वारा लम्बे अरसे से करवाई जा रही गुप्तचरी, यानी 'रेक्की' के आधार पर, एकाएक मारे गए, जिनमें लगभग सवा दो सौ इन्कम-टैक्स ऑफिसरों एवं अन्य कर्मचारियों ने हिस्सा लिया। कंट्रोल-रूम से सभी छापों का संचालन किया मिसेज अग्रवाल ने। कार्रवाई ऐसे फर्राटे के साथ अचानक की गई कि श्रीगोपाल सब-कुछ अपनी आँखों से देख रहा था और फिर भी यक़ीन नहीं कर पा रहा था।

आयकर विभाग की फाइलें साफ़ बता रही थीं कि सबसे ज़्यादा काला धन मिठाई की फैक्टरी में छिपा होने की सम्भावना है। संयोगवश, छापे के वक़्त श्रीगोपाल फैक्टरी में ही मौजूद था। आश्चर्य और आघात से थरथरा गया था वह, लेकिन फिर एक आत्म-विश्वासी मन्द मुसकान थिरक उठी थी उसके होंठों पर।

फैक्टरी पर पड़े इस छापे को संचालित कर रहा था जनक। अभी हाल में जनक की तरक़्क़ी हुई थी और उसे इन्स्पेक्टर से ऑफिसर बना दिया गया था। आकाश ने विशेष दिलचस्पी लेकर जनक की यह तरक़्क़ी करवाई थी। एक ऑफिसर के रूप में जनक का यह पहला ही छापा था। पहले ही अभियान में जनक यदि कुछ विशेष कर दिखाए, तो कितना अच्छा रहे। आकाश के मन में यही उमंग थी।

जनक के, एवं अन्य सभी ऑफिसरों के, छापों की ताज़ा रपट पाने के लिए इतना आतुर था आकाश कि इन्कम-टैक्स कॉलोनी में, ट्रक से, उसका सामान अभी उतर ही रहा था कि उसने शालिनी से कहा, "सुनो...सामान उतारने, ऊपर चढ़ाने और रखने वग़ैरह में मेरा क्या काम? तुम्हारी निगरानी में नौकर यह सब करेंगे ही। मैं ज़रा ऑफिस का एक चक्कर लगा आता हूँ।"

शालिनी तल्ख़ होकर बोली, "मैं कौन होती हूँ रोकने वाली।"

श्वेता और प्रतीक ने भी नज़रें फेर लीं।

आकाश हँसा। ढिठाई के साथ हँस देने और फिर मनमानी करने की उसकी अपनी एक अदा है। अपनी उसी अदा में आकाश हँस रहा था। शालिनी समझ गई, उसे रोकने का कोई अर्थ नहीं, क्योंकि रोकने पर भी वह रुकने वाला नहीं।

आकाश की कार वार्डन रोड क्रॉस कर चुकी थी। क्रमशः आकाश मैरीन-लाइन्स की दिशा पकड़ रहा था। शीघ्र ही आयकर भवन सामने उभरने लगा। कार पार्क कर आकाश तेज़ी से लिफ्ट की ओर बढ़ा।

कंट्रोल-रूम में ज्यों ही उसने क़दम रखे, मिसेज अग्रवाल सहित सब चौंक गए। आख़िर आज आकाश के लिए छुट्टी का दिन था। अगले ही पल सबके चेहरों पर राहत की रेखाएँ उभर आईं, जैसे वे, अनजाने में, आकाश के ही प्रकट होने का इन्तज़ार कर रहे थे। मिसेज अग्रवाल बोलीं, "याद है, आकाश जी? पिछले छापे में आपने मुझे टेलीफोन पर एक हिप्नोटिक-सजेशन दिया था, जिसके ज़ोर पर मैं कई करोड़ के हीरे पहचानकर, उन्हें ज़ब्त करने में सफल हो गई थी।"

"हाँ, याद तो है। क्यों?" आकाश की भौंहें उठीं।

"उसी तरह के हिप्नोटिक-सजेशन की ज़रूरत शायद जनक को भी है..."

"ओह! सारी बात बताएँ।"

"जो बताया गया, उसके अनुसार, मिठाइयों की फैक्टरी की तलाशी पूरी निर्ममता से ली जा चुकी थी, किन्तु कहीं भी कुछ ऐसा नहीं मिला था, जो ज़ब्त करने लायक़ होता, जबकि...जनक के दिल में, न जाने कैसे, लगातार एक गूँज-सी बनी हुई थी कि ज़रूर यहाँ कोई बड़ा ख़ज़ाना छिपा है।"

"ज़रा जनक का नम्बर मिलाइए।" आकाश ने कहा और मिसेज अग्रवाल ने डायल घुमाया...बचपन में जनक ने कल्पना भी नहीं की थी, मिठाइयाँ और नमकीन बनाने की भी बाक़ायदा कोई फैक्टरी हो सकती है। छोटे गाँवों और शहरों में जनक ने सिर्फ़ एक-दो चूल्हों पर मिठाइयाँ आदि बनाते हलवाई देखे थे।

किन्तु बम्बई की गति न्यारी है। इज़राइल जैसे देश से भी बड़ा है यह अकेला शहर। यहाँ छोटी-से-छोटी चीज़ का भी उत्पादन औद्योगिक स्तर पर किया जा सकता है और किया जाता है। जनक आज अपनी आँखों से देख रहा था, 'श्रीगोपाल स्वीट्स एंड नमकीन प्राइवेट लिमिटेड' की उस फैक्टरी को, जहाँ गैस के अनेकानेक विशाल चूल्हों पर कई-कई कड़ाह चढ़े थे। कहीं नमकीन तला या भूना जा रहा था, तो कहीं मिठाइयों का मीठा उत्पादन जारी था। स्वादिष्ट सुगन्ध के बादल-पर-बादल उड़े जा रहे थे। धुएँ के तार और भभाके वायुमंडल में लम्बे डग भर रहे थे। अनेक हलवाई, अनेक नौकर-चाकर, मिठाइयों आदि की पैकिंग कर रहे अनेक कर्मचारी...

स्वयं श्रीगोपाल! आह! उसे देखकर जनक का मन परम सन्तोष से सन गया। पैकिंग विभाग में खड़ा था श्रीगोपाल। कर्मचारियों के कन्धों से कन्धे भिड़ाकर,

चाशनी और चिकनाई से सनी मिठाइयों की स्वयं अपने हाथों से पैकिंग कर रहा था श्रीगोपाल।

जनक ने नहीं सोचा था, श्रीगोपाल कभी भी ऐसी मशक़्क़त करता दिखाई पड़ेगा। लाख नहीं, करोड़ के स्वामी को अपने हाथ चाशनी और चिकनाई से सानने की क्या ज़रूरत? लेकिन लोगों को अपने कर्म से प्यार भी तो होता है। श्रीगोपाल चाहे कितना ही अमीर हो जाए, करोड़पति क्या अरबपति हो जाए, मन से तो वह एक हलवाई ही रहेगा। जनक को श्रीगोपाल का यह कर्म-प्रेम अटपटा लगा, तो अच्छा भी लगा। चाशनी और चिकनाई से सनी श्रीगोपाल की उँगलियों को जनक दो पल देखता रह गया।

"आयकर विभाग! सर्च-वारंट।" इन शब्दों के साथ जनक ने श्रीगोपाल की ओर सर्च-वारंट बढ़ा दिया, उसके दस्तख़त के लिए।

"फैल जाओ चारों तरफ़।" जनक का आदेश गूँज उठा। आयकर विभाग के दर्जन भर कर्मचारी दर्जन भर दिशाओं में दौड़े और मौक़ों की जगहों पर रुक गए।

दो मिनट में ही पूरी फैक्टरी थम चुकी थी। गैस का हर चूल्हा बुझ गया। नमकीन और मीठे पदार्थ—अधबने, अधपके—चूल्हों से नीचे उतार लिये गए।

जनक ने सबसे पहले चूल्हों के ऐन नीचे खुदाई करवाई। कहीं कुछ न निकला। श्रीगोपाल मुसकराकर बोला, "आप ग़लत जगह आए हैं, साब। हम जैसों के पास कहाँ कोई काला धन।" लेकिन जनक ने पूरी फैक्टरी जैसे रौंद ही डाली।

ज्यों-ज्यों समय बीता, जनक की निराशा बढ़ती चली। ज़ब्त करने लायक़ कुछ तो मिलता कहीं! तो क्या...'रेक्की' के तमाम निष्कर्ष झूठे थे? नहीं-नहीं, यह नहीं हो सकता।

और फिर...अन्तर्प्रेरणा जैसी भी तो कोई शक्ति होती है। जनक का दिल नहीं मान रहा था कि यहाँ 'कुछ भी' नहीं है।

श्रीगोपाल के आत्म-विश्वासी चेहरे का अर्थ समझने का लगातार प्रयास कर रहा था जनक। श्रीगोपाल का वह आत्म-विश्वास किसी निर्दोष, निर्भीक व्यक्ति का आत्म-विश्वास नहीं था। वह आत्म-विश्वास तो एक शठ, ढीठ व्यक्ति का आत्म-विश्वास था।

हार-थककर जनक ने कंट्रोल-रूम में, मिसेज अग्रवाल को फोन कर, हाथ-लगी निराशा की सूचना दी, किन्तु साथ-साथ यह भी कहा कि सर्च को अभी वह ख़त्म करना नहीं चाहता।

जनक ने रिसीवर रखा। दस मिनट मुश्किल से बीते होंगे कि स्वयं कंट्रोल-रूम ने जनक से फोन-सम्पर्क किया। रिसीवर में आकाश की आवाज़ सुनते ही जनक की बाछें खिल गईं।

जनक के मुँह से सारी बात सुनने के बाद आकाश ने कहा, ''जनक! कई बार साधारण में असाधारण और असाधारण में साधारण छिपा होता है। साधारण और असाधारण के इस रिश्ते को जो जितनी गहराई से समझ सकता है, वह उतना ही अच्छा आयकर अधिकारी बन सकता है।''

''सर! आपकी बात इतनी ऊँची है कि मेरे सिर के ऊपर से निकली जा रही है।''

''जनक! तुम वहाँ जो कुछ भी देख रहे हो या देख चुके हो, उसका विश्लेषण करो...साधारण में असाधारण और असाधारण में साधारण की खोज करते हुए दृश्य और मानवीय व्यवहार को समझो। गुड-लक, जनक।'' और आकाश ने फोन रख दिया।''

जनक के मन में तर्क-वितर्क के अनेक चक्र उसी पल गतिमान हो गए। दसेक मिनट बीते होंगे कि जनक की दृष्टि एक साधारण दृश्य पर केन्द्रित होने लगी—चींटियाँ। चींटियों की कतार। चली जा रही थी चींटियों की कतार। कितना साधारण दृश्य। मिठाइयों की फैक्टरी में, जहाँ चाशनी और चिकनाई का ही साम्राज्य हो, कतारें चींटियों की न चलेंगी, तो क्या ऊँटों की चलेंगी?

किन्तु उसी साधारण में कितना कुछ असाधारण था। चींटियों की वह कतार घुस रही थी, लोहे के एक रैक में, एक छिद्र के अन्दर। उस रैक में छोटी-बड़ी साइज़ के सैकड़ों डिब्बे भरे हुए थे—गत्ते के ख़ाली डिब्बे। ये ख़ाली डिब्बे मिठाइयों की पैकिंग करने के लिए थे। पैकिंग के बाद, भरे हुए डिब्बों को, नज़दीक के ही एक अन्य रैक में सजा दिया जाता था। असाधारण बात यह थी कि जिस रैक में केवल ख़ाली डिब्बे रखे थे, उस रैक ने चींटियों को आख़िर कैसे आकर्षित कर लिया था? रूखे-सूखे, स्वादहीन गत्ते से बने डिब्बे चींटियों को आख़िर कैसे अपनी ओर खींच सकते थे?

नहीं, नहीं...चींटियों को खींचने वाला तत्त्व गत्ता नहीं है। चींटियाँ तो रैक में बने एक छिद्र से अन्दर जा रही हैं और गत्ते के डिब्बे छिद्र के अन्दर थोड़े ही सजे हुए हैं। डिब्बे तो, रैक में, बाहर-बाहर सजे हैं। तो? क्या है उस सूक्ष्म छिद्र के अन्दर? जो चींटियों को खींच रहा है?

जनक मेटल-डिटेक्टर यंत्र लेकर आया ज़रूर था, किन्तु फैक्टरी में तो चारों तरफ़ लोहे की मौजूदगी थी। लोहे के कड़ाह...लोहे के रैक...कलछुल और चिमटे...जाने क्या-क्या...लोहे के ऐसे भंडार के बीच मेटल-डिटेक्टर भला कैसे काम करता? रैक के सूक्ष्म छिद्र के अन्दर आख़िर क्या है, इसकी जासूसी, किसी भी तरह, मेटल-डिटेक्टर से नहीं हो सकती थी।

किन्तु अन्दर कुछ है ज़रूर। चींटियाँ बता रही हैं...साधारण में असाधारण और असाधारण में साधारण।

गूँज उठा जनक का आदेश, ''खोल दो हर स्क्रू, इस रैक का।''

ज्यों ही स्क्रू खुले, रैक की दीवारों के अन्दर की पोल मुसकरा उठी, जनक की आँखों के ऐन सामने, ढिठाई के साथ। चमचम! चमचम! चकाचक–सोना! आह! कितने प्यारे सोने के बिस्कुट। सजे हैं कतारों में। बिस्कुट ही बिस्कुट। जैसे रैक की पूरी दीवार ही सोने की।

चींटियाँ घूम रही थीं उन बिस्कुटों पर। धन्यवाद, चींटियो! तुम्हीं ने मार्ग-दर्शन किया...कि कुछ है–अन्दर। रैक की दोहरी दीवारों के अन्दर। श्रीगोपाल ने सोने के ये बिस्कुट जब चुपके-चुपके छिपाए होंगे, तब...बेचारा हलवाई, चिकनाई और चाशनी से सने अपने हाथों को श्रीगोपाल ने पोंछा ज़रूर होगा, किन्तु...सिर्फ़ पोंछने से थोड़े ही निकल जाती है सारी चिकनाई, सारी चाशनी। सोने के न जाने कितने बिस्कुटों पर श्रीगोपाल की उँगलियों की चिकनाई और चाशनी चिपकी रह गई होगी...इसी चिकनाई और चाशनी ने आकर्षित किया चींटियों की पूरी कतार को...

ट्रिन-ट्रिन। ट्रिन-ट्रिन। कंट्रोल-रूम में बज रहा था टेलीफोन। रिसीवर आकाश ने उठाया और जनक के स्वर में यह शुभ समाचार पाया, "सर, बधाई! सोने के बिस्कुट पकड़े गए हैं। कम-से-कम पाँच करोड़ रुपयों के।"

आकाश की ओर से सिर्फ़ एक हिप्नोटिक सजेशन। और जनक के पूरे कैरियर को कितना अनोखा टेक-ऑफ मिल गया था।

सुन्दर-सलोनी-श्वेता। आकाश-शालिनी की लाड़ली बिटिया। आत्म-विश्वासी, आत्म-सम्मानी, साहसी, चतुर...किन्तु कितनी नादान। यह नादानी नहीं तो क्या थी कि श्वेता अभी तक स्वयं को बच्ची ही समझती रहे! ब्याह की कल्पना तक जिस लड़की ने न की हो, भले ही उम्र बीस बरस की हो चली हो, उसे नादान न कहें, तो क्या कहें!

किन्तु कड़वी-मीठी सच्चाई यह थी–लड़के वाले श्वेता को देखकर जा चुके थे। मामा जी ने जो लड़का चुना था श्वेता के लिए, वाक़ई लाखों में एक था। सुन्दर, स्वस्थ, गोरा, संस्कारी, कमाऊ, ऊँचा-पूरा, हँसोड़ आदि-इत्यादि। श्वेता के साथ उसकी जोड़ी ऐसी जमेगी, ऐसी जमेगी...

श्वेता, बस, क्रोधम्-क्रोधम्।

डोर-बेल बजी। आकाश ने उठकर अपने ड्राइंग-रूम का दरवाज़ा खोल दिया। सामने खड़े थे–श्रीगोपाल वर्मा। आकाश एक पल तो उन्हें पहचान ही न पाया। कितना बदला हुआ था उनका चेहरा।

पाँच करोड़ का सोना जिनके यहाँ से अभी दो दिन पहले ही ज़ब्त हुआ था, उन श्रीगोपाल वर्मा का चेहरा अगर उतना अधिक बदला हुआ था, तो अजूबा क्या था! क्यों आए थे श्रीगोपाल वर्मा, आकाश के नए, सरकारी फ्लैट में? बहस करने? घूस देने? सोचते ही आकाश भीतर से खौल गया...

"आइए! आइए। नमस्कार।" आकाश ने दरवाज़े का रास्ता छोड़ दिया, ताकि श्रीगोपाल प्रवेश कर सकें। हाथ जोड़ते, अस्फुट स्वर में नमस्कार करते श्रीगोपाल ने प्रवेश किया। आकाश ने बैठने का इशारा किया, किन्तु वह बैठे नहीं। आकाश अकेला ही सोफे पर बैठ गया और वह खड़े रहे। आकाश ने फिर से बैठने का इशारा किया, तो वह हौले से बोले, "अब क्या बैठूँ! आपने तो सभी कुछ बिठा दिया।" —और उन्होंने, जैसे अनिच्छा के साथ, सोफे पर स्थान ग्रहण किया।

आकाश ने ऊँचे स्वर में पुकारा, "अरे, शालिनी। श्रीगोपाल जी आए हैं।"

शालिनी ने आकर हाथ जोड़े। पूछा, "तिलोत्तमा जी कैसी हैं?"

"आपकी कृपा है।" बुझे स्वर में श्रीगोपाल ने कहा। शालिनी चली गई।

नौकरानी ने आकर पानी के गिलास रखे। नौकरानी भी चली गई। थोड़ी देर में फिर आएगी—चाय-बिस्कुट लेकर। आकाश ने मुसकान बिखेरी, "कहिए, श्रीगोपाल जी। कैसे आना हुआ?"

"यह तो मैं भी नहीं जानता।"

"मैं...समझा नहीं।"

"शिकायत करने आया नहीं हूँ, क्योंकि इसका मुझे हक़ नहीं है। समझौता करने या सौगात देने भी नहीं आया हूँ, क्योंकि आप न तो समझौता करते हैं, न सौगात लेते हैं।" श्रीगोपाल का स्वर थोड़ा जीवन्त होने लगा था, "कोई सवाल करने भी नहीं आया हूँ। आपसे सवाल करने की योग्यता मुझमें कहाँ! सचमुच मैं नहीं जानता, अभी आख़िर क्यों आया हूँ!"

"मैं आपके आक्रोश को समझ सकता हूँ।" आकाश गम्भीर हो उठा, "चलिए, यह सवाल उठाते ही नहीं हैं कि आप क्यों आए हैं, लेकिन आ गए हैं, यह तो मानते हैं न? तो...इस मौक़े पर...आपसी मशवरा की तरह...थोड़ी गपशप ही कर लेते हैं।"

"उससे क्या होगा?"

"अगर गपशप भी नहीं करेंगे, तो क्या करेंगे?"

"हाँ...सो तो है..." श्रीगोपाल ने नज़र झुकाकर सिर हिलाया।

श्रीगोपाल पर नज़र पड़ने के साथ भीतर से खौल जाने की जो अनुभूति आकाश को हुई थी, उस पर वह काबू पा चुका था। चाय की चुस्कियों के बीच आकाश ने जो पहला मूलभूत सवाल किया, वह यही था कि अगर पाँच करोड़ रुपयों के सोने

के बिस्कुट, श्रीगोपाल की फैक्टरी में, न पकड़े गए होते, तो आख़िर उतने सोने का श्रीगोपाल ने क्या किया होता? उस विशाल, छिपे धन को श्रीगोपाल खुलकर तो इस्तेमाल कर नहीं सकता था। यानी, उसके पास दो ही चारे रह जाते—या तो उस छिपी सम्पत्ति को वह इस्तेमाल भी छिप-छिपकर ही करे, या फिर, कभी इस्तेमाल ही न करे। ज़िन्दगी भर उसे सिर्फ़ छिपाकर ही रखे।

इन दोनों ही स्थितियों का आकाश ने अलग-अलग विश्लेषण किया। आकाश का स्वर, सहसा, इतना आत्मीय हो उठा कि उसकी ठंडी निष्पक्षता भी, श्रीगोपाल के लिए, सहज स्वीकार्य हो गई। श्रीगोपाल का विवेक मानो पहली बार जगाया जा रहा था किसी के शब्दों द्वारा...

"ऐसा है, श्रीगोपाल जी..." आकाश का स्वर धीमा किन्तु स्पष्ट था, "गुप्त धन गुप्त ख़र्च की ओर, और गुप्त ख़र्च हमेशा गुप्त गतिविधियों की ओर, ले जाता है। गुप्त गतिविधियों के तो बने-बनाए, गिने-गिनाए स्वरूप ही हैं। गुप्त धन ख़र्च होने लगता है दारू पर, चरस-गाँजे-हेरोइन पर, वेश्याओं और रखैलों पर। ये नशे ब्लैक-मनी के, काले धन के सगे भाइयों की तरह हैं, जो इनसान के तन और मन को चौपट कर डालते हैं।"

"मैं तो धन कमाने के पीछे इतना व्यस्त रहा हूँ कि इन नशों की ओर...इन आदतों की ओर...कभी ध्यान गया ही नहीं।" श्रीगोपाल ने ऐसा कहा तो अवश्य, किन्तु उनके स्वर में सच्चाई की खनक नहीं थी।

"...और अगर काले धन को ख़र्च ही न किया जाए," आकाश ने जारी रखा, "सिर्फ छिपाकर ही रखा जाए, तो...उसे लगातार छिपाने की चिन्ता में उसके स्वामी को न दिन को चैन मिलता है, न रात को नींद। ईर्ष्यालु दोस्तों और लालची रिश्तेदारों में से कब कौन ग़द्दारी कर, आयकर विभाग को सूचना दे देगा, इसकी आशंका में...अच्छे-से-अच्छे नाते-रिश्तों में भी दरार पड़ने लगती है...और फिर...ज़रा यों भी तो सोचिए—अगर कोई धन ऐसा है, जिसे न तो प्रकट किया जा सके और न ख़र्च, तो ऐसे धन में और मिट्टी के ढेले में फ़र्क़ ही क्या है?"

श्रीगोपाल वर्मा, आकाश की ओर, चुपचाप देखते रह गए। मानो सुन्न पड़ गए थे वह...

आकाश ने उनके सामने क्रमशः स्पष्ट किया कि कैसे काले धन से संचालित काली गतिविधियाँ पहले तो व्यक्ति की, फिर परिवार की, फिर समाज की और फिर समूचे राष्ट्र की अस्मिता को अपनी लपेट में ले लेती हैं। बल्कि अब तो एक नया ही ख़तरा है सम्पूर्ण मानवता के सामने—एड्स। सोचने की बात है, क्या काला धन इनसान को एड्स के प्राणघाती खन्दक में नहीं गिराता? काला धन हमेशा उन्मुक्त यौनाचार का हिमायती रहा है और उन्मुक्त यौनाचार से ही फैला है, फैलता जाता

है वह एड्स, जिसकी विनाशकता को रोकने का कोई उपाय नहीं है आज के मानव के पास। साक्षात् यमदूत जैसा यौन-रोग—एड्स। और काला धन...

"ओह। नहीं।" श्रीगोपाल एकदम अकुला गए। फिर वह ज़्यादा रुके नहीं। उठकर जब वह जा रहे थे, उनके चेहरे का लहू जैसे पीछे हट गया था...

चौथे दिन श्रीगोपाल वर्मा आकाश के ऑफिस में प्रकट हुए। उनका चेहरा दमक रहा था। भीतर आते ही उन्होंने आकाश के सामने एक पैथॉलॉजिकल लैब की रिपोर्ट रख दी।

"क्या है?" आकाश ने रिपोर्ट उठाते हुए पूछा।

"मेरी ब्लड-रिपोर्ट।" श्रीगोपाल ने ज़रा झेंप के साथ जैसे रहस्योद्घाटन किया, "बच गया मैं"

"बच गए? किससे?"

"देखिए...यहाँ 'निगेटव' लिखा है।" श्रीगोपाल ने अपनी ब्लड-रिपोर्ट के एक कॉलम पर उँगली रखी, "अगर यहाँ 'पॉज़िटिव' आ जाता, तो मैं...मर जाता।"

"मरना तो एक दिन सबको है।" आकाश मुसकराया।

"निगेटिव' का मतलब...मुझे एड्स नहीं है।" श्रीगोपाल ने खूब फैली हुई मुसकान के साथ कहा। अचानक वह फैली हुई मुसकान सिमटकर छोटी हो गई, किन्तु लुप्त न हुई।

आकाश के लिए चौंकने की बारी थी। पलकें उठाकर उसने श्रीगोपाल की ओर देखा, "एड्स?"

"भाई साहब! सुनकर आपको चाहे जो लगे, किन्तु...सच यह है...काले धन को मैं अपने ढंग से ख़र्च करता रहा हूँ। लगभग हर रात कोई-न-कोई नई लड़की...मेरे लिए आती रही है...सोचा भी न था, उन्हीं में से कोई मुझे एड्स देकर भी जा सकती है।" श्रीगोपाल गहन-गम्भीर होकर स्पष्ट बोले, "आप पहले व्यक्ति हैं, जिन्होंने मुझे इस ओर से सावधान किया।"

"ओह। मैंने तो यूँ ही, सिद्धान्त के स्तर पर बात की थी।"

"आपने मेरी आँखें खोली हैं। पाँच करोड़ तो इसी में वसूल हो गए। इन्कम-टैक्स में अगर पूरे पाँच-के-पाँच करोड़ ज़ब्त हो जाएँ, तो भी ग़म नहीं।"

'लेकिन आप जानते हैं, पाँच-के-पाँच करोड़ ज़ब्त नहीं होंगे। टैक्स और जुर्माना काटकर जो रक़म आपको लौटाई जाएगी, वह कोई मामूली रक़म न होगी।"

"भाई साहब! आपने मुझे जीवनदान दिया है। न सिर्फ़ काले धन की मोहमाया से, बल्कि बाज़ारू सेक्स के शिकंजे से भी छूट जाने का पक्का फ़ैसला मैंने कर लिया

है। इसके पीछे आप ही से मिली दृष्टि ने काम किया है। आपको धन्यवाद देने के लिए मेरे पास शब्द नहीं हैं।"

"मुझे खुशी है, मैं आपके किसी काम आ सका।" आकाश ने हार्दिक प्रसन्नता से कहा। इस प्रसन्नता ने आकाश को सारा दिन अच्छे मूड में रखा, किन्तु शाम को घर पहुँचने पर मूड एकदम ही बिगड़ गया। मामाजी की चिट्ठी आई रखी थी। आकाश-शालिनी की लाड़ली श्वेता को देखकर, खूब पसन्द कर, वह जो संस्कारी लड़का घर में चाय पीकर गया था, उसके श्रेष्ठ माता-पिता ने कहलवाया था कि श्वेता को बहू बनाकर ले आने के लिए हम कम उत्सुक नहीं हैं, किन्तु पहले...दहेज सम्बन्धी स्पष्टता हो जानी चाहिए।

यह सारी बात मामा जी ने बहुत ही खेदपूर्वक सूचित की थी।

दहेज! आकाश की साँसें गरम हो उठीं। चिट्ठी को थामे वह खड़ा रह गया।

शालिनी ने शान्त स्वर में कहा, "अभी तो शुरुआत है...ऐसे न जाने कितने आएँगे!"

दो दिन बीते और एक सुन्दर, सलोनी, गोरी, ऊँची-पूरी युवती ने आकाश के ऑफिस में प्रवेश किया—गम्भीर, दृढ़ चेहरे के साथ। उस पर नज़र पड़ते ही आकाश को लगा, इसे कहीं देखा है...कहाँ? सहसा याद न आया। नमस्कार के साथ युवती सामने की कुर्सी पर बैठ गई और बोली, "माफ़ कीजिएगा, सर! लेकिन मैं...यह कहने आई हूँ कि...मेरी जो बर्बादी आपने की है, उसकी पूरी ज़िम्मेदारी आप ही को अपने कन्धों पर उठानी होगी।"

"कौन हैं आप?" आकाश का पहला सवाल छोटा, किन्तु सीधा और सटीक था। युवती ने आश्चर्य से देखा उसकी ओर, "आपने मुझे पहचाना नहीं?"

आकाश बोला, "लगता तो है कि आपको कहीं देखा है, लेकिन...क्या किसी ने हमारा परिचय करवाया था? याद नहीं आता।"

"जी नहीं, हमारा परिचय नहीं करवाया था किसी ने, लेकिन आप मुझे भूल कैसे गए? कुछ महीने पहले आपने मुझे, सुबह-सुबह, जॉकिंग-पार्क में देखा था।" और युवती ढिठाई से, मादकता से, ज़रा हँसी।

"ओह..." आकाश तत्काल सावधान हो गया। वेश्या! यह शब्द आकाश के मन में एक गूँज-सी पैदा कर गया। श्रीगोपाल वर्मा द्वारा, प्लेट में रखी मिठाई की तरह, ऑफर की गई वेश्या। हाँ...यही तो थी वह...आकाश ने भौंहें सिकोड़ीं, "तो...आप हैं। कहिए, मैं आपके लिए क्या कर सकता हूँ?"

युवती ने मुसकान समेट ली। नज़र झुकाई। नज़र उठाई। ठंडे, शान्त स्वर में कहा, "मुझे बर्बादी से बचाना आपकी ज़िम्मेदारी है।"

"ज़िम्मेदारी हो चाहे न हो, लेकिन आपको—या किसी को भी—अगर मैं बर्बादी से बचा सका, तो मुझे दिली खुशी होगी।" आकाश बोला, "क्या मैं पूछ सकता हूँ कि आप अपनी बर्बादी का कारण मुझे क्यों मानती हैं? मैंने क्या बिगाड़ा है आपका?"

"सॉरी, सर। मैं अपने शब्द वापस लेती हूँ। आपके सामने कुर्सी पर बैठने के साथ मुझे ऐसे शब्द इस्तेमाल नहीं करने चाहिए थे।" युवती पश्चात्ताप के स्वर में बोली, "प्लीज़! मुझे माफ कर दें।"

"ओके। कोई बात नहीं। आगे कहिए।" और आकाश ने अपनी कलाई-घड़ी में देखा, "मुझे दस मिनट बाद कहीं जाना है।"

"पता नहीं, मैं दस मिनट में अपनी बात कह पाऊँ या नहीं।" युवती उलझन में पड़ गई।

"दस मिनट कम नहीं होते।"

"जी...मैं...श्रीगोपाल जी के यहाँ...नौकरी पर थी। मुझे आठ हज़ार रुपए का मासिक वेतन दिया जाता था। सौगातें अलग से मिलती थीं। श्रीगोपाल जी ने मुझे झोंपड़पट्टी से उठाकर फ्लैट में पहुँचाया। मैं उनकी शुक्रगुजार, हूँ, लेकिन...अब उन्होंने मुझे नौकरी से निकाल दिया है। अचानक। बताइए, मैं क्या करूँ? कहाँ जाऊँ?"

"मैं...मैं क्या बता सकता हूँ?" आकाश को सिवा इन शब्दों के और कुछ सूझा ही नहीं। ऑफिस में, सामने, एक वेश्या की मौजूदगी उसे असहज किए दे रही थी। अपनी तरह का यह पहला अनुभव था आकाश के लिए।

युवती ने जारी रखा, "मैंने अपनी बर्बादी का कारण आपको इसलिए माना कि आप ही की दी सलाह पर श्रीगोपाल जी ने फ़ैसला किया कि वह...मुझसे दूर रहेंगे...दूसरी लड़कियों से भी दूर रहेंगे। न आप श्रीगोपाल जी को वैसी सलाह देते, न मुझे मुसीबत में फँसना पड़ता।"

"लेकिन आप मुझसे आख़िर क्या मदद चाहती हैं? कुछ तो सोचा होगा आपने?" आकाश ने चौकन्नी मुद्रा में पूछा।

"आप मेरी नौकरी कहीं और लगवा दीजिए।"

आकाश का चेहरा तमतमाकर लाल हो गया, "आपका मतलब है, जैसी व्यवस्था आपने श्रीगोपाल जी के साथ कर रखी थी, वैसी ही व्यवस्था मैं आपके लिए कहीं और करवा दूँ? आप मुझे समझती क्या हैं? लड़कियों का दलाल? उठिए। इसी वक़्त उठिए। चली जाइए यहाँ से।"

युवती न उठी। टप-टप उसके आँसू गिरने लगे। आकाश मन-ही-मन बोला, 'सावधान, बच्चू। ये एक खेली-खाई सुन्दरी के ख़तरनाक आँसू हैं।'

सेक्रेटरी मिसेज जो को भीतर बुलाने के लिए आकाश ने घंटी की ओर हाथ बढ़ाया ही था कि युवती तपाक से उठ पड़ी और बोली, ''अभी चलती हूँ। फिर मिलूँगी। मेरा मतलब वह नहीं था, जो आपने समझा। श्रीगोपाल जी की तरह अब मैं भी सही राह पकड़ना चाहती हूँ। कोई भी ढंग की नौकरी...इज़्ज़त की नौकरी आप दिला देंगे, इस आशा में आकर बैठी थी। डेढ़-दो हज़ार की नौकरी भी अगर न मिली, तो...भूखी-प्यासी तो मैं रहूँगी नहीं। आप अगर चाहेंगे, तो मेरे भी जीवन को एक नई दिशा मिल जाएगी। इसीलिए आपके पास आई। आपने कुछ और समझा। सॉरी, सर! मुझ जैसी लड़कियों को भी अपने जीवन की दिशा बदलने का हक़ है। मैं दुबारा आऊँगी, आपसे मिलने...'' युवती ने पर्स से रूमाल निकाल अपने आँसू कब के पोंछ लिये थे। उसके दग्ध चेहरे पर जो चमक थी, क्या वह वास्तविक थी? या केवल एक छलावा? आकाश समझ सकता, इससे पहले युवती अपनी पीठ घुमा चुकी थी और दरवाज़े से निकलने ही वाली थी। पल भर को आकाश को लगा कि वह उसे रोककर कम-से-कम इतना तो पूछे, 'आपका नाम क्या है?'

किन्तु आकाश चुप रहा और युवती कमरे से निकल गई।

अगली बार जब वह ऑफिस में आई, उसके प्रति अरुचि का भाव, आकाश के मन से, काफ़ी निकल चुका था। युवती के ये शब्द आकाश सहसा भूल नहीं पाया था, मुझ जैसी लड़कियों को भी अपने जीवन की दिशा बदलने का हक़ है। इसीलिए आकाश ने, ऑफिस में युवती के प्रवेश के साथ जो मुसकान प्रदर्शित की, वह केवल औपचारिक मुसकान नहीं थी। सबसे पहले उसने युवती का नाम पूछा।

''बेला...''

सरनेम युवती छिपा गई और आकाश ने भी इस बाबत पूछा नहीं।

''बेला जी। आप पढ़ी-लिखी कहाँ तक हैं?'' आकाश ने इसलिए जानना चाहा कि जहाँ भी नौकरी की बात वह चलाएगा, वहाँ इस जानकारी की ज़रूरत पड़ेगी।

''मैं हायर सेकंडरी पास हूँ। सेकंड क्लास में। टाइपिंग जानती हूँ। अंग्रेज़ी और हिन्दी, दोनों।''

''हफ़्ते भर बाद आप मुझे फोन कर लें।'' आकाश ने सुझाव दिया।

''मैं आ ही जाऊँगी।''

''उसके लिए भी पहले फोन तो करना ही होगा। कभी मैं ऑफिस में नहीं भी होता, या होता भी हूँ, तो बहुत व्यस्त हो सकता हूँ...'' कहते हुए आकाश ने अपने स्वर को ज़रा कड़क कर लिया।

बेला चली गई।

शाम तक आकाश ने आयकर की अनेक फाइलें निबटाईं। ऑफिस के सब लोग चले गए, मगर आकाश बैठा रहा। उसके अवचेतन में बेला लगातार मौजूद थी। किसी भी साधारण, घरेलू युवती को नौकरी दिलाना आकाश के लिए बाएँ हाथ का खेल रहता, लेकिन बेला इस अर्थ में असाधारण थी कि...

बेला की सिफ़ारिश कहीं भी करते वक़्त...क्या यह बता दिया जाए कि उसका इतिहास क्या रहा है? नहीं, नहीं, इस हद तक राजा हरिश्चन्द्र बनना ज़रूरी नहीं। इस तरह तो मिलती हुई नौकरी भी नहीं मिलेगी। ज़िन्दगी में न जाने कितने हादसे ऐसे होते हैं, जिन्हें छिपाकर रखना ही समझदारी मानी गई है। तो क्या...बेला को सती सावित्री के रूप में नौकरी दिलाई जाए? यह तो उस व्यक्ति के साथ सीधी बेईमानी होगी, जो उसे नौकरी पर रखेगा। बेईमानी! आकाश करे असम्भव! लेकिन बेला के रहस्य की डोंडी पीटते हुए भी तो उसे नौकरी के बाज़ार में नहीं उतारा जा सकता।

शुद्ध धर्म-संकट!

गहराती शाम...जगमग सड़कें...मन्त्रमुग्ध करते ट्रैफिक का शोर...कार चलाता आकाश...और धर्म-संकट। फ्लैट में दाख़िल होते वक़्त भी आकाश के चेहरे पर यही धर्म-संकट लरज रहा था। शालिनी ने पूछा भी, "क्या बात है? उखड़े-उखड़े लग रहे हो?"

"कुछ नहीं। रूटीन टेन्शन्स।" बुदबुदाकर आकाश बेड-रूम में चला गया।

टेन्शन्स का सबसे सुन्दर इलाज। स्नान। आकाश देर तक नहाता रहा। स्वच्छ, सुगन्धित होकर स्नानागार से जब बाहर निकला, जैसे एक नया ही व्यक्ति था।

टेन्शन्स का एक और बेहतरीन इलाज—गरम कॉफी। शालिनी के हाथ की बनी। यह इलाज भी आकाश को सहज ही उपलब्ध हो गया। गरम चुस्कियाँ लेते आकाश के दिमाग़ में एक निर्णय आकार लेने लगा।

फोन उठाकर उसने श्रीगोपाल वर्मा का नम्बर मिलाया।

"हैलो?" यह स्वर श्रीगोपाल का ही था, आकाश ने पहचाना।

"नमस्कार। मैं...आकाश।"

"ओह, भाई साहब। नमस्कार। धन्य हो गया मैं। ज़िन्दगी में पहली बार आपने अपनी ओर से फोन किया। आज की तारीख़ तो डायरी में नोट करके रखनी चाहिए।"

"आप ग़ज़ब के ड्रामेबाज़ आदमी हैं।" आकाश ने भरपूर प्रशंसा के स्वर में कहा।

"भाई साहब! अब कहाँ का ड्रामा! ज़िन्दगी का सारा ड्रामा तो छोड़-छाड़ दिया। अब तो बुद्धं शरणं गच्छामि। हुकुम करिए।" श्रीगोपाल ने आश्चर्य, आनन्द और आतुरता से पूछा।

आकाश कुछ बोलने से पहले ज़रा हिचक गया।

'कॉपर चिमनी' का सुन्दर, सम्भ्रान्त, शान्त वातावरण...कोने की मेज़ पर लंच की बानगियाँ सजी थीं। गम्भीरता से भोजन कर रहे दो व्यक्ति—आकाश और श्रीगोपाल वर्मा।

''मैं आपसे बेला के बारे में बात करना चाहता हूँ।''

आकाश ने ज्यों ही यह कहा, श्रीगोपाल ने आश्चर्य से पूछा, ''आपको उसका नाम कैसे पता चला?''

''वह खुद आकर मुझसे मिल चुकी है।'' आकाश ने श्रीगोपाल की नज़र से नज़र मिलाई।

''ओह!...मेरी शिकायत कर रही होगी।''

''नहीं, लेकिन वह अपने जीवन को एक नई दिशा देना चाहती है, जैसा कि स्वयं आपने किया है।''

''वह जो चाहे जो करे। कोई उसे रोक थोड़े सकता है।''

''जी हाँ, लेकिन हम...यानी मैं और आप, हम दोनों...अगर उसकी सहायता नहीं करेंगे, तो वह फिर से उसी राह पर चल सकती है, जिस राह पर चलती रही है।''

''भाई साहब! जाने दीजिए उसे, जहाँ जाए। छोड़ दिया, तो छोड़ दिया।''

आकाश दो पल चुप रहने के बाद बोला, ''उसने मुझसे सहायता माँगी है। मैं उसे सहायता दूँगा।''

''आप मुझसे बड़े हैं। समझदार हैं। मैं आपसे क्या कहूँ, सिवा इसके कि...ख़ैर! छोड़िए।'' कहते-कहते श्रीगोपाल वर्मा बहुत सावधान हो चुके थे।

क्रोध की एक सूक्ष्म रेखा आकाश के मन से उठी और श्रीगोपाल की तरफ़ रेंगने लगी। आकाश को तीव्र प्रयास करना पड़ा, उस रेखा को बुझाने के लिए। ठंडे पानी का घूँट खींचकर आकाश ने गला और सीना शान्त किया, फिर कहा, ''स्त्री का इतिहास कभी उसका पीछा नहीं छोड़ता। मान लीजिए, मैं बेला की नौकरी कहीं लगवा देता हूँ और यह बताता नहीं हूँ कि उसका इतिहास क्या रहा है। मेरे न बताने के बावजूद...क्या बेला का काला इतिहास उसका पीछा करता हुआ वहाँ कभी नहीं पहुँचेगा? ज़रूर पहुँचेगा। नतीजा? बेला की नौकरी छूट जाएगी।''

''मगर, भाई साहब! इसमें हम क्या कर सकते हैं?'' श्रीगोपाल के स्वर की सावधानी तीखी होने लगी थी।

''आप बेला को अपने स्टाफ से मत निकालिए।'' आकाश ने दो-टूक लहजे में कहा, किन्तु श्रीगोपाल चौंके नहीं, जैसे उन्हें पहले से मालूम था, यही कहा जाएगा। भरवां पराँठे का गस्सा श्रीगोपाल शान्ति से चबाते रहे। मौन तो आकाश को ही तोड़ना पड़ा, ''देखिए...मैं बिलकुल नहीं कह रहा कि आप उसे सात-आठ हज़ार के वेतन पर ही जारी रखें...न यह कह रहा हूँ कि उसके साथ नाता भी वही पुराना ही

चलने दें...लेकिन आपकी तिरालीस दुकानें हैं। सैकड़ों कर्मचारी आपके यहाँ काम करते हैं। आप उन्हीं सैकड़ों कर्मचारियों के बीच बेला को खपा लें। किसी भी दुकान के काउंटर को सँभालना बेला के लिए मुश्किल नहीं रहेगा। वह डेढ़ हज़ार के वेतन पर काम करने को तैयार है।''

''लेकिन मुझे नहीं लगता कि मेरी किसी भी दुकान पर उसकी इज़्ज़त हो सकेगी।'' श्रीगोपाल वर्मा ने तटस्थ भाव से जवाब दिया, ''ज़्यादातर कर्मचारी उसका चेहरा पहचानते हैं और मेरे-उसके पुराने नाते को भी। मानता हूँ, अब तक किसी कर्मचारी ने मुँह नहीं खोला है, मगर कब तक? दूध में भी दूध की मक्खी आख़िर कब तक तैरती रह सकती है?''

यह एक ऐसी बात थी, जिसका हिसाब आकाश ने पहले से नहीं लगाया था। उसे चुप रह जाना पड़ा।

''भाई साहब, बुरा न मानें, तो एक बात कहूँ।''—श्रीगोपाल का स्वर।

''कहिए।''

''आप बहुत...मेरा मतलब...बहुत भावुक हैं आप।''

''निर्मम, निर्मोही होने से तो बेहतर है भावुक होना।''

''निस्सन्देह। लेकिन भावुकता किसके प्रति? बेला जैसी लड़कियों की अहमियत क्या है? दुनिया में उसके जैसी लाखों क्या, करोड़ों घूम रही हैं। करोड़ों की इस भीड़ में उसे खो जाने दीजिए। सब अपनी-अपनी किस्मत लेकर आते हैं। मेरा दिया काफ़ी रुपया उसने जोड़ रखा होगा। फ्लैट से भी मैं उसे कोई आज-के-आज नहीं निकाल रहा। तत्काल कोई मुसीबत नहीं है उस पर। वह अपना रास्ता आप निकाल लेगी।'' श्रीगोपाल ऐसे बोल रहे थे, जैसे पहले से तैयारी करके आए हों, ''आप बिलकुल ऐसा न सोचें कि उसे अन्धे कुएँ में धकेल दिया गया है।''

''फिर भी...अगर उसके लिए महीने के डेढ़ हज़ार का भी इन्तज़ाम न किया गया तो...जो कुछ भी उसके पास जमा है, फुँक जाते देर न लगेगी।''

''यह बात हम दोनों से ज़्यादा वह समझती है।'' श्रीगोपाल ने ठंडे पानी का घूँट खींचकर मुँह में बिलोया, फिर गटकते हुए कहा, ''बल्कि मुझे तो आश्चर्य है कि आप चाहते क्यों हैं कि मैं ही उसे नौकरी दूँ।''

''सिर्फ़ इसलिए कि किसी भी दूसरी कम्पनी में बेला का काला इतिहास उसका पीछा करेगा, जबकि आपके यहाँ...सब पहले से ज्ञात और स्वीकृत है।''

''बस? इतनी-सी बात?''

''हाँ, यही।''

''यह तो कोई समस्या ही नहीं। बेला जैसी लड़कियाँ इन मामूली बातों से निबटना खूब जानती हैं।''

"वह मेरे ऑफिस में आने लगी है। मैं नहीं सोचता कि..."

"आप कुछ सोचिए ही नहीं। बेला से साफ़ कह दीजिए...या, चाहें तो आपकी ओर से मैं कहलवा दूँ...कि वह कभी न आया करे आपके ऑफिस में। फोन भी न किया करे। उसे गुम हो जाने दीजिए।"

आकाश ने बेचैनी से घुटने हिलाए, "नहीं, श्रीगोपाल जी। आप न कहलवाएँ। जब भी ऐसा लगेगा कि कह देने का मौक़ा आ गया है, मैं ही कह दूँगा उससे..."

श्वेता का बी.कॉम. का रिज़ल्ट आ गया था। कम नहीं, 95 प्रतिशत नम्बर लेकर पास हुई थी वह। उसकी ख़ुशी का ठिकाना नहीं था, किन्तु ख़ुशी की रंगत फीकी करने वाला दुष्ट तत्त्व भी तो लगातार मौजूद था—शादी। लड़की को ब्याह कर विदा कर देने के लिए कितने उत्सुक होते हैं तमाम माँ-बाप। यहाँ तक कि...आकाश-शालिनी जैसे सुसंस्कारी माता-पिता भी बिटिया को धकियाकर घर से निकाल देने के लिए कितने सुनियोजित ढंग से, खुल्लमखुल्ला साज़िश कर रहे थे।

साज़िश। श्वेता के मन में यही शब्द उभरता था। आकाश-शालिनी ने उसका वैवाहिक विज्ञापन 'टाइम्स' में प्रकाशित करवा दिया था और अब, रिस्पॉन्स की प्रतीक्षा में मस्त थे। जात-पाँत का बन्धन नहीं, दहेज देने का प्रश्न ही नहीं, कन्या की नौकरी लगने के बाद ही शादी, अभी केवल सगाई, शादी के बाद भी कन्या नौकरी अवश्य करेगी...सारी बातें आधुनिकता की चमक लिये...किन्तु...आह! साज़िश! अपनी ही बिटिया को धकियाकर घर से निकाल देने की साज़िश। एकान्त मिला नहीं कि श्वेता के आँसू झर-झर, झर-झर। लेकिन क्या करे बिटिया! जवानी को धक्के मारकर पीछे हटा नहीं सकती, लिहाज़ा ख़ुद ही धक्के खाकर निकल जाना होगा घर से...

'मुझे श्रीगोपाल वर्मा के सामने निवेदन करने की ज़रूरत क्या थी?' रात के दो बजे, आँखें मूँदकर, चुपके-चुपके जाग रहा आकाश, अपने आपको डाँट रहा था, 'मैंने सोच कैसे लिया कि श्रीगोपाल मेरा कहा टालेगा नहीं? तो क्या...मैं ही मान लूँ श्रीगोपाल का कहना? छोड़ दूँ बेला को उसके हाल पर? बेला मेरी लगती ही क्या है?'

कुछ लगती हो या न लगती हो, बेला को उसके हाल पर छोड़ देना आकाश के लिए सम्भव हुआ ही नहीं। बल्कि उसने तो बेला की एक और ज़िम्मेदारी ले ली अपने कन्धों पर। मकान का इन्तज़ाम। ऑफिस में आई हुई बेला ने ज्यों ही उससे कहा था कि उसे किराए के मकान की तत्काल ज़रूरत है, क्योंकि श्रीगोपाल वर्मा

के लिए फ्लैट से जितनी जल्दी निकल जाया जाए, उतना ही अच्छा, त्यों ही आकाश के मुँह से ये ही शब्द निकले थे, "कुछ प्रॉपर्टी डीलर्स मेरे अच्छे परिचित हैं। उन्हें सिर्फ़ फोन करने की ज़रूरत है।"

सात दिनों में ही, अँधेरी पश्चिम के डी.एन. नगर में, बेला को एक छोटा फ्लैट किराए पर मिल गया। बीमार माँ और दो छोटी बहनों के साथ बेला वहाँ रहने चली गई। स्वयं श्रीगोपाल वर्मा को आश्चर्य हुआ कि बेला मुफ़्त में मिले फ्लैट को इतनी जल्दी कैसे छोड़ रही है।

उस रात, शालिनी ने आकाश को बाँहों में भरकर, आँखों-में-आँखें पिरोकर पूछा, "यह...बेला कौन है?"

आकाश चौंके बिना न रह सका। बेला का नाम घर तक पहुँच जाएगा, उसने सोचा नहीं था। बेला का सारा झमेला वह अपनी ऑफिशियल ड्यटी के तहत ही निबटा रहा था और ऑफिस की हर बात की चर्चा घर में करना ज़रूरी तो नहीं। आकाश ने शालिनी की सुन्दर आँखों की मौन भाषा पढ़ने की चेष्टा की...

"पूछोगे नहीं, आकाश? कि बेला का नाम मुझे किसने बताया?" शालिनी के स्वर में उलाहना था, व्यंग्य था, आघात था, ठेस भी थी।

आकाश उसके बाहुपाश से अलग हो चुका था। बोला, "किसी शुभचिन्तक ने ही बताया होगा। शुभचिन्तक का नाम तुम छिपाकर ही रखो, तो बेहतर।"

"तिलमिला गए न?"

"नहीं, शालिनी। लेकिन अब सफ़ाई देना आवश्यक हो गया है। बेला मुझसे मिलने अकसर आती है। कई बार मैं उसे अपनी कार में बिठाकर इधर-उधर ले गया हूँ।"

"इधर-उधर यानी?"

"मैंने उसे किराए का मकान दिलाया है। नौकरी भी आज या कल में कहीं फाइनल हो जाएगी। उसकी माँ हमेशा बीमार रहती है। वे लोग सही डॉक्टरों को पहचानते नहीं हैं और मैं नहीं चाहता, कोई ग़लत डॉक्टर उनकी चमड़ी उतारे। इसके अलावा...बेला की दो छोटी बहनें भी हैं, जिनकी पढ़ाई अधूरी छूट गई थी। दोनों बहनों को पार्ट-टाइम नौकरी दिलानी है, ताकि आधा वक़्त पढ़े-लिखें और आधा वक़्त नौकरी करें। बेला की...अकेली की नौकरी से उन सबका गुज़ारा कैसे होगा? बेला सिर्फ़ हायर-सेकंडरी पास है। डेढ़ हज़ार की नौकरी भी मुश्किल से फाइनल हो पाएगी। इन डेढ़ हज़ार में से नौ सौ रुपए तो फ्लैट के किराए में निकल जाएँगे...बहुत ज़रूरी है कि बेला की बहनें भी कुछ कमाएँ-धमाएँ..."

"लेकिन, आकाश, किसी को मकान दिलाना...या नौकरी दिलाना...इसके लिए तुम स्वयं साथ-साथ घूमो, यह ज़रूरी तो नहीं? ये काम तो तुम सिर्फ़ टेलीफोन करके भी निबटा सकते हो।"

"हाँ, शालिनी, लेकिन...मेरा साथ पाकर बेला का हौसला बँधा रहता है। मैं नहीं चाहता, वह अपने आपको बेसहारा समझने लगे।"

शालिनी की आँखें भर आईं।

"नहीं, शालिनी, प्लीज़, वह बात नहीं है, जो तुम समझ रही हो।" और आकाश ने शालिनी की दोनों पलकों को बारी-बारी चूम लिया।

"कितने दिनों से है तुम्हारी और बेला की दोस्ती?" शालिनी ने दो-टूक जानना चाहा।

"दोस्ती है ही नहीं। सिर्फ़ परिचय है।"

"परिचय ही सही, लेकिन कितने दिनों से है?"

"यक़ीन करोगी? मुश्किल से बीस दिन पहले बेला मेरे ऑफिस में पहली बार आकर मिली थी।"

"और बीस दिनों में ही बात इतनी बढ़ गई कि कोई मुझे बाक़ायदा घर पर फोन करे और बेला का नाम बताए? ज़रूर तुम दोनों की दोस्ती इतनी पुरानी है कि..."

"प्लीज, शालिनी। 'दोस्ती' शब्द इस्तेमाल मत करो, मत करो।" इस बार आकाश अपनी बौखलाहट को पूरी तरह न छिपा पाया, "खुद मुझे आश्चर्य है कि बीस ही दिनों में बात तुम तक कैसे पहुँचा दी गई। कौन है इतना चुस्त जासूस, जो मेरे पीछे पड़ा है?"

इसके साथ ही आकाश के मन में एक चौंध-सी लपलपा गई—श्रीगोपाल।

"क्या उस जासूस का नाम श्रीगोपाल वर्मा नहीं?" आकाश ने खिन्नता से, किन्तु तपाक से पूछा।

शालिनी ढिठाई से हँसी, "सही पहचाना।"

आकाश ने शालिनी को विस्तार से बताया कि बेला और श्रीगोपाल के बीच क्या रिश्ता था और आज उस रिश्ते की शक्ल क्या है। आकाश क़तई समझ नहीं पा रहा था कि श्रीगोपाल वर्मा बेला को अकेली क्यों नहीं छोड़ सकते? खुद श्रीगोपाल का दावा तो यही था न कि उन्होंने बेला को छोड़ दिया सो छोड़ दिया, अब बेला के साथ उनका कोई सरोकार नहीं। जो बेला श्रीगोपाल के लिए कहीं है ही नहीं, उसी अस्तित्वहीन बेला के विरुद्ध शालिनी के कान भरने की क्या ज़रूरत?

आकाश को समझते देर न लगी कि यहाँ श्रीगोपाल वर्मा की शुभ कामनाएँ काम नहीं कर रही थीं, बल्कि यह तो उनके मन-मस्तिष्क की अपरिपक्वता ही थी, जो बेला को कुचल डालने को बेताब थी।

पुरुष का अहं यहाँ अपनी खीसें निपोर रहा था।

इसका तो अर्थ यह हुआ कि बेला को श्रीगोपाल वर्मा कभी भी अस्तित्वहीन नहीं मान सकेंगे। जाने या अनजाने में वह हमेशा बेला के पीछे पड़े रहेंगे और शायद तब तक चैन नहीं लेंगे, जब तक बेला बम्बई शहर को ही छोड़कर चली न जाए।

लेकिन क्या यह बेला के साथ ज़्यादती नहीं? अगर श्रीगोपाल को हक़ है अपने जीवन की दिशा बदलने का, तो बेला को क्यों नहीं?

"तुम तो मुझे पहचानती हो, शालिनी।" आकाश ने धीर-गम्भीर स्वर में कहा, "मैं एक निश्छल व्यक्ति हूँ और जो निश्छल होता है, वह निर्भीक भी होता है। मैं किसी के भी साथ, यहाँ तक कि बेला जैसी लड़कियों के भी साथ, आता-जाता दिखाई दूँ, तो भी मुझे न भय लगता है, न आशंका होती है। मुझे पूरा यक़ीन है कि मेरी निर्मल, निश्छल छवि को कोई आँच आने वाली नहीं है, चाहे मेरा सम्पर्क किसी के भी साथ हुआ हो..."

अगली सुबह, आठ बजने से पहले ही, शालिनी को मौजूद रखकर, आकाश ने श्रीगोपाल से फोन पर बात की और साफ़-साफ़ जता दिया कि बेला को बेचैन या अस्थिर करने वाली कोई हरकत श्रीगोपाल वर्मा न करें। श्रीगोपाल ने भी आकाश के आदेश के अनुसार ही चलने का वादा कर तो लिया, लेकिन...क्या उनका स्वर बेहद उखड़ा हुआ नहीं था?

मामा जी ने तीव्र आपत्ति उठाई थी इस बात पर कि श्वेता के लिए रिश्ते की खोज बिरादरी से बाहर भी की जाए। अख़बारों के वैवाहिक विज्ञापन, रिश्ते की खोज के कठिन कार्य को आसान कर देते हैं, इस बात से तो मामा जी पूरी तरह सहमत थे, किन्तु उनकी दृढ़ राय थी कि बिरादरी से बाहर लड़की देना, लड़की की किस्मत के साथ खिलवाड़ करना ही है। मामा जी का तर्क, अपनी जगह, ग़लत भी तो नहीं था। आकाश और शालिनी को दुनियादारी का सबक सिखाने जैसे लहजे में वह बोले, "लड़की अगर बिरादरी में ही ब्याही जाए, तो ससुराल में लड़की के साथ अन्याय होने का ख़तरा कम रहता है, क्योंकि लड़की की पीठ-पीछे केवल उसके माँ-बाप नहीं, बल्कि पूरी बिरादरी खड़ी रहती है।"

आकाश ने मुसकराकर जवाब दिया, "मैं तटस्थ हूँ। न बिरादरी की तरफ़, न बिरादरी के विरुद्ध। मेरा केवल एक कहना है, दहेज लेकर लड़का नहीं ब्याहूँगा। और दहेज देकर लड़की नहीं ब्याहूँगा।"

माता-पिता तो श्वेता के लिए लड़का ढूँढ़ रहे थे, लेकिन श्वेता अपने लिए सिर्फ़ एक अदद अच्छी नौकरी की तलाश में थी। 'टाइम्स' के 'रिक्त स्थान' के हर विज्ञापन

को श्वेता जैसे चाट जाया करती। श्वेता ने आकाश से कह रखा था, "पप्पा! पहले मैं अपने ही बूते पर नौकरी खोजूँगी। अगर नाकामयाब रही, तभी आप मेरे लिए कोशिश करिएगा, किन्तु छह महीने से पहले नहीं।"

बिटिया के स्वाभिमान पर आकाश गर्व से मुसकरा उठा था।

'टाइम्स' में प्रकाशित वैवाहिक विज्ञापन के जवाब में जो पचास से ज़्यादा चिट्ठियाँ आई थीं, उनमें से पाँच का चुनाव कर उन्हें पत्र लिख दिए गए थे। इन पाँच में से तीन तो बिरादरी के ही लड़के थे, शेष दो बिरादरी से बाहर के।

बेला! उसे कांदीवली के इंडस्ट्रियल एरिया में, एक फार्मास्युटिकल कम्पनी में, नौकरी मिल गई। वेतन पौने दो हज़ार। मकान का पचास प्रतिशत किराया कम्पनी की ओर से। पूरे परिवार का दवा-दारू फ्री। बॉस की एक सेक्रेटरी पहले से थी, किन्तु उस पर काम का बोझ अत्यधिक होने के कारण एक और सेक्रेटरी की तलाश की जा रही थी। यह तलाश बेला पर पूरी हुई—आकाश के सुझाव पर।

वैसे तो आकाश अपने प्रभाव का उपयोग कर, किसी भी व्यक्ति को, सात दिनों में नौकरी दिला सकता था—ऐसे अनेक संस्थान थे, जहाँ अगर कोई पद ख़ाली न होता, तो भी, आकाश की ख़ातिर नए पद की रचना हो सकती थी—किन्तु बेला को नौकरी दिलवाने में आकाश को ख़ासा डेढ़ महीने का वक़्त लग गया। आकाश किसी भी ऐसे उद्योगपति से बेला की सिफ़ारिश नहीं करना चाहता था, जहाँ बाद में स्वयं आकाश से ही, अहसान का बदला अहसान से माँगा जाए। इसीलिए...'इससे कहूँ या उससे कहूँ' की उधेड़बुन में आकाश का बहुत वक़्त ज़ाया हुआ था।

फिर...जैसा कि स्वयं आकाश ने चाहा था, आगामी दो महीने ऐसे बीते, जब बेला ने आकाश के साथ नहीं के ही बराबर सम्पर्क रखा।

तीसरे महीने...आकाश ने दो ऐसे अनुभव लिये, जिन्होंने उसके मन में तीव्र कसक पैदा की और उसे यही लगा—मंज़िल अभी दूर है...बहुत दूर...

पहला अनुभव : नौकरी छोड़कर, किराए का फ्लैट भी छोड़कर, समूचे परिवार सहित, बेला एकाएक ग़ायब हो गई। ज़रूर वह शहर छोड़कर ही चली गई। अपने ऑफिस में, आकाश को, बेला की लिखी एक चिट्ठी प्राप्त हुई, 'सर! मुझे किसी से शिकायत नहीं, लेकिन जहाँ आपने नौकरी दिलवाई, वहाँ दो हफ़्तों के भीतर ही, बॉस की ओर से दबाव पड़ने लगा था—बॉस को हर इतवार खुश करने का दबाव। यह बात किसी को भी बताने पर चेहरे पर तेज़ाब फेंकने की धमकी भी दी गई। शायद बॉस को, किसी तरह, मेरे पिछले इतिहास का पता चल गया हो...न पता चला हो, तो भी...ये लोग किसी भी खूबसूरत लड़की को छोड़ते कहाँ हैं? मैंने आपको कुछ

नहीं बताया। एक तो तेज़ाब फेंके जाने का भय और फिर...आप पर मेरे अधिकार की सीमा भी तो है आख़िर कब-कब, कहाँ-कहाँ, आप मेरी रक्षा करते फिरेंगे? सब सोचकर, निराश और पस्त होकर, आख़िर मैंने एक फ़ैसला कर लिया है—मैं जा रही हूँ। कहाँ? कैसे? कब? कुछ न पूछिएगा। एक डरावना, काला बादल-सा घुमड़ रहा है मन में...खुन्नस का बादल...कि अगर ज़िन्दगी में उबरने के लिए वही करना है, जिसमें बॉस की साप्ताहिक सेवा शामिल हो, तो ठीक है, इस काम को पूरी व्यवस्था के साथ, पूरी ढिठाई और बेशर्मी के साथ क्यों न किया जाए? पौने दो हज़ार के वेतन के लिए साप्तहिक सेवा की मजबूरी? अरे, इस लाइन में तो एक-एक रात के दस-दस हज़ार मिलते हैं...आपसे एक प्रार्थना है। बॉस के साथ कोई डाँट-डपट न करिएगा। अब उसका क्या मतलब? मैं तो चली। दूसरी प्रार्थना—आप मुझे भूल जाएँ। आप जैसे इनसान भी हैं इस दुनिया में...शुक्रिया। और अलविदा...—आपकी अपराधिनी, बेला...'

आकाश चिट्ठी थामे कितनी देर तक बैठा रह गया था, खुद उसी को पता नहीं चला था...

दूसरा अनुभव : इस अनुभव की धुरी में बैठी हुई थी—लाड़ली बिटिया श्वेता। जितनी भी जगह बात चली श्वेता के रिश्ते की—विज्ञापनों के ज़रिए, चाहे बिरादरी के ज़रिए—हर जगह एक ही अड़ंगा...बिना दहेज सब शून्य...

'अरे, आप तो इन्कम टैक्स में इतने बड़े ऑफिसर हैं। आपके यहाँ तो ऊपर की कमाई छप्पर फाड़कर बरसती होगी। अगर आपसे भी कुछ नहीं लेंगे, तो किससे लेंगे? आपके यहाँ तो समुद्र है समुद्र। एकाध डोल भरकर हमें दे देंगे, तो कौन-सा समुद्र में से कुछ घट जाने वाला है।''—इसी आशय के तर्क सुन-सुनकर आकाश जैसे स्तब्ध हो गया था। यही दशा शालिनी की थी।

बिरादरी में सभी के सामने साफ़ जता दिया गया था, वैवाहिक विज्ञापनों में भी हर बार साफ़-साफ़ प्रकाशित होता था—दहेज नहीं देंगे, फिर भी...ज्यों ही वर पक्ष को पता चलता कि यह तो इन्कम टैक्स वाले हैं, त्यों ही उनका रंग बदल जाता। दहेज का राक्षस पहले से ही अधिक शक्तिशाली हो गया है आज के समाज में—आकाश ने पहली बार देखा-जाना।

''लेकिन, शालिनी!'' आकाश ने दृढ़ता से कहा, ''मैं कभी नहीं मानूँगा कि बिना दहेज के श्वेता को सही वर मिलेगा ही नहीं। मैं तो इसे केवल एक संयोग ही कहूँगा कि शुरू में केवल ऐसे ही लोभियों से हमारा सम्पर्क हुआ, जो दहेज के बिना हिलना भी नहीं चाहते। संयोग का चक्र इस वक़्त उलटा घूम रहा है, लेकिन यही चक्र जब सीधा घूमेगा, हमारा परिचय ज़रूर किसी ऐसे परिवार से होगा, जो हर कसौटी पर सही निकलेगा और जो दहेज का सवाल उठाएगा ही नहीं...कोई ऐसा परिवार, जो